# Disability Claims Management

## Second Edition

# Disability Claims Management

## Second Edition

Ann Leckie, C.E.B.S.

Manjit Grewal

with contributions by
Margaret Bellman, Dr. Donald Butt, Carmen Churcott,
Brian Draheim, Michael Droke, Dr. Errol Ferguson,
Amy Friedland, Sue Jordan, Nancy Gallup, Terri Heffel,
Diane McElroy, Alyson Gates, Patricia Monteath,
David Overstreet, Sandra Pellegrini, Alan Ross,
Brenda Rusnak, Dr. Warren Shepell, Carol Vine

Butterworths
A Member of the LexisNexis Group

Disability Claims Management, Second Edition
© Butterworths Canada Ltd. 2002
January 2002

The *Butterworth Group of Companies*

*Canada*:
75 Clegg Road, MARKHAM, Ontario L6G 1A1
and
1721-808 Nelson St., Box 12148, VANCOUVER, B.C. V6Z 2H2
*Australia*:
Butterworths Pty Ltd., SYDNEY
*Ireland*:
Butterworth (Ireland) Ltd., DUBLIN
*Malaysia*:
Malayan Law Journal Sdn Bhd, KUALA LUMPUR
*New Zealand*:
Butterworths of New Zealand Ltd., WELLINGTON
*Singapore*:
Butterworths Asia, SINGAPORE
*South Africa*:
Butterworth Publishers (Pty.) Ltd., DURBAN
*United Kingdom*:
Butterworth & Co. (Publishers) Ltd., LONDON
*United States*:
Michie, CHARLOTTESVILLE, Virginia

National Library of Canada Cataloguing in Publication Data

Leckie, Ann, 1967-
    Disability claims management

2nd ed.
Includes index.
ISBN 0-433-43822-3

    1. Disability insurance claims—Canada—Management.
2. Handicapped—Employment—Canada. 3. Vocational
rehabilitation—Canada. I. Grewal, Manjit, 1971- II. Title.

HD7256.C3L42 2001          658.3'0087          C2001-903915-8

Printed and bound in Canada.

## Ann Leckie

To my daughter – Robin Rose Landry
"At the center of creation there is love"


## Manjit Grewal

To all of the wonderful individuals that I have had the privilege of working with and getting to know throughout my career. I have learned so much from each one of you. And to my family Kashmir, Daljit, Parkash, Paul, Simmie, Gary, Dave, Am, Terry, Shunney, and Susan for without your ongoing support and encouragement I would not be where I am today.

# ACKNOWLEDGMENTS

A textbook is more than the chapters that comprise the book. It is the love and encouragement of our supportive group of friends and family both near and far that created this book. A few of these important people are listed below:

Lucinda McMaster, Towers Perrin
Jane Deane, AON consulting
Sandi Pierce, AON consulting
Rachel Barbour, WCB
Simon Tang, PWC
Geoffrey Crampton, VP Human Resources, South Fraser Valley Health Region
Walter Klatt, VP IT, Overwaitea Food Group
Jim Brisimitzis and Amanda McMaster, of PeopleSoft
Our wonderful editor Karen Davidson at Butterworths
And our wonderful assistant Dawn Torroba

The critical components of this text were provided by the willing and capable disability specialists who devoted their time to providing the reader with an understanding of their craft. Their chapters highlight the diverse and specialized skills of modern disability management.

# TABLE OF CONTENTS

**Chapter 12: Communication Strategies — Consultant's Perspective to Enhance the Disability Management Process ...... 243**

# CONTRIBUTORS

## MARGARET (MARG) BELLMAN

As a Disability Management Consultant, Marg provides a broad range of both macro (organizational) and micro (individual) disability management services including program evaluation/development, training and business development.

Marg has 16 years of experience in disability management. Prior to starting her own consulting practice, she was employed as VP, Service Operations at Aetna Health where she was responsible for both business development and for the delivery of professional services. Marg has worked in the benefits consulting field and has extensive experience with disability insurers including Sun Life, Aetna Life, Prudential Group Assurance and Constellation Assurance. She is recognized for her expertise in the areas of health/disability management and rehabilitation.

Marg earned her Bachelor of Science degree in Physical Therapy and her Master's degree in Adult Education from the University of Toronto.

## DR. DONALD BUTT

Dr. Donald Butt graduated from the University of Toronto, B.Sc Phm., in 1956, and M.D. in 1960. Following his internship at St. Michael's Hospital in Toronto, he practised for six years in Hazelton, British Columbia and Baie Verte, Newfoundland, for the United Church Home Mission Hospital program. He then returned to Mississauga, Ontario. He was an Associate Professor in the Department of Family and Community Medicine at the University of Toronto and, with his interest in in medical education, served as the 1985-1986 president of the College of Family Physicians of Canada. In addition to the demands of a busy practice, he began consulting for insurance companies in disability claims, expanding this to full time by 1992, including underwriting and special risk. He is currently retired in British Columbia and consults for Sun Life on a part-time basis. His awards include Mississauga Civic Recognition Award and 1992 Canadian Family Physician of the Year.

## CARMEN CHURCOTT

Carmen Churcott is the Director of Employee Development for the Overwaitea Food Group (OFG), which has almost 16,000 employees and operates just under 100 retail grocery stores under several different banners in Western Canada. As the leader of Employee Development, Carmen is responsible for Recruitment and Selection, Internal Communications, Health & Safety, and Training & Development. She is a member of the international Food Marketing Institute Training & Development Committee, as well as the national Canadian Food Wholesale/Retail Transition Committee. Carmen has Bachelor's and Master's degrees in Applied Science (Kinesiology) from Simon Fraser University in British Columbia and is a Certified American College of Sports Medicine Exercise Specialist. She is also one of two Jim Pattison Group Personal Achievers for 1999 for OFG.

Included in her 12-year career in the retail industry are several years in disability management for both Canada Safeway and the Overwaitea Food Group. Her disability management experience includes designing and implementing disability management and return-to-work processes for short-term disability, long-term disability, and workers' compensation. Her experience also includes designing and delivering management training and employee communications to support these initiatives.

## BRIAN DRAHEIM

Brian Draheim is a graduate of Simon Fraser University. Brian earned a Bachelor of Arts degree in Economics. His degree is complemented by an Honours Diploma in Human Resources Management from the British Columbia Institute of Technology. He is currently participating in the Certified Employee Specialist program.

## MICHAEL DROKE

Michael Droke is a partner with Dorsey & Whitney LLP (resident in the Seattle office), and is a member of the firm's Labor and Employment Practice. His practice focuses on assisting clients on every aspect of employment and labor law, including discrimination, disability rights, and family and medical leaves of absence. He is a graduate of the University of California at Berkeley, and the Santa Clara University School of Law. Before joining Dorsey & Whitney, Mr. Droke was a shareholder in Littler Mendelson, P.C., practicing in their Seattle and Silicon Valley offices. He is a frequent speaker on employment law topics.

## DR. ERROL FERGUSON

Dr. Errol Ferguson graduated with Honours from the University of Manitoba Medical School, winning the silver medal in 1967. After a rotating internship at the Toronto General Hospital in 1967, Errol started residency training in Respiratory Medicine at the Royal Victoria Hospital in Montreal. Before completion of this four year program, Errol moved to Mississauga, Ontario and began a 25-year career in General Practice with a strong focus on Occupational Medicine. In 1992, Errol began working for Sun Life Assurance Company and held the position of Medical Director for Canada for the Group Division until 2001. Since then, Errol has provided several national employers with occupational medicine expertise. This extensive background has given Errol wide-ranging knowledge and experience in general and occupational medicine, as well as disability management from both insurance and employer perspectives.

## AMY FRIEDLAND

Amy Friedland is an associate with Dorsey & Whitney LLP (resident in the Seattle office), and is a member of the firm's Labor and Employment Practice. She is a graduate of the University of Washington, and the University of Miami School of Law.

## NANCY L. GALLUP

Nancy Gallup is a partner with Dorsey & Whitney LLP (resident in the Seattle office), and is co-chair of the firm's Employee Benefits Practice. Her practice focuses on the design and implementation of qualified and non-qualified employee benefit plans, including welfare plans, and in handling the employee benefits aspects of corporate acquisitions and dispositions. She advises a number of Canadian companies regarding employee benefits issues that arise in their U.S. operations. She is a graduate of Georgetown University and the National Law Center of George Washington University. Before joining Dorsey & Whitney, Ms. Gallup was chair of the Employee Benefits Practice of Bogle & Gates, in Seattle, and has practised with Jones, Day, Reavis & Pogue in their Washington, D.C., Los Angeles, and New York offices. She is listed in *Best Lawyers in America* (employee benefits).

## ALYSON GATES

Alyson Gates is the Director of Operations in British Columbia for CBI Health, Canada's leading provider of integrated rehabilitation solutions. Her history with this company has enabled her to utilize her 12-year background in education and medical management to coordinate and organize rehabilitation services, assist in the development of and training for new programs, and provide intercommunication with patients, employers, insurers, service providers, and members of the medical community.

## MANJIT GREWAL

Manjit Grewal has 10 years of work experience specializing in the health and well-being of workers at the workplace. Her experience includes working in the private and public sector which includes the supermarket, transportation, and healthcare industry.

Manjit's experience includes designing and implementing return to work programs, and managing short-term, long-term, and WCB claims. Her expertise in this area and passion for it has led to recognition for her in the areas of health & safety, prevention, early intervention, disability management, and claims management. Her understanding of and sensitivity to the many different stakeholders in these industries such as union representatives, supervisors, human resources professionals, and health care providers makes her successful in her role.

Manjit has earned a Bachelor of Science degree in Nursing at the University of British Columbia and a Master's of Education specialization in Community Rehabilitation and Disability Studies from the University of Calgary.

## TERRI HEFFEL

Terri Heffel has gained her expertise in a large range of both public and private organizations. Currently, she is employed with Overwaitea Food Group (OFG), which has almost 16,000 employees and operates just under 100 retail grocery stores under several different banners in Western Canada. In this role, she was an integral part of the successful development of the customized Disability Claims Management Module for the PeopleSoft system implementation. She is now working with Retail Accounting and is again exercising her flair for business process engineering, providing the critical link between programmers and user groups to develop a new Point of Sale system. She has been part of various payroll and HRIS system implementations for companies ranging from Labatt Breweries to Summit Logistics (formerly Safeway warehouse and distribution centre).

Terri is originally from Creston B.C., a small community in the East Kootenays. She earned her Business Administration Diploma at East Kootenay Community College in Cranbrook, B.C.  In 1991 she was transferred by the Columbia Brewing Company to Labatt Breweries in Vancouver, B.C. where she lives with her son Devon.

## SUE JORDAN

Sue Jordan, ALHC, has worked in the insurance industry for 20 years and has become a professional in managing claims. Sue attends disability management seminars and workshops to keep on top of changes. She has worked with many employers to streamline their internal disability programs with the insurance companies' initiatives. Currently a case manager with Maritime Life in Vancouver BC, Sue specializes in managing disability plans for large companies.

Maritime Life is a leading provider of individual life insurance and living benefits, investment products, pensions, and group life and health products and services. Maritime Life provides benefits to over two million Canadians served from offices in Halifax, Montreal, Toronto, Kitchener, Calgary and Vancouver.

## ANN LECKIE

Ann Leckie has been an employer relations consultant and project manager for the last 11 years. She has worked with a wide range of HR departments in a variety of industries and sectors.  Ann has specialized in designing and leading best practice initiatives in both Canada and the United States. Recently, she has been project manager for HRIS initiatives for two large Canadian companies.  Her work has bridged the connection between technology and claims management.

Out of her work, Ann has written numerous publications in such journals as "Benefits Canada", "Canadian HR Reporter", and the "HRMA News".  In 1998 this work culminated in the first edition of "Disability Claims Management".  Edition Two evolved from her more current research into the impact of technology and communication on disability management.

Ann earned an Honours degree in Arts at Queens University. Her degree is complemented by a Post Diploma in Human Resources from the British Columbia Institute of Technology. Ann has also earned the Certified Employee Benefits Specialist designation.

## DIANE MCELROY

Diane McElroy, Senior Vice President, Aon Consulting, heads the Toronto communication consulting practice. Diane has over 30 years of experience in the development and execution of human resources communication strategies related to disability management, pension, benefits, compensation, and change management. Diane is a Human Resources web specialist who leads the design and implementation of many Human Resources websites and web communication tools. Her strategies and innovative web solutions have received worldwide recognition through the receipt of many prestigious communication awards. Awards received include 2 IABC Gold Quill Awards, 2 IABC Ovation Awards, 1 Silver Quill Award, International Silver Mercury Award, Business Insurance and Best of Show Award.

## PATRICIA MONTEATH

Patricia Monteath is a Senior Consultant in the Health Strategies Practice department of Aon Consulting. She has over 15 years of experience in disability and absence management from a clinical and consultative perspective. Her expertise includes disability management, Employee Assistance Programs (EAP), reporting systems, audits, benchmarking and analysis. Patricia's hands-on disability management and rehabilitation background includes assessment, planning and implementation of cost-effective vocational reintegration plans, in concert with the broader multidisciplinary team. She also has experience in creating and executing early intervention processes for several large unionized employers.

Patricia is a registered nurse, holding certificates in Occupational Health, Safety and Environment and Disability Management. She also holds a LOMA certificate and is actively pursuing her Bachelor's degree of Applied Arts in Disability Studies. Pat is a member of the Registered Nurses Association of Ontario (RNAO) and the Canadian Association of Rehabilitation Professionals (CARP).

## DAVID OVERSTREET

David Overstreet is an associate with Dorsey & Whitney LLP (resident in the Minneapolis office), and is a member of the firm's Employee Benefits Practice. He is a graduate of the University of Minnesota, and the University of Minnesota Law School.

## SANDRA PELLEGRINI

Sandra Pellegrini is Vice President of Health Strategies at Aon Consulting. She is responsible for the development and integration of health strategies with employee benefits and policy design. Sandra consults in all aspects of managed care, health promotion and benefit design, with particular emphasis on approaches to workplace wellness, managed pharmacy, disability management and reducing workplace absence to support business objectives. As well, she is a frequent speaker at various industry seminars and regular contributor to industry publications.

Sandra has extensive experience in Group Benefits. Before beginning to consult in 1990, she held senior positions at a major insurance company over a nine-year period. Sandra holds a degree in Economics from the University of Toronto.

## ALAN ROSS

Alan Ross is an associate with Dorsey & Whitney LLP (resident in the Seattle office), and is a member of the firm's Employee Benefits Practice. He is a graduate of the University of Washington, and the University of Washington School of Law.

## BRENDA RUSNAK

Brenda Rusnak, BSc(PT), graduated from the University of Western Ontario in 1982 with a Bachelor of Science degree in Physical Therapy. Following graduation, she worked for 10 years as a clinician and a manager in private practice physiotherapy, specializing in the assessment and treatment of work-related orthopaedic injuries and general health and fitness issues. Since 1992 Brenda has been the President and CEO of ACTIVE Health Management Inc., of which she is the founder and co-owner. ACTIVE Health Management delivers a wide spectrum of integrated health care services to employers and insurance companies across Canada through independent, community-based practitioners and a strong centralized management system, creating the perfect balance of quality care, accountability, and cost containment. In her current capacity Brenda is involved in the development of quality improvement tools and accreditation of health care providers, the development of treatment protocols and guidelines, and the collection and analysis of statistical data. Throughout her career Brenda has regularly appeared on television and radio talk shows and is often invited to speak at conferences and seminars on a variety of topics. She has had numerous articles published in consumer magazines, newspapers and professional journals such as Canadian Insurance, Canadian Underwriter, Insurance West, and Canadian Occupational Health and Safety News. In addition, Brenda has sat on many professional committees, most recently the Financial Services Commission of Ontario's Auto Insurance Task Force on Accreditation, the Ontario Physiotherapy Association/Motor Vehicle Accident Fees and Protocol Steering Committee and the Institute for Work and Health's Professional Advisory Committee. In October 2000, Brenda was presented with the "Who's Who In Healthcare Technology" award sponsored by several health care and technology partners including Microsoft Canada, Benefits Canada and Canadian Health Care Manager magazines.

## DR. WARREN SHEPELL

Dr. Warren Shepell is Chairman of the Board of Warren Shepell Consultants, a 100 per cent Canadian-owned company that offers comprehensive Employee Assistance Program (EAP) services to more than three million employees and their dependents in as many as 1,500 North American organizations. He has been a leader and innovator in the development of both the concept and the practice of confidential counseling and EAP services for national and local organizations since establishing his own consulting firm in 1979. Dr. Shepell holds a Ph.D. in Clinical Counselling and Psychology from the University of Pennsylvania, and a Masters of Applied Psychology from the University of Waterloo.

## CAROL E. VINE

Carol Vine is the Manager, Client Services for the British Columbia Workers' Compensation Board in the Victoria Office. Carol is responsible for managing all aspects of the claims and return to work services. This includes case management in the areas of medical recovery, return to work, claims duration and customer satisfaction. She works with a multidisciplinary team to ensure quality control, quality of service and timeliness of service.

Prior to joining the Workers' Compensation Board, Carol had extensive and diversified experienced as a consultant, manager and educator in developing policies, procedures and programs relating to all aspects of disability management. She specialized in the design of cost-effective programs for disability management, return to work programs, short term disability management and attendance management. As a consultant she developed, implemented and evaluated return to work education initiatives and programs to reduce time loss and duration of absences associated with injury and illness. Carol is an Occupational Health Nurse with a Bachelor of Science in Nursing Degree.

# Part I

# THE EMPLOYER'S DISABILITY MANAGEMENT PROCESS

# Chapter 1

# WHAT IS DISABILITY MANAGEMENT ?

ANN LECKIE AND MANJIT GREWAL
*with assistance from Brian Draheim*

## DISABILITY MANAGEMENT DEFINED

As a term, "disability management" enjoys no widely accepted definition. It encompasses the many acts that individual employers, unions, insurance companies, and third party providers (consultants, employee assistance plans (EAP) and other health professionals) have performed to effect change in the management of an individual's disability. For the purposes of this discussion the term will be more precisely defined as "the careful control and measure of disability-related concerns in regards to decreases in time away from work when combined with medically valid return-to-work programs. Such programs can lead to lower costs, improved health and increased productivity."

Disability management includes both non-occupational and occupational absences. The following types of programs cover most non-occupational absences: salary continuance, accumulated sick leave, weekly indemnity and long-term disability. Occupational absences, due to disabilities that arise out of and during the course of work, are covered by benefits provided through the Workers' Compensation Boards of the provinces. To be effective, disability management must take a holistic and integrated approach to managing all types of absences. It must cover a broad spectrum, from measures preventing disability from occurring to programs for the successful reintegration of disabled employees into the workplace.

This book does not directly deal with the issue of occupational disabilities. However, the concepts and programs outlined within apply equally to the process of helping to manage an employee with an occupational disability.

## WHY IS DISABILITY MANAGEMENT AN IMPORTANT TOPIC FOR TODAY'S MANAGERS?

Today, disability management is a hot topic. Articles are popping up on the front page of many national newspapers; human resources magazines are sponsoring editorials on the topic, and conference organizers are continually offering disability management courses. This raises the question of whether it is really such a new topic.

Disability management has been an occupational concern for a long time; however, it has only recently begun to be addressed in a cohesive and planned manner. In the past it was seen as a "one off" occurrence, with employers tending to deal with the occasional occurrence of disability on an *ad hoc* basis. Few formal programs had been established for controlling the costs of disability management and bringing employees back to the workplace in a timely, meaningful and medically acceptable manner. In unionized environments programs such as weekly indemnity plans were offered, but these were seen as a benefit of unionization and as an income replacement plan, not as a component of a formal disability management program.

### The Changing Nature of Work/Skilled Labour

The nature of the workforce has changed the way companies approach disability management. Increasingly, employees are becoming skilled labourers who are not interchangeable. Therefore, not only do companies have to plan strategies around the cost of disability, they now have to plan strategies around the use of this productive workforce. Employees have unique skill sets that are generally specific and unique to the individuals. Absences require intensive management effort to fill in production gaps. In addition, co-workers are demanding that management take the necessary steps to return employees to work because the remaining employees are required to "pick up the slack" as a result of the absent employee.

## International Competition

In addition to the changes in the demographics of the workforce and the type of work performed, the markets in which Canadian organizations compete have changed drastically. In the past, competition came primarily from other local and regional companies in the same industry. Today, however, the marketplace is global with potential competitors scattered throughout the world. Employers have had to slash costs to stay competitive in the international market place. Although employees are no longer viewed as commodities or as interchangeable as the goods or services they create, the markets do not care if the product comes from Canada or Taiwan. Instead, buyers want a product that is competitively priced while offering maximum value. Excessive absenteeism and poorly managed disability programs increase production costs and can reduce the ability of the company to compete in international markets, both in terms of price and quality.

## The Impact of Downsizing

While employers are looking for ways to decrease disability costs, many employees are using disability programs as lifelines to financial survival during the turbulence of downsizing. Employees who are either threatened by or have been let go due to downsizing may lose their loyalty to the company that employs them. Workers with legitimate complaints such as injured backs may no longer force themselves to come to work out of a sense of loyalty and begin to be absent more often.

Several landmark cases have made it difficult for employers to terminate employees while they are receiving disability benefits. Therefore, some employees view disability plans as a safe, albeit temporary, haven from the swift and indiscriminate axe wielded by companies that are downsizing.

An employee seeking a short-lived boost in job security is not the primary reason why disability costs spiral upwards upon the onset of downsizing. The real reasons include the following:

1. Pressures resulting from increased workloads due to fewer workers which can lead to feelings of being overwhelmed and demoralized;
2. The individuals responsible for managing disability programs are often the first to lose their jobs. Therefore, important elements of disability management may be performed inadequately due to lack of time or training;

3. The failure of return-to-work programs due to a lack of jobs to return employees to, or a lack of "light" duties in the workplace to return employees to on a trial or short-term basis.

Employees' fear of the unknown may increase the number and duration of disabilities during downsizing. If their current employer were willing to let them work at 90 per cent capacity because of their excellent employment record, would a new company do the same? Older, more vulnerable employees worry about finding jobs in increasingly competitive markets and believe that since they are partially disabled, they may be better off filing for disability benefits to be protected financially from the impact of downsizing rather than continue to work and face the threat of losing their job.

### The Aging Workforce

Exacerbating the increase in disability costs is the aging workforce. The workforce has and will continue to incur a slight increase in the number of disability claims as the baby boomer generation ages. As people age they are less able to do the work they once did. Through the 1980s and early 1990s, disability plans needed to incorporate an aging workforce in a relatively short period of time. As a result, disability costs soared and changes were made to the way in which disability was managed.

## FUNDING OF DISABILITY PLANS

The changes in the nature of disability plus a greater need to control costs have changed the free flowing "pay as you go" disability strategy to a more determined cost control strategy. As much as possible, employers need to be able to forecast expenses. In order to plan for disabilities and create strategies for controlling costs, employers need a clear understanding of all disability-related costs. They must maintain statistical data of current disability trends including absence by department, length of absence, types of injuries or illnesses, day of the week and time of the year of absence, occupation and other demographic information. They must also track both the direct and indirect costs of absence from the workplace within the organization. By doing so they should be able to budget for these costs.

## LEGISLATION

### Mental and Nervous Clause Removal

Until the late 1980s, the majority of insurers included a mental and nervous condition clause in their short- and long-term disability policies. This clause excluded claimants who were suffering from a psychological condition from receiving disability benefits. However, for the most part, these clauses have been removed from disability policies because they violate human rights laws. All illnesses, whether they are physical or psychological, must be treated in the same manner by the insurer and employer.

In the past, a supervisor who felt comfortable contacting an employee who was disabled with a broken leg was, in effect, performing proactive disability management. With the proliferation of psychological disabilities, that same supervisor may feel significantly less comfortable calling an employee about his or her psychological condition. Thus, the disabled employee may feel alienated from the workplace, which may exacerbate the condition. Individuals who are absent from work due to a psychological claim often are more difficult to reintegrate into the workforce than someone who broke their leg skiing.

The net results of the removal of the mental and nervous clause are as follows:

1. Increase in the number of psychological claims — this is not to indicate that these claims are fraudulent — only that the number of people who are now eligible for benefits has increased and that psychological claims are now more widely accepted throughout society;
2. Increased complexity of disability management for supervisors and employers; and
3. Increased complexity of return-to-work situations for all parties involved.

In addition, by failing to intervene early in the disability, the employer faces the prospect that the disability may be much longer than necessary. For psychological claims the simple accommodations, for example, a foot stool or seated duties, are not sufficient to bring the employee back to work full-time.

## Duty to Accommodate

In the past, the employer, the employee and the employee's union made informal accommodation efforts to return the employee to work. These efforts were sometimes successful, but often met with failure. Most important, they were inconsistently applied.

The 1990s have seen the advent of numerous legal cases which have challenged both employers' and unions' accommodation attempts. The law continues to evolve on this issue, but the courts have ruled that employers have a duty to accommodate disabled workers to the point of undue hardship. To minimize the threat of a successful lawsuit against them, employers must take a strategic and formal approach to their duty to accommodate. They must be able to show the courts that they have return-to-work policies and procedures in place to manage disabled employees. The existence and practice of formal policies will help ensure that disabled employees are being treated consistently and fairly.

The duty to accommodate a physical injury is relatively straightforward. A determination is made concerning the physical abilities of the individual and her or his job requirements. Changes are made to the job description to meet the disabled employee's needs.

The duty to accommodate a psychological illness is more complex. How does a company accommodate an employee who is returning to the workplace when the stress of the workplace is literally making the employee sick? Furthermore, some co-workers may not want the employee back because he or she may be seen as a malingerer who has been difficult to work with in the past.

These issues have led to the current demand for a logical, clear, practical and planned approach to disability management.


## Litigious Environment

Today, the need for planned and coherent action is imperative, as disability benefits have become more litigious. It has now become acceptable in society to sue employers if they have done something that an employee disagrees with or considers inappropriate. In the past "whistle blowers" were forced out of companies. Now they are protected by a variety of laws.

Regardless of how one feels about these changes, all parties to the disability management process must work within the new confines of disability management.

## MEDICAL CHALLENGES

### Medical Changes

Unfortunately, in today's workplace, there are few instances of disability where such simplistic determinations of illness or injury exist. Shades of grey — how ill or injured the individual is — are far more commonplace. Furthermore, the cost of disability has increased to the point that it is becoming a drain on profits. As described below in more detail, changes to the social, medical and legislative environment have altered the role of disability management in most organizations or union sponsored plans.

### The Medical Community

The medical community is beginning to recognize the increasing prevalence of subjective disabilities. They have responded to pressure from both employers and insurers to provide more detailed notes for an employee's absence. For example, instead of simply providing a note that states Jane Doe will be absent from work for two weeks, doctors are drafting notes which state, among other things, the limitations Jane Doe faces in returning to work in a medically-safe manner, the expected duration of absence, and details of the extent of disability. These changes have significantly impacted on how disabilities are managed. Case managers and employers are able to use this information to document the needs of the disabled employees and match them with creative accommodations within the workplace.

### Designer Diseases

Unfortunately, improvement in the medical community's detailing of illnesses and injuries tends to be restricted to more physical ailments. It is relatively simple to state that Jane Doe can not lift weights over 10 kg due to a recurring dislocated shoulder. It is far more difficult to detail the limitations of the new "designer diseases" of the 1990s. Several of these diseases are outlined below in general terms.[1]

---

[1]    Chapter 6 details these "designer diseases" more thoroughly.

## Chronic Fatigue

Chronic Fatigue, otherwise known as Immune Dysfunction Syndrome, Chronic Epstein-Barr Virus, or Myalgic Encephalomyelitis, is one of the most recognizable of the so-called designer diseases. It is a controversial diagnosis that is often misunderstood. It is difficult to diagnosis because the majority of symptoms claimants have are subjective in nature. This does not mean that these complaints are false, only that they are difficult to measure and diagnose, and thus are difficult to evaluate.

## Fibromyalgia

Like Chronic Fatigue, Fibromyalgia is considered to be a relatively new illness. There is significant debate as to whether Fibromyalgia is a new type of illness or just the proper classification of a variety of traditional illnesses.

## Repetitive Strain Injuries (Tenosynovillis/Tendinitis, Carpal Tunnel Syndrome, Bursitis, Epicondylitis)

These conditions are not new, but they are becoming increasingly prevalent in the areas of the wrist and hands due to the repetitive nature of computer keyboard operations.

1. Tenosynovitis/Tendinitis — Tenosynovitis or tendinitis is the inflammation of the tendon, which attaches muscle to bone. The cause of this disease may be from a traumatic incident, such as a fall, or it may be caused by other medical conditions such as arthritis.
2. Carpal Tunnel Syndrome — The carpal tunnel is the space inside the wrist through which the median nerve and tendons of the hand are channeled. Carpal Tunnel Syndrome refers to a specific pattern of hand pain. In the early stages the pain is worse at night and localized in the hand and wrist with some pain in the forearm, shoulder, neck or chest. As the disease progresses the pain becomes constant and the individual can lose the full use of the thumb.
3. Bursitis — a related infliction, is the inflammation of the synovial sac in a joint. The causes of the inflammation may be from repetitive use, sudden trauma, arthritis or infections.
4. Epicondylitis — is a form of tendonitis, which is caused by inflammation of the forearm muscle connected to the epicondyle (bony knob) on the elbow. Lateral epicondylitis is also known as

"tennis elbow" and medial epicondylitis is also known as "golfer's elbow". Epicondylitis is usually caused by repetitive use of the arm or a sudden injury to the area.

Repetitive strain injuries are not new occurrences. They are, in fact, the third largest type of industrial disease claim. The key factor in any disability management case, from the perspective of the insurer, is the determination of whether the strain was caused by work-related factors or from illnesses such as arthritis or from a sudden trauma outside of the workplace, for example, tennis elbow.

There are several common denominators found in all of these disabilities:

1. They are complex and involve several components and potential solutions;
2. They tend to be subjective and difficult to diagnose;
3. Effective return-to-work programs or specific return-to-work dates are hard to set; and
4. They have a significant psychological component in addition to the physical ailment.

## Stress

Stress is becoming an increasingly common diagnosis for disability claims. Yet unlike the above noted illnesses, stress is the only one that is not in and of itself a disease. In fact, stress can actually be quite healthy for an individual. Stress can enable an individual to react positively in a crisis.

This natural occurrence can become negative when one's coping mechanism breaks down or is insufficient to handle the crisis or conflict. Stress, to the point of incapacitation, for one person may be a minor annoyance to another. Stress and tolerance is highly individualized. This makes the disability management process exceedingly difficult; a one-size-fits-all program will not work.

Until the late 1980s, most insurers would not accept a stress claim except for extreme cases such as a critical incident in the workplace like robbery or violence. One of the primary reasons for the increase in disability costs to organizations is the acceptance of a wider variety of stress claims for disability benefits. Since stress-related disability and the resulting absenteeism has increased significantly over the past decade, key challenges in disability management are to eliminate unnecessary stress in the workplace and increase the availability of programs to assist employees in managing their stress.

Slow progression claims are another difficulty in managing stress-related disabilities, that is, the individual becomes increasingly unable to cope at work and at home. Co-workers and family become more frustrated as the previously capable employee or family member gradually becomes unable to perform routine tasks. Inability to perform routine functions causes friction in the work and home which exacerbates the problem. From the perspective of the employer, the inability to effectively manage stress has a negative impact on productivity and the financial success of the employer.

## THE FUTURE

Much has changed over the last few years in the manner in which employee absence is managed. As was discussed earlier, changes have taken place in the composition of the workforce, the nature of work, the environment employers compete in, the types of disabilities, the structure of disability management processes and the emphasis that employers are placing on managing disability. Employers' and insurers' attitudes towards disability management have changed from simply "paying the claim" and accepting the absence to actively intervening in employee absence and assisting in a timely return to work. This trend will continue in the future. Several other trends are also on the horizon.

### Types of Claims

As was detailed earlier in the chapter, there has been a significant decrease in the number of objectively diagnosed physical illnesses and an increase in the number of subjective diseases, many of which have a psychological component. This trend will only continue in the future. Both employers and insurers must take steps to manage these claims effectively, while continuing to provide necessary support to disabled employees. Currently, mental and nervous disorders account for more than 25 per cent of all short- and long-term disability claims. These numbers will likely increase in the future.

Many of the steps employers and insurers must take to manage subjective disabilities are outlined throughout the book.

## Environmental Illnesses/Multiple Chemical Sensitivity

A more recently identified illness that is beginning to receive considerable attention is the disorder known as Multiple Chemical Sensitivity.

Multiple Chemical Sensitivity (also known as environmental illness) is a controversial disorder that involves the potential combined effects of a broad range of environmental substances (*e.g.*, exhaust fumes, smoke, perfumes, chemicals in food) that may cause a wide variety of subjective symptoms. Symptoms occur in the absence of objective physical signs, abnormalities or laboratory diagnostic criteria. Because of the lack of objective, verifiable clinical and laboratory signs, most health care professionals question whether such a disorder actually exists.[2]

Regardless of whether this disorder is commonly accepted by the medical profession, there are increasing numbers of individual doctors who believe their patients are suffering from this illness. This pattern of individual doctors supporting a disorder that is not commonly accepted helped increase the numbers of reported cases of disorders such as Fibromyalgia. Thus, it is important for individuals involved in managing disability to be aware of emerging trends.

## Surgical Techniques

Although there are many new illnesses requiring management's time and effort, there has also been a considerable lessening of demand on management's time due to the reduction in the number of days needed to recover from many common surgical procedures. Many operations are now being performed using less invasive arthroscopic techniques, which have cut recovery times in half over the last 15 years. As a result, claims managers will have to keep abreast of changes in surgical procedures to ensure that employees are returned to meaningful, safe employment at the earliest possible date.

## Focus on Health Prevention and Health Promotion

One of the more promising developments taking place in disability management is the renewed emphasis on health prevention and health promotion. Traditional disability management strategies focus on

---

[2]   Presley Reed, *The Medical Disability Advisor*, 2nd ed. (Horsham, Pennsylvania: LRP Publications, 1994).

returning injured employees to the workplace in a timely manner. Health prevention strategies emphasize keeping employees healthy and at work. Common techniques and programs include:

1. Employee Assistance Programs;
2. Wellness programs, such as stress management training, smoking cessation, blood pressure clinics, flu shots, *etc.*;
3. Ergonomic assessments;
4. Health and Safety programs (as mandated by law);
5. Flexible work arrangements, including flextime, job sharing, compressed work weeks and telecommuting.

All of these programs take a proactive approach to managing absence, and when combined with early intervention, clear and consistent disability management policies and procedures, integrated disability plans and a favourable work environment, such programs should result in lower levels of absence and disability claims.

## Partnerships Among Stakeholders

In the past there has been little communication between various players in the disability management process. The insurer adjudicated the claim but did not generally take proactive steps to rehabilitate the employee; the employer did not communicate with the disabled employee; the employee's physician and other medical practitioners did not work with the other parties to return the employee to work.

To effectively manage the complex disabilities taking place today, there is growing realization that regular communication and partnering is necessary to minimize disability costs. Employers, employees and their unions are beginning to collaborate with their insurers and the medical community to develop effective return-to-work programs. Evidence of the increased level of partnership also comes from the Canadian Medical Association's (CMA) position paper on the physician's role in the return-to-work process. The CMA supports "a shift away from complete reliance on physician certification for work absences to cooperation between the employer and his or her employee with the use of medical input, advice and support from the employee's attending physician and other involved health care professionals."[3]

---

[3]   "The Physician's Role in Helping Patients Return to Work After an Illness or Injury", Canadian Medical Association Journal (March 1, 1997), p. 680A.

The future of disability management will likely see a continuation of communication and partnership among the stakeholders in the disability management process.

## Legislative Changes

The legal system will continue to play a greater role in the future of disability management as both case law and government legislation set standards and rules with which employers must comply. For example, the government of Ontario passed legislation which substantially changed the workers' compensation system in Ontario.[4] Among the most significant changes are increased emphasis on return-to-work and labour market re-entry provisions. The legislation places an obligation on employers to provide suitable employment and forces employers to explore return-to-work options and provide accommodations to employees who are returning to work from workers' compensation claims.

In British Columbia, the new WCB Occupational Health and Safety Regulations, which came into effect in April 1998, require all workplaces covered by the WCB to identify and correct or minimize factors in the workplace that may expose workers to a risk of musculoskeletal injury.[5] This legislation obligates employers to take steps to assess and improve their workplaces and should lead to a reduction of workers' compensation claims.

Both human rights and employment standards legislation will continue to evolve and will require careful watching in developing and implementing return-to-work protocols and other disability management policies and procedures.

## Litigation

It is becoming increasingly common for employees who are denied disability to reapply or challenge the ruling. John Grisham's novel *The Rainmaker* exposes the corrupt medical payment system of an unethical insurance company. In this story the insurance company denies everyone's claim on the first try. This fictitious company hopes that many claimants won't bother to reapply. Those who do are usually successful. This is not the way insurance companies operate, but it is the perception

---

4  *Workplace Safety and Insurance Act, 1997*, S.O. 1997, c. 16, Sch. A.
5  Occupational Health and Safety Regulation, April 15, 1998, Part 4.47, 4.48.

that many claimants have. Thus, the number of claims being appealed is increasing and this trend is expected to continue.

## Changing Nature of Absence

In the past, virtually all short-term absences were due to illnesses or injuries, such as a flu or bad back; however, over the past decade absence due to personal or family reasons has increased dramatically. For example, in 1995 the absenteeism rate in Canada was 9.1 days per year, of which illness or injury accounted for 5.9 days, and personal or family reasons accounted for 3.2 days. Total workdays missed by full-time employees for personal or family reasons amounted to more than 81 million in 1995.[6] As the demographics of the workplace continue to change and employees are increasingly required to make tradeoffs between family and work, the rate of absence for personal or family reasons is expected to continue to rise, while the rate for illnesses or injuries should continue to decline.

To combat the rising rate of absenteeism for personal or family reasons, employers should take steps to make the workplace more "family friendly". Some of the programs that have been successfully implemented in organizations across Canada include flexible working hours, job sharing or part-time work, employer-sponsored day care, personal leave for family emergencies, training in time and stress management, and a myriad of other programs. However, programs alone are not enough to reduce the rate of absenteeism for personal or family reasons; employers must change the culture of the organization to have a greater balance between work and family.

## Focus on the Bottom Line

For a disability management program to be successful, support from senior management is critical. However, senior management will not endorse a program unless results can be quantified and shown to have a positive impact on the organization's profitability. In this era of downsizing and globalization, the ability to show a return on investment will become even more important in the years to come.

Fortunately, computer software that tracks absenteeism, measures the cost of absence to the organization and shows how much money can be

---

6    Statistics Canada, *Work Absence Rates, 1995*, Autumn 1996 Perspectives, p. 5-1.

saved by reducing the number of disability claims and lowering the level of absenteeism is readily available. One of the fundamental tenets of disability management is that to reduce disability claims, one must first be able to measure the number of claims, their duration and type, and the cost of these claims. Thus, disability management programs will have to meet overall corporate objectives and have a positive effect on the bottom line if they are to be embraced by senior management.

## OVERVIEW OF THE FUTURE

Disability management as outlined in this chapter, is only going to become more complex. It will become increasingly difficult to obtain objective evidence of the nature of disability for diseases for which claimants apply. The methods that companies or unions use to account for disability will become even more stringent. Employees or members of a benefit plan will become more likely to try to use disability benefits as a tool to help them handle the transition between employment. Governments will become more involved in disability management to ensure fair and equitable treatment of all employees or members. Finally and most important, all parties to the disability will become more sophisticated in their knowledge of the power and limitations of a disability program.

Does this mean that we should ignore these trends and carry on with business as it was done in the past? Absolutely not. As employers, unions, insurance companies and third party providers of disability management solutions become more sophisticated, there will be new and better tools developed to help return employees to an active positive role in society. We are already beginning to see greater efforts at preventing disabilities before they occur. Also, early intervention into claims before they become long term in nature is becoming more prevalent. Finally, absence-tracking programs are available to assist in the management of disability costs and trends.

We, as a society, have tended to marginalize many disabled persons. Through sophisticated disability management tools, we can integrate these people into the workforce. We can create a meaningful place within the social structure for these individuals to increase the wealth and knowledge of our society. Everyone stands to gain by a well thought out and caring disability program.

This textbook is an introduction to the specialists who spend their lives designing and implementing disability management programs, policies and services to meet the needs of both employers and employees. The purpose of this book is multifold. It will provide a greater understanding of the challenges facing disability management programs and practitioners, outline the various components of disability management, develop a framework for analyzing disability management issues in the workplace, and offer some tools to resolve these issues in an efficient and cost effective way.

# Chapter 2

# TRAINING MANAGERS TO IMPLEMENT A RETURN-TO-WORK PROGRAM

CARMEN CHURCOTT

## THE ROLE OF TRAINING

The role of training is to answer two questions for managers: "why?" and "how?" Effective training explains the benefits and rationale of a return-to-work (RTW) program for managers, employees and the organization. In this way, the "training" actually serves a communications and marketing role. Successful training also delivers a clear understanding of the role that managers play in the RTW program — from how they communicate with ill or injured workers to how to fill out necessary paperwork. One of the main reasons that many programs fail is due to the lack of a well-developed training effort.

Before you can ask managers to implement and adopt a RTW program, you need to be sure that your RTW program meets the needs of your company, your managers, and your employees. The acceptance and success of the RTW program will depend largely on how well your RTW program meets the needs of these three constituents. Understanding how your RTW program meets the needs of these three groups is half the battle — communicating the benefits and processes involved is the other half of the equation.

## BEFORE THE TRAINING

### Research and Understand the Managers' Needs

With any training or communication effort, start by understanding your audience. The success of your RTW efforts rests in the hands of the managers, so they are the audience you must address first. The way to find out what their needs are is to ask them.

The simplest approach is to meet with a representative group of managers and ask what their claims management challenges are. Listen closely and take good notes. You'll likely hear concerns ranging from displeasure at losing experienced, knowledgeable staff through injury to uncertainty regarding what kinds of work an ill or injured worker can do and impact on employee morale. While you may not see the immediate relevance of such information, these comments present an opportunity to you in communicating the benefits of your RTW program.

For example, in your management training program, you can explain how a RTW program can bring back knowledgeable, experienced staff under modified work conditions, thereby avoiding a situation where inexperienced staff are without guidance. Understanding that managers will have questions about what kinds of work can be performed by ill or injured workers will allow you to give considerable focus to this area in your training program.

Researching and understanding the wants, needs, and concerns of managers is the first step. The more work that you do in this area, the more likely you are to deliver a training program that meets the needs of your managers. If you effectively communicate how the RTW program solves real problems that managers are facing, the RTW program will have acceptance and longevity. If the training gives managers both a conceptual understanding and the "hands on" tools to safely return ill or injured employees to work, managers will embrace the program.

### Involve Managers in the Design Process

Remember that the RTW program, and the training that supports it, should solve an operational challenge. The training program and the RTW program are worthless if they do not address a need that exists. Further, if the training does not effectively communicate how the RTW program improves the operation of the branches or departments, the RTW program will not be successful. Additionally, the training must be complete enough to ensure that, after the training, managers are comfortable implementing the RTW program. The appropriate people to help you with the content and design of the training, then, are your managers.

After carefully researching the kinds of questions and concerns that managers have about claims management, you will have an understanding of the areas that the training must address. These areas should form most of the "content" of your training. Invite a group of managers to evaluate the outline of the information that will be included in the training. Your managers, as the customers of this training, will be able to tell you if the information is complete, what questions remain unanswered, and can help identify any additional needs. This step can assist in focusing the training on the right areas — the areas that matter to your managers.

Conventional wisdom tells us that people will support what they've helped to create. Involving managers in the design of the RTW program, and the training that supports it, gives you the opportunity to communicate the role that they played when you begin training other managers. Managers can also provide valuable guidance around areas such as:

- location for the training;
- preferred training format;
- acceptable costs for the training;
- beneficial activities that could be included:
  - designing user-friendly forms; and
  - additional tools that will assist them in their efforts to implement the RTW program.

One cautionary note is a reminder that you won't be able to satisfy everyone on every issue. Carefully consider every idea and suggestion, accept those with merit and reject only those that you have good reason to discard.

## Understand and Address the "Top 10 Questions"

As part of your initial research into the questions and concerns that managers have, it is very valuable to compile a Top 10 list. These kinds of lists have tremendous appeal, as they are often viewed as "what's really important". They are also very user-friendly, as they provide a quick reference to top issues, thereby circumventing the need to leaf through manuals or other materials.

In your training design, you should make sure that you include a Top 10 list, along with complete answers to each question or concern. Often, a tour of branches after the training will reveal that managers keep such lists readily available for easy reference. It's advisable to include the names and contact information of those who can be contacted for help or information.

The list of Frequently Asked Questions (FAQ) doesn't necessarily need to have exactly 10 points — it can be longer or shorter. However, if the list is too long, it will be seen as less user-friendly and lose much of its appeal.

## Financial Feasibility

Most organizations will not approve the implementation of programs that do not make financial sense. Even organizations that will invest in programs that demonstrate their commitment to their employees will not support a program that is cost-prohibitive. The onus is on the program-developer to research and model the program costs (including the cost of training), program savings and benefits, and Return on Investment (ROI). The role of the training is to communicate those tangible fiscal benefits to managers, to help build the case for the RTW program.

The training should communicate both "why" the RTW program is important and "how" to return ill or injured employees to work. The financial rationale is a critical piece in communicating the necessity of a RTW program. Often, managers do not understand the cost of disability claims; they may see these costs lumped in with other employee expenses on their financial statements and may not understand the true cost for their department, branch, or the total organization. Additionally, advising managers of the potential savings that can be realized through the implementation and ongoing execution of a RTW program can lead to a shared understanding of the positive impact on the bottom line. Often, the communication of the ROI alone can be enough to obtain the support of many managers.

## Relating to Company Culture

A key factor that impacts a RTW program is how the program relates to the company culture and long-term plans. This link has often been overlooked, an oversight that may have contributed to the failure of many RTW programs.

Demonstrating how the RTW program supports the company's mission, values, and long-term strategic goals provides irrefutable evidence that the program is an important business strategy that will help the organization attain its objectives. It provides a framework for shared ownership of the initiative. Shared ownership between the Claims Management Group (or Human Resources) and the operational managers will help to ensure the success of the RTW program.

Obtain a copy of the company's mission and values or company philosophy and examine each statement. Document how the RTW program supports each message or value. This information will serve as the basis for how the RTW program supports the company culture and will be part of the communication to senior management and operating managers.

If your organization has a strategic plan, you should obtain a copy and study it carefully, looking for areas that can be supported or complemented by the RTW program. If your company doesn't have a strategic plan, ask a senior manager what the goals and objectives of the organization are. Again, document how the RTW program can support or enhance those goals and objectives. This information will demonstrate how the program supports the company's business objectives, and why it is a strategic part of the organization's operating procedures.

Taking the time to research how the RTW program fits into the company's business strategies and culture has benefits that go beyond gaining managers' support for the program. This information can also be effectively used to market the RTW program to employees, senior management, and labour unions. Another positive side effect is an increase in your department's credibility with managers. This can be very helpful in facilitating the acceptance and implementation of future programs or initiatives.

## Communicating Benefits of RTW

As described in other chapters, in addition to financial benefits, there are many other tangible and intangible benefits of implementing a RTW program. The training program offers an excellent opportunity to communicate these positive outcomes, thereby gaining the needed support for a successful program launch.

Your organization's unique culture and distinctive values will influence how you communicate these benefits. As described earlier, once you have determined how the RTW program directly supports the company's business plan and mission, share this information with managers. Outlining the direct links between the benefits of a RTW program and the company mission, values, and business plan provides an excellent argument for the importance of successfully implementing the program.

Your company culture will also affect the training and communication in other ways, ranging from the order of presentation of the benefits to the emphasis that each benefit should receive. With few exceptions, the training should begin by outlining the direct financial benefits that managers can expect. The financial case should be outlined in considerable detail, and significant emphasis put on the potential savings. The order and amount of emphasis placed on other benefits will depend on your organization's values and business objectives.

## RTW and the Labour Union

If your company operates in a unionized environment, positively communicating the goals and benefits of the RTW program to the labour union(s) increases support. Gaining up-front support will greatly facilitate implementation of the program. Additionally, a shared understanding of the intent and parameters of the program will decrease any opportunity for misunderstanding or perception of ulterior motives. It can also increase employee acceptance of the program, decrease grievances, and improve labour-management relations. For these reasons, it's advisable to gain union understanding and support for a RTW program before beginning the implementation and training phase.

Just like the management training program, it is necessary to communicate to the union "why" the RTW program is important. The work that you have done linking the benefits to the mission, values, and business objectives will serve as an excellent presentation outline. After obtaining support for the implementation of a RTW program, you will need to communicate the high-level processes of the RTW program that you have designed.

The details of the RTW objectives and processes should be communicated to union business agents and shop stewards. These individuals are the front line for questions and concerns from employees and a thorough understanding of the program helps them field those questions appropriately. You may even want to consider investing in a short training program for these individuals as well as a question and answer (Q&A) document to assist them in addressing employee questions or concerns.

### RTW and Senior Management

Few programs succeed without the full understanding and support of senior management, and a RTW program is no exception. These leaders are the role models of the organization, and their behaviours and messages are given considerable weight. If this group does not fully understand and support the program, there is a potential that mixed messages will be sent inadvertently, resulting in irreversible damage to the program.

As with managers and unions, the communication and marketing of the RTW program should centre on the work done to relate the benefits of the RTW program to the company's mission, values, and business objectives. The presentation to this group should be concise and at a high level, with less supporting information and details than you communicate to managers. The communication should begin with positive financial results and then focus on other key areas, in decreasing order of importance to the organization's business objectives.

A key component of this communications effort should be to outline the things that senior management can do to support the initiative. Keep the list short and high-level, but ensure that it covers off the key items.

## TRAINING DESIGN

### Train the Right People

Whom you train depends largely on the organizational structure and complexity of the company, its branches, and departments. In fact, in some cases, it may not make sense to train anyone up front. While, in other cases, it may be better to provide different types of training to several individuals in one department or branch. Selecting the right managers to receive the training can positively impact the execution of the RTW program.

Involve managers in determining who should be trained. For example, while it may initially seem that the Branch Managers should be trained on every aspect of the RTW program, discussion with Branch Managers may reveal that the Assistant Branch Managers or Department Managers are better candidates, since they are directly responsible for the management of their staffs. By involving Branch Managers in discussions regarding who should be trained on the details of the program, you can ensure that those individuals who are directly responsible for executing the RTW program receive the information that they need.

You should ensure that the direct supervisors of the training participants also receive information regarding the program. This information should be of a higher level and focus on the importance of the program (the "why") and an overview of the procedures.

As mentioned, for some organizations, up-front training may not be necessary. For a company with a low incidence of claims, it may be more appropriate to train managers after a worker becomes ill or injured. A manager who doesn't use the information for a long period of time is likely to forget much of the information, and will need to be coached through the process step-by-step at the time of an incident anyway. In such cases, the initial investment in training is wasted. Understanding the incidence of claims will help you to weigh the benefit of up-front training against an "awareness" communications campaign coupled with just-in-time training for managers.

The scope of responsibilities and level of position of the training audience will play a role in the training design. The training for individuals with the responsibility for the day-to-day administration of the RTW efforts for employees should not only communicate information about why the program is important, but also provide detailed information regarding procedures, paperwork, and how to communicate with ill or injured workers. As mentioned previously the managers to whom these individuals report should fully understand the importance of the program and have a general understanding of the program procedures. Having this level of understanding allows these managers to follow up, continue to emphasize the importance of the initiative, and ensure that the program is being correctly executed.

## Involve Managers in Training Delivery

Almost every piece of this model has encouraged involving operating managers in the process. Training delivery is no exception. Involving managers as training facilitators can add a significant amount of credibility to the training, as other managers see that their peers support the program and have successfully implemented it. This can increase the acceptance of the RTW program.

Including managers as trainers also creates shared ownership of the RTW program. This decreases the perception that the RTW program is "another Head Office program" or "another HR program". Shared ownership also encourages managers to become invested in the success of the program.

Involving managers as trainers requires additional time and energy in the beginning, as you need to conduct a Train the Trainer session to ensure that they completely understand the RTW program and are proficient training facilitators. The Train the Trainer session involves sharing the training content and flow with the manager. Once the manager understands the information, you need to observe the manager as he or she facilitates the training session and provide feedback. Videotaping the facilitator and watching the tape together can be a very effective feedback tool.

## Training Design and Format

One method to train managers to initiate and implement a RTW program is through an interactive workshop. This kind of training not only involves participants in the process, but encourages them to voice questions and concerns. This method of training is especially appropriate for hands-on activities, such as form completion and appropriate communication. Interactive training results in a much higher retention of the information being communicated than a lecture format. Another positive side effect of this kind of workshop is that the camaraderie builds relationships and results in teambuilding.

Training should appeal to different learning styles. The goal is to ensure that all participants, regardless of preferred learning style, receive the same message. Generally, there are four learning styles that trainers try to address:

1. Reading the information;
2. Hearing the message;
3. Seeing images/charts/pictures/videos; and
4. Interacting and performing tasks.

For this reason, it's advisable to include a variety of media for communicating the key messages.

Build some flexibility into your training. The best training programs are facilitator-led, but remain participant-centred. For example, some groups may become involved in a discussion that takes them into an area that is of interest to the group, but is not really part of the training. Ensure that you have sufficient flexibility to allow some of this. Idea sharing is crucial to retaining the group's enthusiasm; cutting off discussions that most participants are interested in can dampen the group's interest. Additionally, some groups may seek the answers to specific questions that are provided later in the training design. Flexibility is the key for any facilitator.

Encourage participation, even if the comments are negative or challenging. In fact, by encouraging participants to voice their opinions openly, you gain the trust of the entire group. By involving managers up front, you should already understand the majority of the concerns that other managers will have. Anticipating some resistance in the training workshop will go a long way to motivate you to be prepared to address such concerns.

When designing training, a general guideline is that questions relating to "why" are addressed by providing information and encouraging discussion, while questions surrounding "how" are answered through hands-on activities. Deal with conceptual issues through providing factual information, as well as a context for that information (e.g., Our projections indicate that this RTW program could save us $20,000 annually, which goes a long way to meeting our objective of increasing profitability by 2 per cent each year). Initiating a discussion regarding philosophical issues can help individuals experience the "a-ha" moment for themselves. Conversely, hands-on activities are retained if participants actually perform them. This is true of everything from completing forms to a one-on-one conversation with an ill or injured worker.

You may not be able to meet every expectation that your managers have. For example, it is unlikely that you will be able to deliver a 1-hour training program that explains the entire RTW program, complete with video examples of role-plays at no cost to your company. But, substituting role-plays will certainly decrease costs, and will have about the same impact on learning. If your training delivers all of the information that your managers need, they will support the investment in a longer training session. Such creative variations and adaptations will help you to deliver an effective training experience.

There are many other possible modes of training, ranging from self-guided workbooks, to CD-ROMs, to web-based training. While such training mediums have merit for many kinds of training, there are some challenges that may hinder the effectiveness of any of these mediums for training managers to implement and adopt a RTW program.

First, the acceptance of the merits of a RTW program often requires an opportunity to question its benefits and rationale and to be convinced first-hand. Additionally, participation in a workshop provides an opportunity to observe peers accept the program, which may help to persuade a manager to get on board. One of the greatest challenges in

RTW training is that there is a great deal of grey area — it is impossible to anticipate every situation that a manager may encounter. However, a workshop allows for tailored discussion that is more likely to provide the kind of framework that can help managers make appropriate decisions. Web-based technology does afford the opportunity for such interaction, but current technology is somewhat limiting in terms of video quality and speed, which can be distracting for participants and negatively impact the experience. Web-based training is expected to show great promise in the next few years. But, perhaps the strongest reason for a workshop format is that it will limit distractions and ensure that you have the undivided attention of your audience.

## Make RTW Important to Managers

The only way to get managers to support a RTW program is to convince them that it's important to them. For that reason, start by explaining how disability claims negatively impact their departments, branches, and the company. Following this with a discussion of how a RTW program can minimize these negative effects, and even create some positive outcomes will gain your audience's interest.

There are some global reasons why people should care about what you're going to tell them. These common interests include the costs of disability claims, comprising the direct costs of claims as well as the indirect costs. They also include the claims cost savings associated with a RTW program, as well as the retention of highly knowledgeable workers. There are many other benefits that relate to corporate citizenship and employee welfare, which can almost always be tied back to the company's mission and values.

Reasons for creating a RTW program include the positive outcomes for employees, as well as the company. Relating this underlying rationale for the RTW program back to the company mission and values will provide an anchor for the program that is hard to refute. It also demonstrates the business case for the program, which will have a significant impact on many managers.

Having linked the RTW program to both a positive financial outcome and the organization's mission/values, you can now make the case for the RTW program as a strategic business direction. This is accomplished by outlining the connection between the objectives and outcomes of the RTW program and the company's strategic plan or business goals. One point to emphasize during this initial communication is that these positive impacts of a RTW program can only be realized if both the implementation and the ongoing execution of the program are solid.

Encourage managers to ask questions during the communication of the rationale for the RTW program. You need to ensure that managers support the initiative before moving on to discussions around processes. Expect some critique and cynicism — there will be some concerns and doubts. In fact, if no one questions the rationale, importance, or viability of the RTW program, you may want to start the discussion by volunteering a couple of concerns that managers raised during the development of the RTW program. The facilitator should be prepared for concerns and then discuss them openly with the group. Ensure that there is sufficient discussion at this point to guarantee that all questions and reservations about the program are addressed — this removes the barriers to a successful launch. Additionally, your openness will communicate your confidence.

Once you are satisfied that the managers support the program, you can begin addressing the processes involved, specialized communication skills required, and proper form completion.

## Elements for Information Retention

To ensure that the training is effective and the information is retained, build in a lot of interaction for participants. Not only is it more interesting for managers if they have an opportunity to participate, it also helps to keep them focused. The interactive format also allows managers to build collateral skills that are needed to be successful (e.g., a role-play allows managers to use their communication skills, in addition to thinking through the correct message). Additionally, include various modes of communication, to ensure that all managers, regardless of preferred learning style, receive the same message.

There are various ways to keep a workshop interesting for all participants.

The use of a written handout or workbook can be very helpful for managers who prefer to read. The use of slides, charts, and flipcharts are another way to communicate information in a different way. Including short "lecturettes", stories, or examples can be a great way to illustrate concepts. The use of appropriate humour can be a great way to keep participants interested and energized. Strategically placing interactive skits or role-plays in between discussions can help to keep managers sharp and involved. Breaking managers into subgroups and having them present back their ideas to the rest of the group can be a great way to increase interaction as well as keep the topic interesting.

## Encourage Questions and Discussion

It is important that all questions about program implementation and execution are answered. Any ambiguity about the expectations of managers or the correct procedures can spell disaster.

In the design of your training, build in ample time for discussion — this will help you avoid cutting off discussion. For every question that you anticipate, there is likely at least one that you do not. So, do not short-change the time that you budget for questions and discussion. Peer discussion is often the most valuable part of the RTW training, so include plenty of time.

Be sure to encourage questions and discussion around examples of injuries and illnesses and appropriate RTW solutions. You should plan a discussion around what-if scenarios — in fact, bringing a list of common RTW examples and discussing what could go right and wrong with each situation is an excellent activity that can stimulate a lot of lateral thinking and creative solutions. A discussion on hot topics — illnesses or injuries that are more difficult or prevalent — can really help managers to understand how to deal with such situations.

Facilitating a discussion of managers' experiences and using them as case studies (What could we do differently?, How does the RTW program help us in a situation like that?, *etc.*) can be a stimulating exercise. The added benefit of this kind of activity is that it uses real life examples that are relevant to the group.

Any or all of these activities can be effective — the key is to encourage interaction and discussion around solutions to RTW challenges. This kind of peer discussion will result in ideas that are practical and realistic with RTW solutions that are easily implemented by operating managers.

## Stimulate Discussion

One method used to initiate a discussion regarding the importance of what managers do and say is to have managers complete a questionnaire regarding what behaviours are acceptable or inappropriate during a RTW program. The point of this activity is not to keep track of who was right or wrong — it's to illustrate the impact of managers' behaviours on the ill or injured worker and the RTW process.

The questionnaire might be a collection of 15 or 20 statements indicating things that managers could say or do, along with a True or False column where managers can indicate whether they feel the statement is acceptable or not. Common mistakes and misconceptions can be included in this list, along with the correct behaviours the training encourages.

The lesson in this exercise is in the discussion of why the statements are appropriate or inappropriate — this is where valuable information can be communicated. Participants' answers can be used to discuss areas such as medical confidentiality, the importance of respect and dignity, timely initiation of the RTW process, common misconceptions about claims management or transitional work, the disability mindset, *etc*. A side benefit of using this kind of activity is that most managers will get at least one answer wrong, which will remind them that they have room to learn.

## Illustrate with Examples

One of the most common criticisms that managers have of training courses is that the information is theoretical, and they are provided with little guidance on how to use the information on the job. To ensure that the training is useful to the managers incorporate real life examples. The more comfortable managers are that the solutions will work for their branch or department, the more likely they are to believe in the feasibility of the program.

To guarantee that the training will be relevant to your audiences review the claims history of your company and ensure that the training covers RTW solutions for the highest frequency illnesses and injuries. Offering examples of how to successfully manage a safe and dignified RTW for these injuries or illnesses will provide useful, relevant solutions for managers, and will demonstrate your commitment to providing pertinent training. Encouraging discussion regarding transitional duties for such examples will provide additional tools for managers.

Another effective example that should be considered is the most difficult RTW that your organization is likely to face. Discussing this kind of RTW, and the correct way to manage it, sends the clear message that there is a solution for every illness or injury, although sometimes the only apparent avenue may be contacting a Claims Specialist or Human Resources Advisor for guidance. Reassure managers that they are not expected to be RTW experts and that they have access to resources that are pleased to support them.

If possible, discuss a wide variety of examples of situations and solutions. The more examples discussed the broader the framework that managers build for how to correctly handle individual RTW programs. Often, there is a significant amount of overlap in how situations should be managed and if enough discussion occurs, managers will pick up on themes and trends.

The importance of using real situations that managers will actually encounter cannot be overemphasised. If abstract situations are discussed theoretically, there isn't a sufficient frame of reference to allow managers to translate them into real actions that they can take. Lack of understanding of either what's expected or ambiguity regarding how to deliver it will negatively impact the acceptance of the RTW program.

## When An Employee is Unable to Work

One of the pivotal points in the claims management process occurs when a worker indicates that he or she is unable to work due to illness or injury. The manager's responses and actions at this point significantly impact the opportunity for an early RTW, as well as the worker's perception of the RTW program.

Because of the importance of this moment in the RTW process, it warrants special attention in the training. Managers need to have a very clear idea of what to say and do at this point. To make it real for managers have them participate in role-plays or skits.

This kind of activity allows managers to see their peers saying and doing the right things in different kinds of RTW scenarios. Because each manager participates in the activity, it also ensures that each manager has actually demonstrated the correct actions at least once. There is often a significant gap between understanding what should be said or done and actually demonstrating the correct behaviour. The strength of role-plays and skits is that they bridge this gap. Including a discussion of which actions were strong and which could have been improved upon can also be very valuable. To inject some fun into the training, consider including a skit of "how not to handle the situation".

One alternative to skits or role-plays is to produce a video that demonstrates the right and wrong actions managers can take when a worker indicates that he or she cannot work due to illness or injury. Video production can be costly, but the discussion regarding which actions are positive and which are incorrect can be very effective. Another alternative is to talk through case studies, again focusing on what is right and what is not.

There are many different ways to communicate the correct actions that managers can take at this point of the claims management process. The key training considerations are highlighting the importance of this point of the RTW process, the fact that this is an opportunity to begin dialogue about the RTW process, and the impact of what managers say and how they say it.

## Use of Forms

The correct completion of paperwork is often a difficult area for managers. Comprehensive training should include an explanation of the purpose of completing each form, as well as detailed training regarding how to complete the various forms.

Managers should understand which forms they are responsible for completing. Further, they should understand the purpose of each form, where the form should be forwarded, and the timeframe within which the form must be received. It's also a good idea to outline the possible consequences of incorrect or late form completion. Since the managers may not retain much of this detail, ensure that the information is documented and can be easily referenced.

The easiest way to ensure that managers really understand how to correctly complete the forms is to have them complete all necessary forms for a couple of different RTW examples. It is a good idea to include examples of both workplace and non-workplace injuries, and to follow these examples right through from the initial claim forms to the RTW paperwork. Managers should complete the forms the same way that they would complete them on the job (*e.g.*, electronically, paper and pen, *etc.*).

## Brainstorm Transitional Duties

One of the advantages of having a group of managers together is that it provides an opportunity for group synergy to produce ideas of greater quality and quantity than any one individual. This creates an ideal environment to brainstorm and compile a comprehensive list of types of work duties that can be assigned to ill or injured workers as they transition back to regular work.

As part of your research in developing the RTW program, you will have compiled examples of modified work solutions appropriate to your company's work environment(s). However, since it is unlikely that your list is comprehensive, it's a good idea to dedicate some time during the training to brainstorming and documenting various transitional duties for different types of injuries or illnesses. The added benefit of this approach is that it demonstrates to the managers that their ideas and input are valued, which is often crucial to the program's acceptance.

Once you have completed all of the training, put together a comprehensive list that includes all ideas generated in each training session. Grouping the transitional activities together into like categories (*e.g.,* transitional duties for a hand or arm injury) can be very helpful for managers. Send each manager a copy of this list as a follow-up to the training. This is also an opportunity for a personalized note of encouragement or thanks for participation.

## Marketing Strategy for the RTW Program

The only way to ensure that managers will implement and execute any program is to present a compelling picture of why it's in their interests. Normally, we think of marketing products and services to our customers, but marketing disability programs to managers and employees is equally as important. Your marketing plan doesn't need to be complicated or expensive, it only needs to be well thought out and reinforce the positive aspects of the program to the various constituents. Additionally, few marketing campaigns are based on a strategy of "send the message once and expect it to stick" — the strategy should use a variety of mediums to communicate the messages you want to send.

Organizations have different forums for communicating with managers and employees, but some of the media that you can consider are employee newsletters, employee brochure(s), posters or bulletins, union shop stewards, emails or memos to managers, an Intranet webpage, presentations at business meetings, and staff meetings. When choosing a communication vehicle, know who your audience is, tailor the message to address the concerns of the audience, and choose a communication method that targets that audience. For example, a reduction in claims costs should be communicated to managers, probably using a memo. Conversely, a human-interest story celebrating the successful RTW of an employee could be communicated in an employee newsletter.

A marketing plan also ensures that the program doesn't fade into the background after the training ends. A strategy that ensures that there will be an ongoing focus on communicating the benefits of the RTW program helps to ensure the success of the program, as it raises the awareness of managers and employees, even if they haven't had direct involvement with the program. Communication also creates an awareness of the program in the general employee population, as well as an understanding that there is an expectation for employees who are medically cleared for RTW programs to participate.

## Testing the Training

Conducting a beta or pilot test of the training that you have designed provides an excellent opportunity for fine-tuning the training. It can help you discover what works well and what does not. It can also uncover anything that may have been omitted.

A pilot test can help you understand the kinds of questions and concerns that managers have, before you face a large group. In this respect, it is an enlightening part of your preparation. It's also a safer environment for the trainer to gain experience handling objections and facilitating discussions.

A pilot test is an opportunity to get feedback regarding whether you have targeted the training to the right group. A smaller group of managers can often provide valuable information about who might handle different aspects of the RTW program, which can help you target your training to the right people. For example, you may discover that the training should be directed at two-person teams from each branch, a manager and an administrator. Or, perhaps the training would be better broken into sections and delivered to different groups.

At the conclusion of the pilot training session, you should devote some time to a focused feedback session. You'll want to ask managers what parts of the training were clear and informative. You'll also want to understand if there are any areas of the RTW program that they feel were not fully or clearly explained. The trainer must try to understand if there are any unanswered questions and if the managers believe that there is value to the program. You can obtain feedback regarding which activities or exercises were particularly useful and which added little value. People have different likes and dislikes, so remember to balance the feedback by determining if there is consensus, or if it's a single opinion.

Part of the informal marketing of any program is the grapevine. A small, influential group of managers who act as advocates and role models for your RTW program can be very powerful and carry a lot of weight with other managers. For this reason, you may want to pick your pilot group carefully, listen openly to the feedback, and embrace the suggestions that will improve the training or the RTW program.

Earlier in this chapter, we alluded to the fact that there is often much to be gained by involving managers as trainers. In every training session, especially the pilot session, ask managers to participate in facilitating future sessions. Even if they play a co-facilitator role, involving managers can go a long way to increasing support.

## Evaluate Training Effectiveness

Try to get feedback from every training session, even if you conduct a pilot. By obtaining feedback, you can understand if you are meeting the needs of the managers. Additionally, there is almost always room for improvement, so every suggestion should be invited and considered. Asking for feedback also provides managers with a sense that you care about what they think.

Written evaluation allows for confidential feedback. If you are going to use this, be sure to include open-ended questions such as, "What suggestions do you have to improve the training?" Leaving an open area for ideas and comments allows managers to share top-of-mind thoughts about the training.

If your culture supports open discussion of the successes and shortcomings of the training, this can be an effective way to get feedback, as it affords an opportunity to get clarification of some of the comments. Do not appear to be defensive, or you will not receive meaningful feedback. Feedback should be what you need to hear, not necessarily what you want to hear. If your culture does not support the candid sharing of shortcomings, this will not be a particularly useful way to get feedback.

Encourage participants to contact you in the future, if they have any suggestions for improvement once they've had an opportunity to put the program into practice. Again, the more open you are to feedback, the better your training will be.

## AFTER THE TRAINING

### Communication Packages

Immediately following the management training sessions, there should be a communications effort to begin a shared understanding of the RTW program throughout the organization. Provide the management training first, to ensure that managers can answer any questions that arise. For this same reason, it is often beneficial to provide any training or information to union business agents and shop stewards (if applicable) before any widespread communication occurs.

This initial communication should be an integral part of your RTW marketing strategy, and the primary objective for this communication should be to lead to a shared understanding of why the RTW program is being introduced. A secondary focus should be a high-level overview of the process, with an emphasis on the benefits of the program for employees. Stress the areas of dignity, respect, and the necessary medical authorization for RTW. This kind of communication that strives to achieve a shared understanding will reduce likelihood that any employees will feel singled-out when asked to participate in the RTW program and will also set up the right expectations for employees and managers.

Additionally, such communication can increase the awareness of other employees regarding why some employees may be working transitional duties and help to reassure them that there is a fair system in place for all employees. It also reassures co-workers that there is an expectation that employees will return to regular hours and duties. This kind of up-front communication is essential to ensuring that employee morale is maintained or improved as a result of the implementation of the program.

## Follow-Up after the Training

Ensure that managers do not associate the RTW program with a one-time training event. As the sponsor or advocate of the program, it is up to you to look for ways to keep the awareness of the program top of mind. Really, it is as simple as keeping in touch with the managers. Regular manager contact is a key part of the marketing of the program.

Ongoing contact with managers can be formal or informal. A simple way to remind managers of what they learned at the training is to include the following exercise in the training. Ask managers to write three objectives on a piece of paper and seal it in a self-addressed envelope. Sixty days after the training session mail the envelope back to the managers. This can serve as a useful and timely reminder of the commitments that managers made at the training.

Phone calls to individual managers to discuss any successes or challenges demonstrate your sincere interest and your availability to provide support. Providing regular updates on claims' statistics or changes in claims' costs is another useful way of keeping managers informed and invested. Sharing success stories with managers can be informative, inspiring, and also inject a little competitive spirit. You may also want to think about whether there is a need for follow-up, or more advanced training in the future.

This ongoing attention to the RTW program will help to prevent the flavour of the month syndrome that plagues many programs. In some organizations, this flash in the pan approach to programs has created a culture where managers simply sit back and wait for the program to fade away. An ongoing focus underscores the company's long-term commitment to the initiative, and furthers the position that it's a valuable part of the strategic business plan.

One of the key responsibilities of the training facilitator is keeping any commitments that were made during the training. Distributing a comprehensive list of transitional duties discussed in your session demonstrates your commitment to following through and providing support. It lets the managers know that their input is valuable and useful. This also represents your first opportunity to follow up after the training.

You can include a personalized note of support or recognition for a recent RTW success. It's also an opportunity to encourage managers to share ideas with each other — either through you, an Intranet or bulletin, or informally. The role of the trainer, after the initial training, is to encourage networking and partnering amongst the managers; it's never too early to start the process.

## Recognition

People like to be recognized for doing a good job. Ways to reward and recognize managers range from a simple thank you to a formal award presentation. The type of recognition varies by organization and culture, what matters most is that there is some recognition, not the type of reward.

You can recognize a manager quickly and easily through an email, voicemail, electronic card, postcard, or memo — possibly also advising the individual's direct supervisor of the accomplishment. Many employees say that the best recognition they ever received was a hand written note outlining an extra effort or accomplishment. Again, the nature of the recognition is not as significant as the fact that it is personalized, specific, and timely.

A key part of your RTW marketing strategy is recognizing managers who are exceptional at managing the RTW program. If your company has management achievement awards, investigate whether support of the RTW program can be included as part of the selection criteria or if a new award can be created. If you have management business meetings or a managers' bulletin, recognize managers who have succeeded in reducing claims' costs or duration.

If you have the support of senior management, investigate whether some members of senior management will invest time in recognizing and rewarding managers who go above and beyond. Again, it doesn't need to be formal, it just needs to be sincere. If you leave a voicemail, note, or email for a senior manager outlining a manager's success, the senior manager may be able to comment positively the next time he or she sees the manager. The more common this kind of communication becomes, the closer you are to instituting the RTW program as part of daily operating procedure.

## Get Testimonials

The marketing strategies for books and movies include reviews and quotes that help convince people of their merits. These kinds of public endorsements can be just as effective in the marketing of your organization's RTW program.

From the pilot test on, solicit and record testimonials from managers. You can include these quotes in presentations, reports to sponsors and managers, and written promotional materials. A newsletter article or bulletin about the RTW program could also include quotes, although you need to ensure that the message is the right one for the audience. Endorsements from operational managers will usually carry the most weight with other operators and senior managers.

If possible, try to get endorsements from employees too. Testimonials from employees who have had positive and successful experiences with the RTW program will be most influential with other employees. It's a good idea to supplement employee testimonials included in marketing materials with additional information and expectations that you want widely understood. Employee quotes can also be included in marketing materials, newsletters, and reports to senior management or sponsors.

If your company operates in a unionized environment quotes from union representatives or leaders can be very influential for your employees. If the union produces newsletters or bulletins, there may be an opportunity to include an article on the benefits of the RTW program. The RTW program can often be an area that both company and union can work together on, providing an opportunity for joint communication of its benefits.

## Be Available

No matter how much training you provide to managers, they will never be experts in Claims Management. Nor should they be. They are responsible for the day-to-day operation of their branches and it's unrealistic to expect the RTW program to be their number one focus. Therefore, be available to answer questions — even questions that you've answered before. Remain patient and provide professional support.

In addition to being available for coaching and questions, it's a good strategy to be proactive by placing follow-up calls with managers to see how everything is going and offer assistance. This is just another way to continue to keep managers focused on the importance of the RTW program.

If you were successful in including some managers as training facilitators, encourage them to act as coaches for other managers. These managers can also be great cheerleaders for the RTW program.

## Obtain Feedback on the RTW Program

Another follow-up to the training is to solicit regular feedback from managers regarding the effectiveness of the program. This will allow you to make modifications to the RTW program, as well as the training program that supports it.

One way to obtain feedback is through the use of surveys. These can range in complexity from elaborate, statistically validated studies to an informal telephone or pen and paper questionnaire. The feedback that you obtain should include information regarding managers' understanding of the RTW program, as well as how well the RTW program is meeting managers' needs. Information regarding the ease of following RTW procedures and form completion should be obtained. Soliciting information regarding the components of the RTW program that are working, as well as those that are not, can be invaluable. All feedback should provide managers with an opportunity to point out shortcomings in the program, as well as offer suggestions for improving the system.

As with other feedback that you have received, remain open and do not be defensive. Remember, although there are some comments you may not want to hear, they are comments you need to hear. Managers will use a system that works, but will quickly abandon a process that doesn't. For this reason, you want managers to raise concerns with you, not with each other — and, it's also why you should thank managers for their feedback.

Communicate the results of the feedback that you obtained, as well as how the information will be used to improve the process. This communication also provides you the opportunity to communicate the positive comments and feedback to the managers. If you don't take the time to communicate the usefulness of the feedback, and how it will be used to improve processes, you may find managers less eager to provide feedback in the future.

## Schedule Regular Training Sessions

Organizational structures rarely remain static in today's business environment. Your organization will experience turnover and growth, resulting in promotions and new incumbents. Thus, you'll likely need to schedule additional training sessions, to ensure that new managers understand the RTW program, and its associated procedures and expectations.

The RTW program often evolves over time, as new suggestions and ideas are incorporated. These changes can sometimes be significant enough to warrant a training update. Even if there aren't any substantial changes to the RTW program, follow-up training to refresh managers' knowledge can be very beneficial. Such follow-up training keeps the awareness high and can be an opportunity to communicate program successes and statistics.

The format of such training depends on the extent and nature of the changes. Some of the formats to consider include meetings, workshops, bulletins, workbooks or manuals, conference calls, videos, CD-ROMs, and web-based training.

## Differentiate Between Training and Accountability

Just as business challenges can not all be solved by training, training can not be held responsible for the ongoing success of the RTW program. Training can provide information and teach new skills. Effective training will result in the communication of the importance of the RTW program and a widespread comprehension of how to follow the defined RTW procedures. However, training doesn't necessarily change behaviour, so the measurement of success must differentiate between training and accountability.

For the program to be successful over time, managers must be held accountable for following the program. If it is acceptable to opt out of the RTW program, and it is easier to opt out of the program, the RTW program will fail. One of the roles that senior managers can play is to ensure that managers are not allowed to "self-select-out" of the RTW program. Senior managers must properly position the RTW program as a business strategy that is as important to the organization's success as any other business practice.

## What the Future May Hold

Tomorrow, like today, the best choice for the training format will be the one that clearly communicates all of the information at a reasonable cost. While there will undoubtedly be changes in technology that will provide new, and possibly less expensive, options for the communication, training, and marketing of RTW programs, the most critical factor in determining the success and viability of the program will continue to be a strong foundation. A simple, convenient RTW program design, supported by user-friendly tools and forms, regular measurement, and meaningful feedback will always be more important than adopting the latest training vehicle.

Technological advancements may allow for faster delivery of more detailed information or training, more sophisticated automated analysis of results, or immediate feedback/advice following on-line form completion. However, what won't change is the need to establish clear program and training objectives, communicate the business imperative to managers, and obtain widespread understanding of the purpose, scope, and processes of the RTW program.

So, in the future, everything will change and nothing will change.

# Chapter 3

# THE TECHNOLOGY TOOL FOR DISABILITY MANAGEMENT

*TERRI HEFFEL WITH ANN LECKIE*

## THE TECHNOLOGY ADVANTAGE

The major reason for disability management technology = cost control + prevention.

Business today has recognized the cost of managing disability claims. However, until recently, many companies have managed claims through a paper and pen system. This adds to the hidden cost of disability management. Employers were not easily able to analyze their data to determine what illnesses/injuries were impacting their workforce or what specific accidents were impacting the individual work areas. Recent technological advances that have streamlined many business functions are now at work in the area of disability management. There are computer programs that are available to any size employer from a simple over-the-counter spread sheet program to the highly sophisticated programming of Enterprise Wide Software (ERPS — Enterprise Resource Planning Systems) such as PeopleSoft.

This chapter uses examples from PeopleSoft. The concepts can be applied to any business or software.

Utilizing a software program will shift your disability management programs' focus from completion and adherence to regulations to true "management" of claims. This will allow the disability management program to focus on active intervention and management of claims using techniques described throughout this book. Software is the base of knowledge and true disability management utilizes this knowledge, experts, and programs to provide a sound return-to-work program that brings the previously marginalized disabled person into the mainstream workplace.

## What is a Relational Database?

Most disability management software programs are based upon relational databases. It is these databases that allow the experts to cross reference or "mine" data from individual claims to find trends and systemic issues. A relational database is an application that works as a "storage" facility for pieces of information that can then be retrieved based on common piece(s) of information.

1. Stores data in central location or database that can be shared;
2. Data is stored in a series of tables;
3. Each type of information is stored in its own table and is divided into rows and columns;
4. This format then enables relationships to be established between data in two ways:

"One to One"                           "One to Many"
1 Employee = 1 EmployeeID          1 EmployeeID = Many Claims

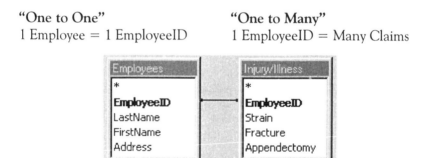

## How does a Relational Database Aid in Disability Management?

The most basic benefit of a relational database is that it allows access to cross reference information, for example, how many bank tellers have carpal tunnel or how many store clerks have low back pain. This information can then be used in many ways: reporting, statistical analysis, providing feedback, prevention and cost control. This information has always been available to the claims experts however, it would take significant amounts of time to consolidate. With a relational database, because the data is "on-line" the information needed is easily and quickly obtained.

For example, within a company, there might be a concern about the number of back injuries. The question then becomes how to quantify the anecdotal stories into statistically relevant information. Also, without the use of a relational database to maintain claims information there is a concern as to the accuracy of the information collected and reported.

With the aid of a relational data base and its reporting capabilities the data collection possibilities are only limited by the amount of data entered into the system. Data collection has a cost associated with it in terms of the time taken to enter it. The database can provide the number of back injuries for a given time period, work related or non-work related or both, specified by location, the length of each disability, the average length of return-to-work, the costs associated, the attending physicians, the average ages; the parameters are endless. The real advantage being that the time to provide this information is only as long as it takes to select the required data fields and print the report. The added bonus, confidence that the data supplied is both complete and accurate.

## Data Collection

From the above example it is clear that the most important concern for any disability management expert is the collection of data. No program can provide any benefit if the necessary data is not collected. With today's highly advanced software, data collection can now be collected with minimal paperwork stored virtually paperless, and used to a much greater extent. Having said that, there is still one very old premise that holds true — GIGO — "Garbage In = Garbage Out". The software will only be as good and useful as the data collected.

In the next several sections of this text, highlighted are critical fields that should be in your disability management software. Not all software programs have these fields. Not all these fields will be used in every disability management program. Outlined for you are commonly used fields. When designing or evaluating your own software, the claims managers should review with the end users of the software reports their needs and wishes. A review of the steps to solicit material from managers is discussed in chapter 2 on Training Managers. The end result is the managers' wishes should be broken down into data collection fields. The lists should be compared to the text below and any unnecessary fields should be reviewed and possibly deleted and any necessary fields should be inserted. Disability management programs differ from company to company. The software and data collection will also differ. Ensure that any program you purchase allows the disability experts to customize to their needs.

## Table Driven — Data Collection

When collecting data for a relational database, there are two major issues — what to collect, and how to ensure that it is collected consistently. For this reason it is very helpful to have software that is table driven. To a computer "sprain" and "sprian" are not the same. Limiting typing input is useful. It is also very important when a database is set up that each fields' associated table has consistent information. Keeping data simple and unique will ensure that the results of any inquiry will provide the desired output.

In the example below, if you want to report all "Dislocation" injuries, Table A will give more consistent results vs. Table B which has too many selections that are similar *e.g.,* "Sprain" and "Sprained".

## <u>Table A</u>                    <u>Table B</u>

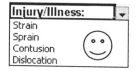
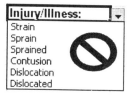

For easier data entry, create forms for the program or database to mimic the same flow of information.

## What Kinds of Flexibility to Look for in a Disability Program

Disability management programs are often difficult to purchase "over-the-counter", as it is a relatively new business tool. Most HRIS (Human Resource Information Systems) have a disability "module" or "component" to the programs offered. Often it depends on how large the organization is, or how extensive the disability costs are, which will determine the type of program selected. There are very large and intricate programs available, however, for smaller organizations there is always the option to "build your own database". This may limit the functionality of the program, but the most important data to the organization will be available.

For larger organizations a program that includes managing the organizational needs, outside service providers, and legislative requirements are important factors to review.

Whether large or small the most important component to look for in your software is the ability to report. Data collection whether it is in a filing cabinet or on your computer is useless without the ability to combine the information into relevant management information reports.

Remember data is NOT INFORMATION until it is formulated into useful reports.

## TRACKING THE INDIVIDUAL

The primary section of any disability management program tracks the individual claimant. This is the area within the software that will allow you to get to know the individual employee, their injuries, their claims trends, and history. This is especially critical in organizations with many offices or work units where a centralized disability manager might not personally know the employee. Some useful data fields are listed below.

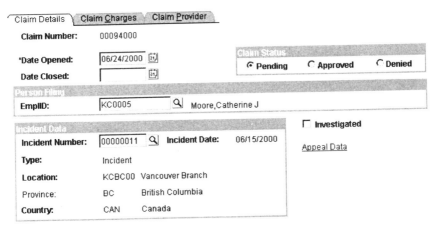

### Important Dates

Tracking the dates of a claim can be instrumental in managing the claim as so many of the factors involved are date sensitive or date required. The important dates to collect are as follows:

- Entry Date — This is the date when the claim is received by management. There are often "rules" with insurance carriers that the claim must be submitted within a specified period of time.

- Start Leave or 1st Day of Disability — This is the 1st day the employee misses due to disability. This is important for both management purposes and WCB regulation. WCB will treat the claim as a "Lost Time Claim" when the employee cannot do their job subsequent to the day of injury.
- Injury/Incident Occurred Date & Time — This is both the date and time of the injury. (WCB Regulation)
- Injury/Incident Reported Date & Time — This is both the date and time the injury was reported. Often there is a "gap" in the time the injury occurred and the time it was reported. (WCB Regulation)
- Start Early Return-to-Work (Estimated) — This is the date that you can establish using published information on "normal" length of disability for related injuries or illnesses. It is usually provided on the basis of light, medium, and heavy duties.
- Start Early Return-to-Work (Actual) — This is the date the employee actually returned to work on any sort of modified or light duty program.
- Full Return-to-Work (Estimated) — This is the date that you can establish using published information on related injuries or illnesses based on the specific job requirements.
- Full Return-to-Work (Doctor Estimated) — This is the date the employees' doctor has established as the full return-to-work. Remember, as a disability management practitioner, doctors need to be educated as to your workforce and your disability program. Often it is up to the employer to ensure the doctor knows the requirements of an employee's job to ensure a safe return. (See medical information and other correspondence)
- Full Return-to-Work (Actual) — This is the date the employee actually returned to work on full-time regular job duties.

The difference between the estimated dates and the actual dates can be used to "measure" the effectiveness of your management skills. A disability management program would want to track three things:

1. Trend towards a decreasing number of work-related accidents;
2. Trend towards decreasing length of absence within your organizational norms; and
3. Trend towards the length of absence being less than the norm for that particular illness or injury in the general public.

A well-managed disability plan should show decreased time away from work for illness/accidents.

## Injury/Illness Information

This may appear to be a relatively easy set of data to collect, unfortunately, it is more complex than it might seem to be on the surface.

Although an employee may report a specific type of injury, after visiting the doctor, the diagnosis may change. In addition, there can be a change in diagnosis during the duration of the claim and can even change from the initially reported body part. For example, a claim might start as low back pain then progress into a diagnosis of depression.

This is an area where a relational database and the flexibility to collect historical information are essential to managing a claim and cost.

The fields required to manage this information are as follows:

1. Injury/Illness Reported — This area should include both injury and illness information. For example strains, fractures, *etc.* and also illnesses or diseases such as diabetes, bi-polar disorder *etc.* to ensure that it encompasses the needs of both work-related and non-work related illnesses and injuries. To "build" a table of illness/injuries that is pertinent to your organization it is helpful to review your specific organization's historical information.
2. Diagnosis — This area is for when there is a difference in the reported injury.

Example:

(a) Reported:  Strain      Diagnosis:    Fracture
    or
(b) Reported:  Strain      Diagnosis:    Fibromyalgia
    These injuries will be managed in <u>significantly</u> different ways.

3. Body Part — This area is to report the affected body part. This should include both standard and technical terms to cover all types of injuries, illnesses, and diseases. In addition, it should include right, left, and both. (Managing a claim for a right hand injury is significant information if the claimant is left-handed.)

Example:
(a) Injury:    Strain        Body Part:      Shoulder - Right

| (b) Injury: | Fracture | Body Part: | Femur - Left |
|---|---|---|---|
| (c) Injury: | Hepatitis | Body Part: | Liver |

Again, when building the database, these fields are very important so keep the labels used as simple and unique as possible for reporting purposes.

## Medical Information and Other Correspondence

Disability management often includes a large amount of correspondence from doctors, employees, service providers and internal company documentation. Keeping the correspondence under control and adding relevant information into the database allows for efficient processing. (Refer to the Reporting section for samples and details.)

A program or database should include a "date driven" area that allows you to access the most current information including the following:

1. Doctor Information — This area should include the name, address, phone and fax number. In addition, the software should allow for multiple entries for historical tracking purposes for when a claimant adds specialists or changes doctors. This information can be included on forms that an employee completes or can be included directly into the software program by requesting the database from the College of Physicians & Surgeons.
2. Correspondence — Can be generic or specific to the organization and may include:

   (a)   Written Correspondence/Reports;
   (b)   Phone calls;
   (c)   Emails;
   (d)   Fax information.

Selected software should include an area that can manage this correspondence and where appropriate include the actual documentation; such as, the ability to attach emails or letters directly into progression or case notes.

1. Types of correspondence that may be helpful in tracking and managing a claim are as follows:

   • Service provider correspondence;

- Claim acceptance;
- Medical information requirements;
- Extension of benefits;
- Return-to-work strategies;
- Transition to long-term disability *etc.*
2. Workers' Compensation Board Correspondence — This area should include both information for claims (time loss and no time loss) as well as appeals:
   - Regulated mandatory claim forms;
   - Claim acceptance or denial letters;
   - Adjudicator correspondence;
   - Work site visit reports;
   - Modified return-to-work reported earnings;
   - Appeal division or review board information *etc.*
3. Medical Professional Reports:
   - Physician reports
   - Physiotherapy reports
   - Psychiatrist reports *etc.*
4. Light Duty Letters — This form is completed by a doctor and outlines the claimants' ability to perform light duties.
5. Work Activity Restriction Reports — This form is completed by a doctor and outlines the strategy for the timing of the transition and progression between light duties and full job duties.

## History and Trends

Once the individual claim is entered into the software it is possible to assess historical trends in relation to the individual. This is extremely useful for the claims manager. For example, a claimant with a history of low back pain may have responded well to a particular light duty program. With this knowledge the claims manager is able to set up a similar program to effectively deal with this particular claim.

History — Individual history can often make the difference in the ability to focus attention toward a specific individual.

Some common historical questions that can be answered through a relational database or program include:

- How many claims has this individual had?
- What type of claims has this individual had?
- What was the duration of each claim?

- What was the injury or illness?
- How much did each claim cost?
- Did the claimant participate in any rehabilitation programs?
- What preventive program was put in place for this illness/injury to ensure there are no repeats?

This information can also be used to determine if this injury is related to another previous injury. If so, it might be possible to reopen the original claim for illness or injury. This might result in a decrease in claims cost for the organization depending upon the length, severity and duration of the claim.

Trends — The historical information reported can then lead to the establishment of individual trends and can often give a much clearer picture of the claimant and thereby enable the manager to plan specific strategies for a safe and timely return to work.

Some common trend identification questions that can be answered through a relational database or program include:

- Were claims for similar injuries or body parts?
- What was the average claim duration?
- Did the claimant participate in a modified return-to-work program?
- Did the claims start at similar times each year?
- Did the claims happen at a specific location?
- How many claims resulted in acceptance or rejection?

## TRACKING THE GROUP

Once the individual is tracked within the system the software makes it possible to track the group. The definition of group can be made as inclusive as the disability management program requires. Using a large bank as an example, the group can be the entire bank, a single branch, or a job classification such as customer service representative. How an organization decides to track groups will depend on the nature of the organization. It is best to discuss fully with end users of the information what they would like to see in any reports. This way, the information will meet the needs of the claims management group as well as the strategic needs of the organization. Knowing the business and identifying these groups can aide in disability management for both cost control and strategic health and safety planning.

An example for an industrial setting might include:

- Management;
- Clerical/Technical;
- Mechanics;
- Welders;
- Fork Lift Drivers.

Each one of these groups have very different dynamics both from a job function and disability management perspective.

## Ability to Target Specific Employee Groups

Although these groups are usually established by area or pay group, with the use of a database, there is the ability to define groups into a more narrow "scope". Although there may be merit in a detailed breakdown, there is a balance that needs to be drawn between the user requirements and volume of data that is entered into the system. There is a cost to the collection of data in terms of data-entry.

| **Useful:** | | **Not Useful - Too** |
| Mechanics: |  | **Narrow:** |
| Journeyman | | Clerical: |
| Apprentice *etc.* | | Typists |
| | | File Clerks *etc.* |

## Statistical Information and Measurements

Data collected and reported on these specified groups will identify statistics and measurements for both setting goals and strategic planning.

Sample Statistical Information:

- What are the total claims for each employee group?
- What types of claims are they?
- Is there a relationship within a group between seniority and number of claims?
- What is the claim duration of the total group?
- What is the claim duration of a specified group?

Sample measurements:
- How do the number of claims differ between mechanics and welders?
- Does the duration of a claim differ between management and ForkLift Drivers?
- Is there a common injury for all welders?
- How does the number of claims compare to the industry average?

### Business Decisions Based on Group Data

The information collected based on group data can impact business decisions in many ways.

- Cost Control Initiatives;
- Health & Safety Programs;
- Training Programs;
- Return-to-Work Programs;
- Maintenance Programs;
- Strategic Plan Development.

Thus, it is in the area of group measurements that the disability program can be cost justified. It is here that the organization can fully understand the nature, duration, and type of disability claims it is facing.

## MANAGING COSTS

Cost control is one of the areas that separate disability management from other Human Resource functions. There is a direct correlation between management intervention and cost savings. Disability costs can be both identified and measured and therefore, they can also be controlled. Controlling these costs become more effective and efficient with the use of technology.

Individual Claim Costs

These costs are specific to an individual claim and include:

- Wage Loss;
- Health Care Benefits;
- Re-Conditioning Costs (*e.g.*, Physiotherapy or Work Conditioning Programs).

Employee Historical Claim Costs

An individual complete claim history including costs can be very informative. These costs can be viewed in several different ways:

- Work Related — Where an individual has WCB claims all costs should be managed as preventable costs.
- Non-Work Related — For non-work related claims the cost control should be managed through the return-to-work programs and through prevention programs such as stress reduction. Please see the chapter on EAP's for more information on these types of programs.

Overall Group Costs

Group costs can be measured for specific groups or for the entire company. These are costs that are not specific to an individual and are more subjective as they include the following:

- Benefit provider premiums;
- WCB premiums.

What about all the "Other" Costs?

There are many ways that a disability can "cost" an individual and a company. These "costs" are the reason that disability management is such an integral component to any management team.

- Costs to the employee:

  1. Quality of Life — both individual and family;
  2. Time away from work;
  3. Confidence in self and ability to perform job requirements;
  4. Time.

- Costs to the employer:

  1. Administrative costs;
  2. Program implementation training and development;
  3. Replacement employee costs;
  4. Modified duty program costs;
  5. Lost production;

6. Re-Training costs;
7. Work force morale.

Any of these costs, quantifiable or subjective, have one thing in common for their control... Prevention!

## RETURN-TO-WORK STRATEGIES

Once the employer has a thorough understanding of the nature of illness and injury in their workplace the next step is to implement Return-to-Work Strategies. Return-to-work strategies using technology takes much of the "guess work" out of creating a comprehensive and workable "plan" for an employees' safe and timely return to work.

The relevant areas that are required within the software to manage any type of return-to-work program require a combination of data collected. By combining this information, it enables the disability manager to plan a strategy based on the broader knowledge of the individual claim and the specifics of the relevant return to work data.

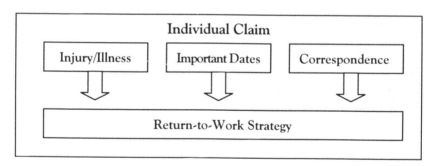

### Light Duty Programs and Their Effectiveness

Many companies have discovered that a light duty or modified duty program can be beneficial for both the returning employee and the productivity of the company. These programs allow continuity of the connection between the employee and the employer.

### Tracking Progression

In order to achieve the ultimate goal of a safe return-to-work, it is necessary to track the claimants' progression from light or modified duties to their individual job or "full regular duties".

## Making the Most of Correspondence and Doctor Reports

The collection of relevant data is essential. Most of this data can be gathered from various correspondence and doctor reports. Relevant data that is usually included in correspondence and how it can be used for return-to-work planning is as follows:

| Relevant Data | Program or Database Use |
|---|---|
| • Doctor Approval | ☐ Comparison of Duration-Doctor vs. Standard |
| • Light or Modified Duty Start Date | ☐ Clearance for duties vs. actual work |
| • Estimated Full Return-to-Work Date | ☐ Comparison of Duration-Doctor vs. Standard |
| • Any Job Restrictions | ☐ Comparison of restrictions vs. injury |
| • Progression Information | ☐ Progression from modified to regular duties |

## Integration to Access Payroll Information

Program integration or access to specific payroll information can be useful for both completing forms and time reporting.

1. Forms are completed using relevant and current payroll information.
2. Forms are completed using relevant and current benefit information.
3. Ensures the employees time is being recorded and paid accurately based on their return-to-work status.
 • Ensures information reported to the benefit provider or WCB is accurate based on return-to-work status.

## THE POWER OF REPORTING

Collection and tracking of data is useful in managing an individual claim or understanding group dynamics. However, for senior executives and management reporting information in a user-friendly manner ensures their "buy-in" of your ongoing disability management program. Thus, the ability to create reports is probably the most useful tool for disability management.

Reporting can be like breathing life and relevance into all the various collected data. The possibilities are endless.

Due to these endless possibilities, for simplification, there are two major categories of reports that should be created:

- Static Reports;
- Ad Hoc Reports.

1. Static Reports — These are also known as "canned" reports. Most software programs have a variety of reports that are available or have a "report writer" function that allows the user to build reports that are required on a consistent basis.

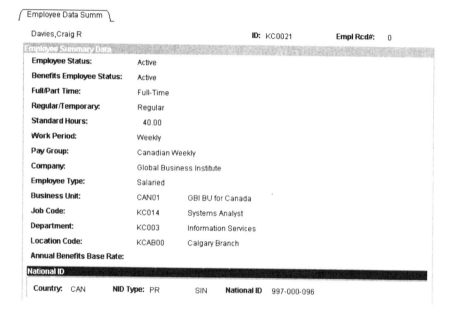

Sample static reports:

- Company Claim Information;
- Total Claims;
- Total Active Claims;
- Total Non-Work Related Claims;
- Total Work Related Claims;
- Total Time Loss Claims;
- Total No-Time Loss Claims;
- Total Cost.

Return-to-work information:

- Average claim duration;

- Total employees on light or modified duties;
- Comparison between estimated light duty start to industry standard;
- Comparison of full return-to-work to industry standard.

Individual claim information — Same as company claim information on an individual basis benefit provider or WCB information:

- Employee listing;
- Return-to-work status;
- Return-to-work hours and payment.

There are more possibilities for these types of reports and the general guideline for the requirement of a "static" or "canned" report should be measured by how often the same report is created. If a report is used weekly, monthly, quarterly or annually it should be a "canned" report. If the report is a "one off" for a specific purpose then it should be an "ad hoc" report.

2. Ad Hoc Reports — These are reports that are created using either a "report writer" or "download" to a spreadsheet for manipulation purposes. These reports can be created with a variety of data and are used for more detailed management or analysis.

CUSTOM01_INJURY_SUMMARY- Custom01-Injury Summary

Download results in : an Excel Spreadsheet (6 kb)

1 - 16 of 16

| | EmpID | Name | Incident # | Incdnt Dt | Type | Treatment | Log Comments |
|---|---|---|---|---|---|---|---|
| 1 | HFE001 | EE Survey testing,Employee 1 | 36151401 | 1990-01-12 | Incident | Medical | |
| 2 | HFE001 | EE Survey testing,Employee 1 | 36151402 | 1990-12-31 | Incident | Medical | |
| 3 | HFE002 | EE Survey testing,Employee 2 | 36151401 | 1990-01-12 | Incident | Medical | |
| 4 | HFE009 | EE Survey testing,Employee 9 | 36151404 | 1990-10-12 | Incident | Medical | |
| 5 | HFE009 | EE Survey testing,Employee 9 | 36151405 | 1990-09-08 | Incident | Medical | |
| 6 | HFE012 | EE Survey testing,Employee 12 | 36151406 | 1990-12-15 | Incident | Medical | |
| 7 | HFE012 | EE Survey testing,Employee 12 | 36151407 | 2001-09-01 | Incident | Medical | |
| 8 | HFEN01 | EE Survey testing,Non Employee 1 | 36151403 | 1991-05-02 | Injury | Medical | |
| 9 | HFEN01 | EE Survey testing,Non Employee 1 | 36151404 | 1990-10-12 | Incident | Medical | |
| 10 | KC0005 | Moore,Catherine J | 00000011 | 2000-06-15 | Incident | Medical | |
| 11 | KF0018 | Chabot,Yves | 00000016 | 1998-10-21 | Veh Acdnt | Medical | |
| 12 | KG0001 | Tendulkar,Indira | 00000013 | 1995-06-15 | Veh Acdnt | First Aid | |
| 13 | KG0003 | Jackson,Ritu | 00000014 | 1999-11-19 | Veh Acdnt | Medical | |
| 14 | KG0007 | Yu,Wai | 00000015 | 1997-08-14 | Injury | Medical | |
| 15 | KU0010 | Santos,Antonio | 00000010 | 2000-06-12 | Incident | Medical | details filed per regulation |
| 16 | L00001 | Rodriquez,Anna Lucia | 00000009 | 1999-10-28 | Veh Acdnt | First Aid | |

When creating any type of reports, keep in mind the matter of both relevance and interpretation by the user.

## Statistical Analysis, Trends and Measurements

These types of reports use only the data collected within the program or database. There is very little manipulation required. These reports deal with specific results and can be created using a "report writer".

Some general guidelines or information for these reports include:

1. Statistical Analysis — These reports include totals, counts, averages and generally answer the question of "how many?"
2. Trends — This kind of report can be used to monitor re-occurring injuries, body parts, and specific time periods.
3. Measurements — These reports show comparisons between data. This kind of report is generally for measuring return-to-work program effectiveness and will include a comparison of industry standard and actual claim duration.

## Budgeting, Bargaining, Planning and More...

These types of reports often require a "download" in order to manipulate the original data collected within the program or database. These reports usually deal with the question "what if?" and can be helpful for planning and analysis.

Some general guidelines or information for these reports include:

1. Budgeting — Reports created that show the actual costs of claims that can then be manipulated to include such variables as inflation, growth, closure, or any change in the business environment.
2. Bargaining — Reports can be created to aide in bargaining or negotiations and could include information about specific groups and their disability statistics to ensure the most effective benefit plans are available.
3. Planning and More... — The area of planning and managing through the use of reports can be an effective tool for any disability professional. These types of reports are really specific to the individual manager and can be as broad or detailed as required.
4. The advantage of the extra reporting capabilities is by far the ability to be pro-active rather than reactive.

### Demographics

Demographic reports can provide useful information that not only allows you to "know your employees", but also can aide in reviewing training or health and safety programs. These reports can answer the questions from employee groups before they're even asked.

Information that may be useful for disability management may include:

• What is the average age of the workforce?
• What is the breakdown by gender?
• How many employees are reaching retirement age?
• How many claims are by employees with less than two years experience?

### Day-to-Day Requirements

These reports are usually simple to create and fulfill specific requirements. Generally these reports provide the answer when faced with the issue of "this task would be a lot easier if I only had a list…"

## HOW TECHNOLOGY CAN AFFECT OCCUPATIONAL HEALTH AND SAFETY PROGRAMS

The use of technology as a tool to review occupational health and safety programs can be useful for prevention, training and review of the disability management program itself. With ever changing workforce dynamics, it makes sense that these programs should be evaluated and modified over time.

### Safety First… How to Avoid a Claim before It Becomes One…

Safety and prevention is by far the most advantageous method of managing disability claims. This is where the disability management professional has to make a commitment as all the data and reports in the world cannot impact claims unless there is a firm action plan to take this historical information to the next level of change and implementation.

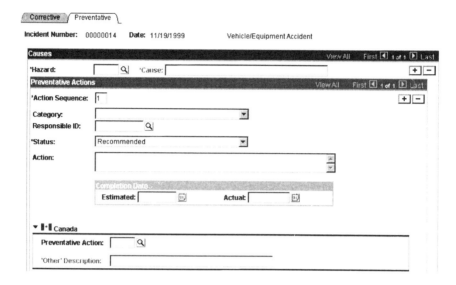

## Targeting Problem Areas

Using technology the ability to target specific concerns is more applicable than ever before. In the past, front line managers may have had a "hunch" about a work area that needed improvement, and with the use of data and reports these "hunches" can now be confirmed and strategies developed and implemented.

These problem areas can include both work-related and non-work related injuries and illnesses.

For work-related issues, software allows for the disability team to report to a front line manager that there is a consistent type of injury that occurs to a specific employee group. This often leads to direct analysis and subsequent change. This analysis could include a physical demands analysis of the specific job or maybe as simple as a slight modification to a work area.

For non-work related issues software can increase the employers' ability to implement programs to aid in sustaining a healthy workforce. These programs could include reviewing or implementing an employee wellness program, an Employee Assistance Program (EAP), or even promoting access to a fitness facility.

All of these programs promote good physical and mental health for all employees regardless of disability. These types of change have long-term impact on the organization.

## Setting Targets and Making Decisions

If all work related injuries are "preventable", then setting targets for reduction and prevention of claims is the basis of any good disability management program. These targets can now be quantified, measured, and reviewed. What may work today, may change tomorrow and to keep a competitive advantage, making the right decisions with the right information for disability management is essential.

## Technology Can "Tailor Make" Your Prevention Plan

The information collected and reported can be used to create a prevention plan that is specific to your business needs. This plan could include simple elements, of where to put fire extinguishers and eye wash stations, to more comprehensive reviews of job factors that may significantly change the workplace; such as, the need for a forklift, due to the level of reported back injuries.

Through the use of technology, experts can tailor make strategic plans that specifically fit your organizational needs.

**\*\* Technology = Cost Reduction + Prevention \*\***

## Keeping Everyone "In the Loop"

If communication is the key... unlock the information.

Historically, due to the confidential nature of disability claims, only disability management professionals were given access to claim files. Through the use of technology, security can be established, thus allowing modified access to other management groups within the organization.

This can actually expand the disability management team beyond the department and into the areas of the organization that could benefit most from the information. For example, an employer could have access to comparative cost data. If one location had no claims and another location had 20 work-related claims the second manager could learn techniques in claims reduction from the "best practices" location.

## INSURANCE CARRIERS AND WORKERS' COMPENSATION

The previous sections have focused specifically on how technology, in particular disability management software, can support your specific business, however, the "electronic age" has also affected agencies outside your business element, and depending on the agencies capabilities, can be integrated into your software packages.

Insurance carriers and Workers' Compensation Boards have recognized the benefits of using technology to provide their clients with more timely and accurate information. One of the most useful resources that can be provided in "download" format is the claim cost statements. These reports are usually available "on-line" and as a customization, can be set up to automatically "up load" into your specific disability management software.

## Are You Getting the Most from Your Insurance Carrier?

Many insurance carriers have used technology to establish similar software systems to the database information included in this chapter. Exploring the capabilities of this technology and the integration into your business software is an advantageous exercise. This integration can be relatively simple or can be explored for more complete service. Some areas that can be investigated are as follows:

- Email access to communicate "on-line" with claims adjudicators and managers;
- Download capabilities for premium statements;
- Download capabilities for wage replacement payments;
- Electronic form filing for application for benefits;
- Electronic sharing of case notes where applicable.

## How to Help Your Insurance Carrier Adjudicate Effectively

The most basic elements to help insurance carriers adjudicate claims is to provide them with timely and accurate forms and any other disability claim information required. For claims that have already been established, providing them with historical information can save time, carrier costs, and ultimately claims costs. Some types of historical information or reports that you could supply are as follows:

- Open claims with no modified duties where there is indication that they are relevant;
- Claims that have been open for a specific period of time. (*e.g.*, three months);
- Claim duration statistics;
- Modified duty hours and earnings.

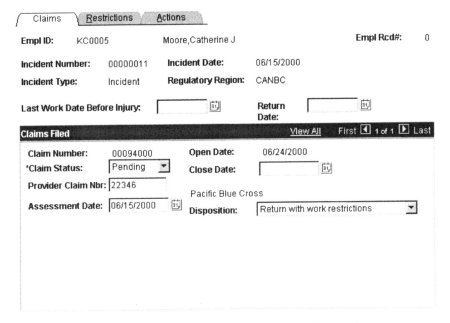

## Workers' Compensation and Legislative Requirements

Many Workers' Compensation Boards have implemented electronic case files. Most boards are expanding to allow employers access to electronic filing of many forms and may even include Internet capabilities. The software program that is selected should be flexible enough to encourage this aspect of disability management. When exploring software packages or creating your own database ensure that the legislative requirements of your provincial board are included.

## How to Keep Your Business and WCB "On the Same Page"

Many of the elements of technology that can be explored with your insurance carriers can be explored with WCB as well. Keep in mind, when building tables of information for your software, it is valuable to contact technical support at WCB as they can supply the foundation for tables for your databases.

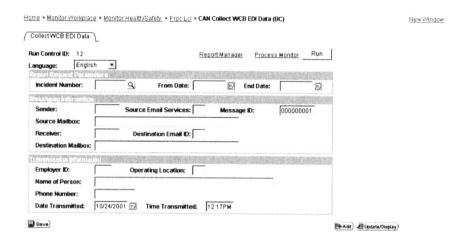

## WHAT DOES THE FUTURE HOLD?

Imagine if…

The amazing pace of growth in the technology field today will ensure that over time the disability management software available will become more comprehensive, fully integrated and "user friendly".

As disability management professionals, it will be a requirement to set the standards and demand the customer service for such an important element of business today. Technology is only limited by our imagination and creativity and how we apply it to expand the horizons of any disability management program.

# Chapter 4

# DISABILITY MANAGEMENT IN THE U.S. — A LEGAL PERSPECTIVE

NANCY GALLUP, ESQ. AND MICHAEL DROKE, ESQ.
(gratefully acknowledging the assistance of David
Overstreet, Esq., Amy Friedland, Esq. and Alan Ross,
Esq.)
DORSEY & WHITNEY, LLP[1]

## A UNITED STATES PERSPECTIVE

### Introduction

Many Canadian companies are now working across the border and they quickly discover that the border is more than an imaginary line across the continent. The requirements imposed by a complicated framework of U.S. state and federal laws change the entire environment in which a company works. Companies in Canada that wish to operate in the U.S. and plan to effectively manage the risk of employee disability must be

---

[1]  With 21 offices worldwide (14 in the United States, 2 in Canada — Toronto and Vancouver, B.C.), Dorsey & Whitney, LLP <http://www.dorseylaw.com> is a full service law firm. It is the 25th largest law firm in the United States with over 600 lawyers and over 800 support staff. The firm's Labor and Employment Law practice group comprises 40 trial and labor law lawyers from nearly all of the firm's offices. These lawyers work closely with 19 Employee Benefits lawyers who serve clients on issues related to employer-sponsored qualified retirement plans and non-qualified deferred compensation plans, group health, life, disability, severance and other employee benefit plans.

aware of these laws and be prepared to modify their disability management programs to satisfy them. To aid these Canadian companies we have provided below an overview of the U.S. statutes that relate to disability management.

Dealing improperly with employee disabilities in the U.S. can result in significant liabilities. A Canadian company should use caution when dealing with U.S. disability issues. Its employment practices and benefit plans that relate to disability should be reviewed by qualified lawyers specializing in U.S. employment law, and U.S. employee benefits law, to ensure that the company is in compliance with all U.S. statutes and regulations.

This chapter first explains the web of U.S. benefits and regulation. Then, some examples of common worker disability scenarios are provided. To simplify discussion, formal citations to the U.S. statutes referred to in this chapter are provided at the end of the chapter. A reference list is also provided for further information about U.S. disability regulation and issues.

## THE U.S. EMPLOYER'S CHALLENGE - COMPETING FEDERAL AND STATE LEGISLATION

There are two primary sources for disability benefits in the United States: governmental programs and employer-sponsored plans. Individuals can supplement these benefits by purchasing disability insurance. The disability legal landscape is not that simple, however, because there are other federal and state laws that govern disability in the workplace, such as the *Americans with Disabilities Act* (referred to sometimes as the ADA), and the *Family and Medical Leave Act* (referred to sometimes as the FMLA).[2]

The interplay between these laws creates a myriad of issues, in part because the laws define disability differently. Furthermore, state and federal laws may have different requirements for employers when an employee becomes temporarily or permanently disabled. Therefore, when employers working in the United States consider employee disability situations, they must successfully navigate through these state and federal laws, not only for the health and safety of their employees, but also as a shield against potential liability.

---

[2] *Americans with Disabilities Act*, 42 U.S.C. §12101 *et seq.* and *Family and Medical Leave Act of 1993* (FMLA), 29 U.S.C. §2601 *et seq.*

## GOVERNMENT BENEFIT PROGRAMS

### The Social Security Act

The *Social Security Act of 1935* (referred to sometimes as the SSA)[3] is a collection of federal welfare programs that generally provide benefits upon retirement, disability and death. A monthly disability insurance benefit is available under the SSA to individuals:

- Who are determined to be disabled (which generally requires a showing that the individual cannot engage in any substantial gainful activity);
- By reason of any medically determinable physical or mental impairment that can be expected to result in death or;
- That has lasted or can be expected to last for a continuous period of not less than 12 months;
- Who have not attained full retirement age (which currently is age 65); and
- Who have achieved disability insured status (which generally requires the individual to have earned a *minimum* number of credits of Social Security coverage).

Disability insurance benefits are payable to an individual who meets the above criteria after filing an application and after a waiting period expires (which generally is five full calendar months). The benefit is equal to the individual's primary insurance amount, which generally is the amount that the individual would have received under the SSA if the individual had retired at full retirement age. It lasts until the earliest of the month in which the individual dies, the month in which the individual attains retirement age, or the third month following the month in which the disability ceases. However, the SSA provides for a possible reduction in benefits where the disabled individual is also receiving Worker's Compensation benefits or disability benefits under certain other government programs, and the combined benefits exceed 80 per cent of the individual's pre-disability earnings. Benefits under the SSA are not reduced when benefits are received under private employer-sponsored plans, however benefits under such plans are typically offset for all government benefits received on account of disability.

---

[3]    42 U.S.C. § 301 *et seq.*

## Worker's Compensation

Individual states have Worker's Compensation laws that require employers to provide temporary and permanent disability benefits to eligible employees who incur work-related injuries and illnesses. It is the exclusive remedy for employees who suffer from such injuries or illnesses. Unlike FMLA, Worker's Compensation is entirely controlled by state law and guarantees compensation but (usually) not leave of absence or job protection. Worker's Compensation statutes cover almost every employer and cover any employee who sustains an injury arising "out of and in the course of" employment. Worker's Compensation also covers employees who have pre-existing conditions that are aggravated or accelerated by the employment relationship.

Worker's Compensation statutes vary greatly by state. States have different requirements for compensation due to total and partial disabilities. The classification of a disability is generally made by a medical professional and there are procedures for disputes over classification. Disability awards may also be subject to state limitations on the amount. States also have various notices, record-keeping, vocational rehabilitation, and reinstatement requirements. However, it is unlawful in every state to terminate an employee for filing a Worker's Compensation claim.

Worker's Compensation benefits can overlap or be qualified by other benefits. For example, an employee's Worker's Compensation absence can run concurrently with a FMLA 12-week leave when the work-related injury qualifies as a "serious medical condition". Additionally, the interaction between Worker's Compensation laws and the ADA brings forth interesting issues such as whether a person with an occupational injury has a disability as defined by the ADA or whether an employer must reasonably accommodate persons with disability-related occupational injuries. These are complicated questions to answer. The best advice to an employer who is faced with a Worker's Compensation issue is to consult the Worker's Compensation statute in the applicable state and, most importantly, an attorney familiar with that statute.

## Non-occupational Temporary Disability Insurance Laws

A few states, including California, Hawaii, New Jersey, New York and Rhode Island, as well as Puerto Rico, have enacted laws creating a state sponsored fund to provide disability income protection for non-occupational temporary sickness or accident. The benefits are principally funded through employee contributions, although some states require employers to contribute also. In lieu of participating in the state program, an employer generally can arrange to provide the benefits through a private insurance arrangement, although any such arrangement must meet state requirements. Eligibility criteria and benefit amount vary by state. However, a minimum waiting period is generally required before the individual can receive benefits (usually seven days) and there is generally a maximum duration of benefits (usually 26 weeks).

## EMPLOYER SPONSORED BENEFIT PLANS

Although employers are not required to maintain employee benefit plans that provide short-term or long-term disability benefits, many employers voluntarily elect to sponsor such plans. They finance their cost either through self-insuring or through the purchase of a group disability policy from a private insurance carrier. Many employers will require employees to pay a premium for coverage under the plan.

Employer sponsored disability benefit plans generally are subject to the *Employee Retirement Income Security Act of 1974* (referred to sometimes as ERISA)[4], which regulates both employee pension benefit plans and employee welfare benefit plans (which include disability plans). ERISA mandates include a written plan requirement, fiduciary standards, reporting and disclosure obligations, and civil enforcement provisions. Moreover, ERISA protects employees from reprisal or discrimination for exercising a right to a benefit, and prohibits employers from interfering with an employee's right to a benefit. Thus, for example, an employer cannot terminate an employee in anticipation that the employee will be receiving disability benefits. However, ERISA generally permits an employer who sponsors a long-term or short-term disability plan to amend the plan to provide lower benefits or even terminate the plan at any time as long as the plan reserves the sponsor's right to amend or terminate.

In addition, most states have enacted laws that regulate insurance carriers and the group insurance policies that the carriers sell. As a result, an employer that funds a disability benefit plan through the purchase of such a group insurance policy will indirectly be subject to such state laws given that the underlying policy will have to comply with state law. However, such state laws do not apply to an employer sponsored plan

---

[4]    29 U.S.C. §1001 *et seq.*

funded through self-insurance (*i.e.*, benefits are paid from the general assets of the employer or through a trust set up by the employer) because of ERISA and its effect of pre-empting state laws.

Perhaps surprising to many, ERISA does not mandate that employer sponsored disability plans provide a minimum level of benefit. In contrast, ERISA allows employers significant freedom in designing a disability benefit plan with respect to eligibility and benefits. Consequently, benefits vary from employer to employer. Of course, where the employees are represented by a labour union, the collective bargaining process usually determines the provision of disability benefits.

Short-term disability plans usually provide benefits for a period between 13 and 26 weeks to employees who cannot perform their normal occupational duties. Such plans typically require a waiting period, usually around one-week, and may be co-ordinated with an employer's sick leave policy. Benefits are either paid as a percentage of earnings, generally ranging from 50 per cent to 70 per cent of the employee's income, or as a flat dollar amount. If disability benefits require no contribution by employees, if they are paid entirely out of an employer's general assets, and if they are, in essence, a payroll continuation arrangement, then the benefits are not covered under ERISA.

Long-term disability plans usually provide benefits when short-term disability benefits expire. While long-term disability plans may use the same definition of disability used by short-term disability plans (*i.e.*, inability to perform one's occupational duties), most long-term disability plans continue receipt of benefits on the individual meeting a more strict definition. Typically the inability to perform *any* occupation based on training, education and experience. Although long-term disability plans may limit benefits to a set period, many plans generally provide benefits until the employee reaches retirement age. Benefits are usually paid as a percentage of earnings. Generally this ranges from 50 per cent to 60 per cent of the employee's income with a flat maximum monthly dollar amount.

One of the most significant duties in administering a disability benefit plan is the disability determination. Often disputes arise between the employer and the employee as to whether the employee meets the definition of disability under the plan. Where a plan contains appropriate language granting the decision-maker discretion when determining eligibility for benefits or interpreting the plan, a decision-maker's decision will be afforded deference by a court of law. As a practical result, a disability determination by the party responsible for administering the plan will be conclusive as long as it is based on reasonable medical evidence regardless of whether a court would have reached a different conclusion from the evidence.

A disability plan administrator must often access health information to determine whether or not a claimant is disabled and entitled to benefits. Health care information is protected under privacy regulations authorized by the *Health Insurance Portability and Accountability Act of 1996* (HIPAA).[5] The HIPAA regulations require that before an employer or disability plan administrator can have access to protected health information of a participant, the participant must give specific written authorization. The information must not be used for any purpose other than the limited purpose detailed in the authorization. Employers or plan administrators should review their claim forms to ensure that they meet the requirements for the authorization found in the regulations, and should ensure that procedures are in place to safeguard participants' health information and limit its use to those authorized.

## OTHER LAWS GOVERNING DISABILITY

### Americans with Disabilities Act

The *Americans with Disabilities Act* (ADA)[6] was enacted in 1990, and became effective July 26, 1992. The purpose of the ADA as it relates to employment is to promote the employment of those who are disabled and who are still able to perform the essential functions of their job with some form of additional assistance that is not unduly burdensome for the employer to provide.

The ADA expressly seeks to eliminate employment decisions being made on the basis of stereotypes, unfounded fears, and assumptions regarding the abilities of disabled persons to work and on the basis of other employees' preference not to work with such disabled persons. Thus, while the ADA is a complicated statute and often difficult to administer, the key to compliance is to evaluate applicants and employees on the basis of their actual ability to perform the job, not on the basis of assumptions.

The ADA requires that employers with 15 or more employees provide reasonable accommodation to "otherwise qualified individuals with disabilities" unless providing such accommodation would impose an "undue hardship" on employers. The ADA protects employees working

---

[5]  Pub. L. No. 104-191 (Aug. 21, 1996).

[6]  42 U.S.C. §12101 *et seq.*

for a United States employer in a foreign country, such as Canada, if they are citizens of the United States. Both applicants and employees are entitled to protection under the ADA. In some circumstances, even former employees may be entitled to protection under the ADA's anti-retaliation provisions.

The employment provisions of the ADA generally only protect "otherwise qualified individuals with disabilities" — i.e., persons with disabilities who are both qualified for the job and able to perform the essential functions of their job with or without reasonable accommodation. Thus, the ADA does not provide protection to persons who are unable to work or who are not able to perform the essential functions of a position, with or without reasonable accommodation.

Exceptions to this general rule are applicants for whom it is not yet known whether they can work or perform essential functions and for whom the employer is required to provide reasonable accommodation in the application process itself. Further, in limited circumstances, an employer may be required to accommodate employees who are unable to perform the essential functions of their current jobs by moving the employees to vacant positions that the employees are capable of performing with or without reasonable accommodation.

The ADA only protects those who are disabled. This means that before an employer is required to provide reasonable accommodation, 1) the person must demonstrate that he or she has a disability as defined by the ADA; or 2) otherwise be regarded as being disabled. Under the ADA, a disability is a physical or mental impairment that substantially limits a major life activity. This means, generally, a long-term or permanent physical or mental condition that actually and substantially currently limits a person's ability to do such things as see, walk, hear, talk, care for oneself, speak, breathe, learn, and work.

Unfortunately, there is no definitive list of what constitutes a "disability" although the regulations of the Equal Employment Opportunity Commission (EEOC) provide some guidance. There are no *per se* disabilities, and what may be a disability for one person may not be for another, depending on how a particular impairment currently impacts a particular person's ability to perform a major life activity. Each person must be evaluated individually for purposes of determining if he has a disability. Thus, a broken leg would not constitute a disability, while an amputated leg may be a disability. Similarly, pneumonia may not constitute a disability, while emphysema may be a disability.

In determining whether a particular person has a disability, the employer should attempt to objectively evaluate all available current medical information, as well as all factors the person uses to "mitigate" his disability — e.g., hearing aids, eyeglasses, medications, canes. Furthermore, employers should not accept without question the conclusion of the person's doctor that the person is disabled. The employer is permitted to have performed at its own expense an independent medical examination of the person, unless the person's disability and concomitant limitations are obvious.

The ADA also provides protections to persons who have a "record of" a disability or who are "regarded" by the employer as being disabled. The "record" provision of the ADA prohibits employers from discriminating against a person because he had, but no longer currently, has, a disability such as a past addiction to drugs. The "regarded" provision of the ADA prohibits employers from discriminating against a person because the employer mistakenly believes that the person has a disability or that the person's actual impairment substantially limits a major life activity, when in fact the circumstances are not so severe. Importantly, however, an employer does not "regard" a person as disabled merely because the employer views that person as unable to meet a particular job qualification standard, such as a lifting or standing requirement.

Upon request by an applicant or employee who is truly disabled, an employer must provide the person with "reasonable accommodation", so long as the accommodation does not impose an undue hardship on the employer. "Reasonable accommodation" may include "job-restructuring, part-time or modified work-schedules, reassignment to a vacant position, acquisition or modification of equipment or devices, appropriate adjustment or modifications of examinations, training materials or policies, and the provision of qualified readers or interpreters".

An employer is obligated to consider re-assignment to a vacant position only where the employee is unable to perform his current job with accommodation, the employee is qualified for and able to perform the vacant position. An employer is also obligated to consider granting leave to the disabled employee, although the employer is not generally required to grant indefinite leave or leaves of unreasonable duration. While an employer may be required to eliminate marginal functions of a position to accommodate an employee, the employer is never required to eliminate "essential functions". This means, for example, that an employer is not required to eliminate the lifting function of a warehouse position if that function is one of the core tasks of the position. Finally, an employer is not required to grant the precise accommodation requested by the employee. Where two or more accommodations are equally effective in permitting the employee to perform the essential functions of the position, the employer is entitled to select which accommodation will be offered.

Finally, the employer is not required to provide any accommodation if doing so would impose an undue hardship on the employer or would result in a "direct threat" to the employee's safety or the safety of others. "Undue hardship" means an accommodation that would impose significant expense on the employer (depending on the employer's size and financial resources) or unduly disrupt its business operations (*e.g.*, placing a ramp in the middle of a cramped production floor). "Direct threat" means an imminent risk of serious harm. The employer bears the burden of making both of these showings. Few situations reach this stage because most are resolved by a conclusion that the employee is not disabled or by the provision of a reasonable accommodation, generally costing less than a few hundred dollars.

Many state statutes also provide parallel or even greater protection to persons with disabilities, although few states require employers with fewer than 15 employees to provide reasonable accommodation. Consequently, employers should carefully analyze the civil rights laws of each state in which they have operations.

## Family Medical Leave Act of 1993

### 1. Generally

The federal *Family and Medical Leave Act of 1993* (FMLA)[7] was passed in order to accommodate families in difficult times by providing a minimum labour standard for leave. FMLA requires covered employers to grant eligible employees 12 weeks of unpaid leave for family and medical reasons in a 12-month period. The statute and its accompanying regulations are much too complex and technical to cover thoroughly in a brief section. However, it is vital for employers operating in the United States to understand the principle components of the statute and to be alert to potential difficulties it poses.

An employer is covered under the Act if the employer "employs 50 or more employees for each working day during each of 20 or more calendar workweeks in the current or preceding calendar year". The Department of Labor (DOL) includes part-time, temporary, and leased employees in the total. The DOL will generally look only to the employer's payroll records to make this determination, and will reject arguments that non-

---

7    29 U.S.C. §2601 *eq seq.*

working individuals on those records should not be included in the calculation.

An eligible employee is an employee who:

- has been employed by the employer for at least 12 months (these months do not have to be consecutive);
- has worked at least 1,250 hours during the 12-month period immediately preceding the commencement of the requested leave; and
- is employed at a work site where the employer employs 50 or more employees within 75 miles of the site.

An employee may take FMLA leave for the following reasons:

- the birth or the placement of a child for adoption or foster care and to care for such child after birth or placement;
- to care for a parent, spouse, or child with a "serious health condition"; or
- an employee's own "serious health condition" which renders the employee unable to work.

The statute and regulations define a "serious health condition" and also provide that an employer may require that an employee submit medical certification, issued by a health care provider, of the serious health condition that forms a basis of their FMLA claim.

FMLA leave is unpaid leave. However, an employer may require, or an employee may request, that an employee's paid vacation or sick/medical leave be substituted for any unpaid FMLA leave. This means that an employer only has to provide 12 weeks of total leave each year and does not have to give an employee an extra 12 weeks of leave after the expiration of an employee's vacation or sick time. When an employee uses paid leave instead of FMLA leave and the employer's procedural requirements for taking that type of unpaid leave are less stringent than the FMLA requirements, the employer can only require that the less stringent requirements be fulfilled. An employer is also responsible for designating leave, paid or unpaid, as FMLA leave, even if the employee's request does not mention FMLA.

FMLA may either be taken in one block of time or as intermittent or part-time leave. For example, FMLA leave taken due to the birth of a child or placement of a child for adoption or foster care must be concluded within 12 months of the birth or placement, and the employer may require that such leave be taken in one block of time. On the other hand, an employer must allow an employee to take FMLA leave to care for a family member with a serious health condition or due to the employee's own serious health condition on an intermittent or reduced leave schedule when medically necessary. If an employee needs intermittent or reduced leave and such leave is foreseeable based on planned medical treatment, the employer may require the employee to temporarily transfer to an alternative position for which the employee is qualified. Such position would better accommodate recurring periods of leave than would the employee's regular position. The alternative position must have equivalent pay and benefits.

There are several notice requirements connected with FMLA both on the part of the covered employer and the eligible employee. An employee must provide an employer with notice of the requested FMLA leave 30 days in advance or as soon as practicable. In turn, a covered employer also has notice obligations including conspicuously posting the pertinent provisions of FMLA in the workplace and must designate the leave as FMLA-qualifying, both verbally and in writing almost immediately after the request is made.

When an employee is on FMLA leave, the employer is responsible for maintaining an employee's group health plan coverage on the same conditions and level of coverage as would have been provided if the employee had been continuously employed during the entire leave. Upon return from FMLA leave, an employee is entitled to be reinstated to the same position the employee held when FMLA leave commenced or to an equivalent position with equivalent benefits and pay. There are exceptions to reinstatement for highly paid employees or for employees who would not otherwise have been employed at the time the reinstatement is requested (*e.g.*, reduction in work force). In certain circumstances, the employer may have to give prior notice of its intent not to reinstate.

Finally, the employer cannot discriminate against employees who request FMLA leave. Rights under FMLA are enforceable by eligible employees through civil actions. Therefore, non-compliance with the statute may subject the employer to serious penalties.

### 2. Interaction with State Laws

Almost every state has family and medical leave laws. Although these laws are typically not as comprehensive as FMLA, several states have laws that are more restrictive than FMLA. It is important, therefore, for an employer to be aware of the applicable state law in order to sufficiently comply with both federal and state law.

For example, some states such as Maine, Hawaii, Massachusetts, and New Jersey have less stringent requirements to qualify as a covered employer or employee for purposes of family and medical leave. Other states provide additional benefits to those provided in FMLA. Massachusetts recently passed a "small necessities" leave Act. This Act entitles an employee who works for an employer with 50 or more employees to take 24 hours of unpaid leave during any 12-month period for participating in certain school activities or accompanying children or an elderly relative to a routine medical or dental appointment. Massachusetts joins six other states (California, Illinois, Louisiana, Minnesota, North Carolina and Vermont) and the District of Columbia by enacting this law. Moreover, several states including Oregon, California, and Tennessee allow employees to take additional leave for pregnancy.

The foregoing are just a few examples of the differences in state and federal family and medical leave laws. It is vital, therefore, to be familiar with both FMLA and the applicable state laws to sufficiently comply with the leave laws in the United States.

## Health Plan Continuation Rules

The *Consolidated Omnibus Budget Reconciliation Act of 1985* (COBRA)[8] is the federal health care continuation law that allows employers or their families who lose group health care coverage to continue that coverage under the employer's group health plan for a limited period of time. The employee simply pays the cost of coverage at group rates. With limited exceptions, COBRA applies to a group health plan sponsored by an employer who has 20 or more employees on a typical business day in the previous calendar year. For the purpose of determining whether a company has the requisite number of employees, employees employed by a company outside the United States are counted even though such employees generally cannot elect COBRA coverage. Thus, an employer who has a Canadian facility with 200 employees and a United States facility with 10 employees will be subject to COBRA with respect to the United States facility.

---

[8]   Pub. L. No. 99-272 (April 7, 1986).

In general, the maximum COBRA period for which an employee or former employee may extend coverage is 18 or 36 months, depending on the event that caused the loss of coverage. In the case of an individual or family member who is or becomes disabled (as determined under the *Social Security Act*) within the first 60 days of COBRA coverage, that individual and his family may be able to extend COBRA continuation for up to an additional 11 months. The purpose of this extension is to permit a disabled individual to remain on COBRA coverage until entitled to Medicare. To be eligible for this disability extension, the initial loss of coverage must be a result of either the employee's termination or a reduction of hours.

## A PRACTICAL COMPLIANCE APPROACH

The first step in developing a coordinating compliance approach for dealing with disability and disability leave issues is reviewing all employer communication and internal policies and procedures dealing with disability. It is critical for U. S. employers to establish policies and procedures that meet at least the minimum requirements of all applicable federal and state regulations. It is equally important for U. S. employers to understand that to the extent the policies exceed the statutory minimums, that they may be bound by those commitments. For example, where an employer has a policy that provides for paid leave to an employee who experiences a serious medical condition, an employer may be obligated to provide such paid leave even though the FMLA may only require an employer to grant unpaid leave to an employee.

Below are some situations that often arise when dealing with disability in the U. S. workplace. Following each scenario is a discussion of the types of benefits often available to the employee. Leave and return-to-work issues are also discussed (including whether the employer can fire the employee and how long the employer has to hold the employee's job for the employee out on disability leave).

### Short-term Disability

Employee who has worked on a substantially full-time basis for one year is injured in a non-occupational accident or is diagnosed with a short-term illness that prevents him from working for a short time period, anywhere from one week to six months. Return to work is a viable option.

## 1. Employment Issues

- **Is the employer required to grant the employee leave (unpaid or paid)?**

The employee's condition would probably qualify as a serious health condition under the FMLA because, at a minimum, the employee requires more than three days of consecutive leave for his condition under the care of a health care provider. As a result, the employer would be required to grant this employee 12 weeks of unpaid FMLA leave, unconditionally, unless the employer does not have sufficient numbers of employees to be a covered employer under the FMLA at the facility in question. The employer would be further required to return this employee to his same or similar job after 12 weeks of leave. The employer could require the employee to take any allowable paid time-off (*e.g.*, sick leave) as part of the FMLA leave. The employee might be entitled to further leave if and only if the person's health condition also qualified as a disability under the ADA. It seems doubtful that the employee's condition would qualify as a disability because it appears to be short-term and/or temporary. The employer is not required to grant paid disability leave. The EEOC takes the position that, if the employer grants leave as an accommodation under the ADA, it must return the employee to his same job; this issue has not been decided by the courts.

- **What amount of leave must an employer give an employee under federal law?**

The FMLA currently requires only a total of 12 weeks of leave in any calendar year for eligible employees. Congress is currently considering an extension of the amount of time and the eligibility requirements. It is not possible to say for certain how much leave is <u>required</u> under the ADA, as it depends on the employee's circumstances, the employer's business needs, and the employer's prior practices.

- **Can the employer terminate the employee's employment?**

Yes, the employer may terminate the employment of an employee who qualifies for FMLA leave or who is disabled provided the termination is not because of:

- the employee's disability or serious health condition;

- the employee's request for FMLA or disability leave;
- an erroneous perception that the employee cannot do his job due to his disability;
- or in an effort to interfere with the employee's exercise of his FMLA or ADA rights.

For example, if an employee on FMLA leave would have been discharged anyway for legitimate non-discriminatory reasons, such as a lay-off, the employer can still terminate that employee on FMLA leave. As another example, an employer may terminate an alcoholic employee for misconduct even if the misconduct is induced by the employee's alcoholism (a disability) because the reason for the termination is misconduct, not the employee's disability.

- **How long is the employer required to hold open the employee's job while the employee is on leave?**

The safer course is to always hold an employee's job open while he is on FMLA or ADA leave. FMLA requires that the employee be returned to the same or a similar job, although effectively the federal government has concluded that it must be the same job. The ADA contains no express mandate whether the employee must be returned to the same job, but the EEOC has concluded that the employer must keep that job open unless it can prove that doing so creates an "undue hardship". If the same job cannot be held open, the next safest course is to provide the employee with a job with identical pay and benefits and, to the extent possible, the same working hours and working conditions. The further the employer strays from providing a nearly equivalent job, the greater the risk will be that the employer will be found in violation of the FMLA or the ADA.

- **Can an employer reassign the disabled employee's job duties to a co-worker?**

Yes, as long as those job duties are returned to the employee after the expiration of his leave. The FMLA requires that the job duties be returned. This has to be done even if the employee's duties were temporarily reassigned to another employee to accommodate the leave. The ADA is less clear on this obligation. However, after the employee returns from leave, an employer is not required to reassign essential functions of the employee's job to another employee as a reasonable accommodation under the ADA. The employer may insist that the employee be able to perform those essential functions, with or without reasonable accommodation. If the employee cannot perform those functions and he cannot be transferred to a vacant position for which he is qualified and which transfer would not violate the seniority rights of others, he can be discharged.

- **Can the employer require medical certification before allowing a leave?**

Yes. The Department of Labor has developed a FMLA medical certification form for employers to use. Employers need not use this form, but must keep in mind that information requested from an employee must relate only to the serious health condition for which the current need for leave exists.

## 2. Employee Benefit Issues

- **What plans may provide benefits during short-term disability?**

In those states that have enacted non-occupational temporary disability insurance laws, a disabled employee may be eligible to collect benefits from the state. For most employees, however, an employer-sponsored short-disability plan is the principal source for benefits. Generally, such plans require an elimination period — a short waiting period during which the individual must be continuously disabled — before benefits are paid out. Many employers coordinate this elimination period with their sick leave policies.

- **May an employee continue health care coverage during short-term disability?**

In general, employees are able to maintain health care benefits during a period of short-term disability. If eligible for FMLA leave, employees of an employer that provides health care benefits under a group health care plan are entitled to health care benefits during their leave that they would have been provided if still working. In many cases, an employer's group health care plan allows an employee to continue to participate in the plan while the employee is on leave or receiving short-term disability benefits. In those cases where an employee loses health care coverage due to the reduction in hours or termination, COBRA continuation rights may be applicable.

## Long-term Disability

Employee is seriously injured in a non-occupational accident or is diagnosed with a serious chronic illness that prevents the employee from working for an extended time or permanently. Return-to-work is an option, if at all, only with significant accommodation and lengthy rehabilitation time.

### 1. Employment Issues

- **Is leave required?**

Generally, the employment issues involved in long-term disability situations are the same as the questions and answers in the discussion above regarding short-term disability. The only issue is that, if the employee concedes at the outset that he is permanently disabled and can no longer work at all and will not be returning to work, neither FMLA nor ADA leave is required.

### 2. Employee Benefit Issues

- **How are long-term disability plans structured?**

Benefits under an employer sponsored long-term disability plan are usually paid out after an elimination period — usually equal in length to the maximum duration of short-term disability benefits. In addition, medical certification is almost always required before an employee becomes eligible for benefits.

- **May an employee continue health care coverage during long-term disability?**

Just as with short-term disability benefits, many employer sponsored group health care plans allow for continued participation by an individual receiving long-term disability benefits regardless of whether the employer classifies the disabled individual as a current employee. However, the eligibility criteria of each plan must be examined carefully on this point.

If the plan does not provide for benefits during disability, COBRA continuation rules may apply.

## Intermittent/Partial Disability

Employee has a disability that prevents full-time work status; employee can only work part-time or has to take a leave of absence every so often.

### 1. Employment Issues

- **Is the employer required to accommodate employees by allowing them to work part-time? If so, are there any limits?**

Under the FMLA, the employer is required to provide up to a total of 12 workweeks of intermittent leave as long as the disability qualifies as a serious health condition. There are certain constraints on the intermittent leave. First, the employer may require the employee to transfer temporarily during the period of intermittent or reduced leave to an available alternative position for which the employee is qualified and which better accommodates recurring periods of leave than the employee's regular position. The alternative position must have equal pay and benefits. Second, spouses who are both employed by the same employer may be limited during any 12-month period to a combined total of 13 weeks of FMLA leave. The leave may be due to the birth of a child or placement of a child for adoption or foster care or to care for a parent who has a serious health condition. Additionally, FMLA leave taken due to the birth of a child or placement of a child for adoption or foster care must be concluded within 12 months of the birth or placement, and an employer may require that such leave be taken in one block of time. After the expiration of the FMLA leave, under the ADA, an employer would be required to allow further part-time and/or intermittent leave so long as the accommodation is reasonable and does not require the employer to eliminate essential job functions. The required duration of such leave under the ADA would depend on the facts of the case.

- **At what point can the employer terminate the employee's employment?**

An employer can terminate an employee's employment after the expiration of allowable FMLA leave in three circumstances. An employer does not have to reinstate an employee's position under the FMLA if:

- the employer can show that an employee would not otherwise have been employed at the time the employee requests reinstatement (*i.e.*, due to a reduction in force);
- the employer can show that the employee is a highly compensated "key employee" whose reinstatement is denied to prevent "substantial and grievous economic injury" to the company and the employee receives the required notice;
- the employee is unable to perform the essential functions of the position because of a physical or mental condition, including the continuation of a serious health condition, and if further leave would not be required as a reasonable accommodation under the ADA.

Even if the employee needs and is granted further leave as an accommodation under the ADA, the employer can terminate the employee once the length of the leave becomes unreasonable or once the employee's leave begins to substantially disrupt the employer's business operations such that it constitutes an undue burden.

- **Does the employer have to treat dissimilar disabilities the same for accommodation purposes?**

Not necessarily. The focus of the ADA generally is on individualized assessments both as to the nature and extent of the disability, as well as to the nature and extent of the required accommodation. The determination of what accommodation is reasonable, effective and required generally depends upon a host of factors specific to the particular case, including what job the employee performs, whether non-essential job functions can easily be assumed by others and what impact the accommodation has on an employer's business operations. Therefore an employer may treat an employee with cancer differently than it might treat an employee with a severe lifting restriction. In some cases such as HIV in a medical setting, or epilepsy in a driving job, the employee's disability may make the employee a "direct threat" to the safety of other employees requiring no accommodation; whereas HIV in a driving job may not make an employee a direct threat. Different accommodations might be required. It is important to note, however, that once an employer provides a particular type of accommodation to an employee that accommodation sets a precedent for future accommodations. If an employer allows a person with HIV to work in the operating room of a hospital with certain accommodations, the employer may have difficulty denying a similar accommodation to another person with a communicable disease if that accommodation would allow the employee to perform the essential functions of the job.

- **Can an employer force an employee back to work?**

The employer can never force an employee to work. It can, however, terminate an employee when that employee fails to return after FMLA leave expires and after any additional leave required as a reasonable accommodation expires or if the employee makes clear that he does not intend to return to work. States may have their own individual laws that provide for leave under different circumstances. Before proceeding with a discharge, an employer should learn the requirements of any such state laws. Further, under certain state Worker's Compensation laws an employer cannot require an employee on Worker's Compensation leave to return to a light duty position. However, the employee risks losing his Worker's Compensation benefits if he refuses to return to such light duty assignments. Finally, under the ADA, the employer can limit light duty assignments to non-occupational injuries and can limit their duration.

### 2. Employee Benefit Issues

Are employer-sponsored disability benefits payable for partial disability?

While it is common for an employer sponsored group disability plan (either short-term or long-term) to provide partial disability benefits, not every plan does so. Generally, group long-term disability insurance policies require continuous total disability during the elimination period, and partial disability benefits are offered, if at all, to limit benefits once an employee is cleared for any return to work, and to encourage rehabilitation and limit the duration of claims. Employers should review the terms of their plans or policies to determine the extent of benefits for partial disabilities.

### Pregnancy

Employee takes time off for the birth of a child. Perhaps there is a complication arising from childbirth that prevents the mother from returning to work for several weeks. Return to work is viable option.

## 1. Employment Issues

As an initial matter, employers need to be aware that there is a specific federal statute (the *Pregnancy Discrimination Act of 1978*)[9] that prohibits discrimination against pregnant women. Discrimination against pregnant women is a form of sex discrimination. Under this statute, it is unlawful for an employer to fire a pregnant employee or to treat her differently with respect to the terms and conditions of her employment simply because she is pregnant and without regard to her ability to perform her job.

Under this statute, an employer also must treat pregnant women the same for all employment-related purposes, including the receipt of fringe benefits, as it treats other non-pregnant employees who are similar in their ability or inability to work. For example, if an employer is willing to assign light duty to non-pregnant employees who are limited in their ability to work due to non-occupational injuries, the employer must also be willing to assign light duty to employees who are limited in their ability to work due to pregnancy (*e.g.*, lifting restrictions). As another example, if an employer allows a non-pregnant employee to return from lay-off status to light duty, it must also allow a similarly situated pregnant employee to return from lay-off status to light duty.

An employer who violates the *Pregnancy Discrimination Act of 1978* is subject to the same penalties as an employer who commits sex discrimination in violation of federal law. State laws can provide even greater protections for pregnant employees.

- **Is the employer required to grant the pregnant employee leave (unpaid or paid)?**

In the situation described above, the employer is obligated to grant the pregnant employee at least unpaid FMLA time assuming the employee has not already exhausted her FMLA leave time of 12 weeks. Under FMLA, an employee is entitled to 12 weeks of unpaid leave time because of the birth of a child, regardless of whether the employee has suffered any complications resulting from the birth. *In fact, the FMLA requires that employers grant job-protected leave to pregnant employees for medical appointments and pregnancy-related conditions such as morning sickness.* The employee would only be entitled to paid leave if she has accrued paid sick or vacation leave time that she can use as her FMLA time.

---

[9] Pub. L. No. 95-555 (October 31, 1978).

If the employee has exhausted her FMLA leave time by the time the complications have arisen, she would not be entitled to any further FMLA leave even if the complications rise to the level of a serious health condition because she has no further leave time available, although state law might require more leave. The employee probably would not be entitled to any further leave time as an accommodation under the *Americans with Disabilities Act* because complications from pregnancy, particularly temporary complications, do not constitute disabilities under that Act. Pregnancy itself is not a disability under the ADA and it would be an extremely rare instance in which a pregnancy-related disability would be a disability.

- **What amount of leave must an employer give a pregnant employee under federal law?**

Under the FMLA, the pregnant employee is entitled to a total of 12 weeks of unpaid time to use for any pregnancy-related complications before and after the birth and for the birth itself. If the pregnant employee has already used a portion of her FMLA leave time for the year (*e.g.*, six weeks), the employer is only required to give her the remainder (*e.g.*, six weeks) as leave for the birth. Because pregnancy is not a disability under the ADA, and pregnancy-related complications are rarely disabilities, the employer would not be required to give any further leave time under the ADA for pregnancy or pregnancy-related complications. State law, of course, might allow for greater leave.

- **Can the employer terminate the pregnant employee's employment?**

The employer can terminate the pregnant employee's employment so long as the termination is not because of the employee's pregnancy, the termination is not designed to interfere with the employee's exercise of her leave rights under the FMLA or state law, and the employer would have terminated a non-pregnant employee for the same reasons that it terminated the pregnant employee. For example, if as a result of a downturn in business, the employer eliminates three engineering positions and one of them just happens to be held by pregnant employee about to go on FMLA leave, the employer may still eliminate those positions and fire the pregnant employee. The reason is that the pregnant employee is being discharged for legitimate non-discriminatory reasons — a downturn in business — and she would have been discharged regardless of whether she was pregnant or whether she would soon go on FMLA leave.

An employer, however, should be careful about discharging a pregnant employee (or any employee) on FMLA leave because the employer realizes during the leave that there is no need for that employee's position (e.g., as a result of her leave, it becomes clear to the employer that other employees easily could absorb her job duties). The distinction between firing an employee for legitimate business reasons and firing an employee to interfere with the exercise of FMLA rights (e.g., the right to return to a same or similar job) could be difficult to draw in this case. The better result would be to allow the employee to return to work and then make a reasonable, business-driven decision as to whether the employee's position was truly superfluous.

- **How long is the employer required to hold open the pregnant employee's job while she is on leave?**

Under the FMLA, an employer is not required to hold an employee's job open while he or she is on leave, although the best course is to keep the job open. The reason is that the FMLA requires that the employee be returned after leave to the same or similar job. The requirements for the job to be "similar" are so stringent that they are tantamount to requiring that the "similar" job be identical to the position the employee had before leaving.

The federal Equal Employment Opportunity Commission also takes the position that an employer must hold open the position of a disabled employee (if the employee meets the definition of "disabled" under the ADA) on leave as a reasonable accommodation, unless holding open that position constitutes an undue hardship. The EEOC takes the position that the leave is not an accommodation if the employee can be "punished" by losing their job for taking the leave. Nothing in the ADA expressly requires the employer to hold open the position of a disabled employee on leave as a reasonable accommodation and the courts are not necessarily in agreement with the EEOC on this point. Nonetheless, the safer course is to keep the disabled employee's job open during the leave unless the employer, for legitimate business reasons, needs to permanently place another employee in that job. Under those circumstances, the employer should then consider the disabled employee for any vacancies for which the employee is qualified when the leave ends. Of course, these requirements will rarely apply to any pregnant employee since pregnancy and pregnancy-related complications generally are not disabilities.

- **Can an employer re-assign the pregnant employee's job duties to a co-worker?**

It depends. Because a pregnant employee is usually not disabled for purposes of the ADA, an employer would not be required to re-assign the pregnant employee's job duties as a form of reasonable accommodation. Furthermore, even if pregnancy were a disability, an employer is never required to re-assign an employee's essential job functions as a reasonable accommodation and should rarely, if ever, do so. The reason is that the reassignment of essential job functions both sets a precedent for future reasonable accommodations as well as suggests that those job functions were not truly essential.

Notwithstanding, if an employer re-assigns job functions, including essential job functions, for non-pregnant employees (e.g., gives them light duty by removing lifting functions), the employer will be required to re-assign such job functions for pregnant employees should they request such re-assignment.

Moreover, it is a rare circumstance in which an employer should re-assign job functions over the objections of the pregnant or disabled employee. The reason is that, if it does re-assign those functions in these circumstances, an employer may be perceived as acting on untrue stereotypes about the abilities of pregnant or impaired employees, and not based on the actual abilities of those employees. In these circumstances, the employer would run a greater risk of liability for pregnancy discrimination and disability discrimination under the "regarded as" test of the *Americans with Disabilities Act*. If the employer has real doubts about the actual ability of the pregnant or impaired employee to perform their job, it should send the employee for a fitness-for-duty examination where a medical doctor can render an objective opinion about whether it is unsafe for the employee to continue working.

Finally, an employer can re-assign job functions of a pregnant or impaired employee if that employee agrees. The better course is to obtain such agreement in writing. The employer should be aware, however, that it cannot explain to the co-worker to whom the job duties have been re-assigned the basis for the re-assignment, even if the co-worker's morale appears to be adversely affected by the re-assignment.

- Can the employer require medical certification before allowing a leave?

No, the employer may not require a pregnant employee to provide certification of need for FMLA leave, unless the employee claims that she suffers from a pregnancy-related complication that rises to the level of a serious health condition and needs the leave for that purpose. The FMLA does not allow for medical certifications for leaves taken "because of the birth of a son or daughter" or "because of the placement of a son or daughter with the employee for adoption or foster care". However, the employer may require that a pregnant employee provide a certification of ability to resume work after she has taken the FMLA leave provided the employer requires such certifications from all employees returning from FMLA leave.

## 2. Employee Benefit Issues

- Must the employer continue health care coverage for the employee?

A pregnant employee eligible for FMLA leave will be entitled to the same health care benefits during such leave that she would have been provided if still working. An employer's health plan may also provide for certain continued coverage. If health care coverage is lost due to a reduction in hours or termination, COBRA continuation rights may be applicable.

- Is the employee entitled to disability benefits?

Under the terms of the PDA, employer-sponsored short- and long-term disability plans, whether insured or self-insured, must generally provide benefits for pregnancy-related disabilities on the same terms as they provide benefits for any other illness.

## Work-Related Injury

Employee is injured on the job. The length of time away from the job and whether the employee can return to work depends on the severity of the injury.

## 1. Employment Issues

Many of the answers to the following questions will track the previous sections with respect to the FMLA and ADA if the work-related injury rises to the level of a serious health condition or disability. The main difference between the prior situations and a work-related injury is the application of the Worker's Compensation statutes. As discussed earlier in this chapter, Worker's Compensation is controlled entirely by state law and therefore will differ in each state. All of the nuances between the differing state laws is beyond the scope of this article. It is worth repeating, therefore, that when faced with a Worker's Compensation issue it is imperative to consult state law and an experienced attorney.

- **Is the employer required to grant the employee leave (unpaid or paid)?**

Yes. When an employee sustains a job-related injury, Worker's Compensation provides paid leave to the employee. If the employee has a serious health condition, then he or she qualifies for the 12-week FMLA leave which can be used concurrently. An employee with a work injury may also be disabled under the ADA and additional leave may be warranted.

- **What amount of leave must an employer give an employee under federal law?**

Once again, unlike FMLA leave, there is no maximum time allotted for Worker's Compensation leave. Worker's Compensation leave can run concurrently with FMLA, which allows for 12 weeks if the injury qualifies as a serious health condition. If the employer wants Worker's Compensation leave to count toward FMLA leave, it must notify the employee of this desire. Unlike FMLA leave, employees cannot take intermittent leave under the Worker's Compensation laws. ADA leave may be required after the FMLA leave expires.

- **Can the Employer require a return to light duty if the employee qualifies for FMLA leave?**

No. Light duty refers to particular positions that provide alternate work for those employees who cannot perform some or all of their normal duties. These may include tasks such as answering the telephone and other administrative work. Light duty may be required under Worker's Compensation as a rehabilitative position. However, an employer cannot force an employee to take a light-duty position if the employee qualifies for FMLA leave. If a light-duty position is offered under those circumstances and the employee refuses a light-duty position which he or she is able to perform, that employee could sacrifice his Worker's Compensation benefits. The worker could still be entitled to FMLA leave, however, if he or she has a serious health condition.

Light duty can also be considered a reasonable accommodation under the ADA. Under the ADA, the employer can distinguish between on-the-job injuries (OJI) and non-OJI disabilities for the purposes of determining who gets light duty; the employer can also limit the duration of light duty. That is, the employer can lawfully have a policy that limits light duty to those with OJIs (disability or not) and for 90 or 120 day periods. The policy, however, should be consistently maintained. Finally, an employer can require an employee with a disability that is not a serious health condition or whose FMLA leave has expired to take light duty as a reasonable accommodation. If the employee refuses to take the light duty position, he or she can be terminated.

- Can the employer terminate the employee's employment?

Yes. There are circumstances in which an employee who has been injured on the job can be terminated. For example, if a physician determines that an employee is too injured to return to work in any capacity including a light duty capacity, he or she may be terminated but may qualify for long-term disability in which the employee would receive a portion of his or her pay. Once again, FMLA and ADA must be taken into consideration in any decision to terminate.

- How long is the employer required to hold open the employee's job while the employee is on leave?

Unlike FMLA, Worker's Compensation laws usually do not require an employer to hold the employee's job open or give an employee his or her job back after a Worker's Compensation leave. Likewise, employers are not required to continue providing benefits to employees receiving Worker's Compensation. However, depending on the state, the employee may have job protection rights such as being reinstated to a light duty position until he or she can resume working in the old position. Employers should be careful when deciding whether to hold a job open because an employee with a serious health condition could be receiving Worker's Compensation benefits and also be on FMLA leave. Under those circumstances, there may be a requirement to return the employee to the same position after completion of the 12-week leave. Thus, as stated earlier, the safer course is to hold an employee's job open if he or she qualifies for FMLA or ADA leave.

- **Can an employer re-assign the disabled employee's job duties to a co-worker?**

Yes. During the employee's absence, the employers can hire temporary workers, shift work priorities and assignments, or ask another employee to temporarily fill the position. The difficulty arises when the employer is faced with the question of whether to give the employee his or her job back. As discussed before, this is not required under Worker's Compensation laws, but is required under FMLA.

- **Can the employer require medical certification before allowing a leave?**

Yes. In fact, when an employee is injured on the job, the employer can require an injured employee to undergo a medical examination at the employer's expense. The doctor can provide important information such as whether the employee's disability is partial, temporary, or permanent; whether intermittent leave will be required; whether the employee can accept light duty; and whether an accommodation under the ADA will be required.

## 2. Employee Benefit Issues

- **What plans cover medical expenses incurred in connection with work-related illnesses or injuries?**

State-mandated Worker's Compensation programs provide medical coverage for workplace injuries or illness. These programs are not subject to ERISA. Employer sponsored medical plans may exclude coverage for such injuries or illnesses — or provide a right of subrogation by a plan which advances the expenses of a workplace injury. An injured worker eligible for Worker's Compensation benefits while at the same time covered under an employer's health plan, will otherwise have all the benefits of other covered participants — that is, to continue benefits under COBRA if coverage is lost because of a reduction in hours or termination of employment. If the employee is disabled for U.S. Social Security purposes, the COBRA period is extended up to nine months, as described above.

• **Are disability benefits payable?**

Worker's Compensation programs provide disability benefits that vary by state. Employer-sponsored short-term disability plans either exclude such injuries or illnesses from coverage, or offset any benefits received from Worker's Compensation plans. Employer-sponsored long-term disability plans invariably offset the benefits payable by any disability benefits received from Worker's Compensation programs.

## THE FUTURE

This chapter is intended to provide Canadian employers operating in the United States with a basic understanding of the complex and overlapping system of state and federal regulation, and a basic understanding of the interplay between government and privately sponsored benefit programs. Now and in the future, a basic understanding of these concepts may not be enough. For almost any disability management situation involving U.S. employees, Canadian companies are urged to seek competent U.S. legal advice. Such advice will undoubtedly become ever more important in the future, as the laws and regulations relating to disability rights and benefits are changing at an ever-increasing rate. Employers who ensure that they comply with U.S. laws relating to disability management, and deal appropriately with their U.S. employees in disability management situations will have more productive and stable work forces, and will shield themselves from significant potential liabilities.

## U.S. STATUTES

All citations to U.S.C. refer to the *United States Code*. In the case of ERISA, it is common practice to cite sections as they were numbered in the Act itself as opposed to United States Code. For instance, ERISA § 510 corresponds to 29 U.S.C. § 1140.

• Americans with Disabilities Act (ADA), 42 U.S.C. §12101 *et seq.*

- Family and Medical Leave Act of 1993(FMLA), 29 U.S.C. § 2601 *et seq.*
- Employee Retirement Income Security Act of 1974 (ERISA), 29 U.S.C. § 1001 *et seq.*

An on-line copy of the United States Code can be found at www4.law.cornell.edu/uscode.

## USEFUL RESOURCES

### Printed Materials

Hairston, Abby G. Esq., *The Leave and Disability Coordination Handbook*, Thompson Publishing Group, 1999.

*Corporate Counsel's Guide to the Family and Medical Leave Act* Business Laws, Inc., 1999.

Detlefs, Dale R. *et al.*, *2001 Guide to Social Security and Medicare* William M. Mercer, Inc., 2000.

U.S. Department of Labor, Bulletin No. 2517, *Employee Benefits in Medium and Large Private Establishments*, USGPO ,1997.

*1998 Social Security Explained*, CCH, 1998.

The U.S. Equal Employment Opportunity Commission has issued guidelines, including questions and answers, interpreting the *Pregnancy Discrimination Act* 29 CFR 1604. 10.

### On-Line

U.S. Department of Labor Pension and Welfare Benefits Administration Website — www.dol.gov/dol/pwba. This website contains links to Department of Labor regulations pertaining to ERISA, Department of Labor Publications and Reports, and Department of Labor Advisory Opinions.

U.S. Department of Health and Human Services questions and answers regarding HIPAA privacy regulations — aspe.hhs.gov/admnsimp/final/pvcguide1.htm.

BenefitsLink Website — www.benefitslink.com.

EEOC Website — www.eeoc.gov.

Department of Labor Website — www.dol.gov.

# Chapter 5

# THE OCCUPATIONAL HEALTH NURSE AND DISABILITY MANAGEMENT

CAROL VINE

## INTRODUCTION

The majority (75 to 80 per cent) of employees off work due to illness or injury will return to work without difficulty. However, for some intervention is needed by the immediate supervisor to facilitate a smooth transition back into the workplace or to refer the employees for more extensive case management. The challenge in the business of today appears to be in creating, adopting and adapting policies, benefit plans and workplaces to enable employers to manage all aspects of the disability management process for the 20 to 25 per cent of employees who require assistance.

Managing disability begins with the recruitment and selection process and is followed by a health and safety program, health promotion programs, injury prevention programs, early intervention when an employee is absent, an established return-to-work program, data systems integrated with human resources, payroll and occupational health, coordination of the company benefits plan, appropriate referral for case management by the occupational health nurse, and program evaluation. The presence of disability management, a rigorous safety program specific to the company, and a supportive corporate culture can be expected to reduce physical, emotional and financial costs for the employee and the employer.

## THE OCCUPATIONAL HEALTH NURSE

The occupational health nurse is the member of the health and safety team that is more closely aligned with the human resource department because of the association with the personal aspects of the resources of the company that are dealt with on a daily basis. There is a natural affiliation with other confidential services such as the employee assistance program. The occupational health nurse as a specialized clinician, manager of a service, educator, researcher and health consultant is the vital link among the employee, family members, the employer, community resources, treating practitioners, family physicians, specialists, and benefits plan.

## OCCUPATIONAL HEALTH NURSING PRACTICE

Occupational health nursing practice is a highly specialized field of nursing that has its major emphasis grounded in prevention of illness and injuries at the workplace and health promotion programs specific to the needs of employees. Occupational health services and programs are planned, implemented and evaluated to raise the level of health of the workforce. The ultimate goal is to improve, protect, maintain and restore the health of the individual employee and the company workforce through management and delivery of services. The occupational health program is co-ordinated to obtain optimum results. Priorities are established following a needs assessment in order to be efficient and cost-effective. The occupational health nurse brings a unique combination of professional, occupational health, administrative, educational, supportive and cost-effective experience which directly benefits both the employees and the employer.

Disability management is central to all of the programs and services offered. Through this commitment to innovation and a proactive approach, an organization can prevent and minimize the devastating effects of illness and injury.

## UNIQUE POSITION OF THE OCCUPATIONAL HEALTH NURSE IN DISABILITY MANAGEMENT

The occupational health nurse is strategically positioned within the company to be the most effective professional to co-ordinate the provision of disability management. Since the occupational health nurse spends a great deal of time with the employees beginning with the pre-placement assessment, a rapport is developed. The employees share confidential information regarding themselves and respective personal and family relationships in a very non-threatening environment. This relationship grows and when the employees are affected by stress in the workplace, the occupational health nurse has a full understanding of the complex often extenuating circumstances that the employees face.

The occupational health nurse is knowledgeable about the plant, the work environment, each physical worksite, the materials used and the processes. A comprehensive worksite assessment and risk assessment is conducted routinely using a team approach whenever possible. This is composed of many facets: management's role and commitment to occupational health and safety; the plant, the product, the process and the people; familiarization with the workforce characteristics and health status; a comprehensive review of existing programs and services; a worksite walk-through survey identifying potential and actual hazards; and a review of workplace hazardous substances and the effects on employees.

The data collected and reports generated by the occupational health nurse pin-point specific areas and employees at risk of exposure and subsequent illness or injury. The statistical analysis together with the walk-through survey indicate where investigation is required or changes need to be made. This information is useful in placing new employees and in returning them to work following an absence due to illness or injury.

The occupational health nurse is the natural link between the employee and health care services provided in the community. Assessment of the community resources initiates communication and establishes co-ordination of services when required for employee treatment and return to work. Ongoing liaison and collaboration ensures the appropriate treatment, identifies barriers to rehabilitation and expedites the return-to-work process. The occupational health nurse is in the best position to initiate the insurance claims process for short-term and long-term disability and workers' compensation claims and also to assure, where appropriate, the uninterrupted provision of these benefits. Progress is documented and changes recommended as the employees participate in rehabilitation and prepare for return to work.

## HUMAN RESOURCES PROFESSIONALS AND THE OCCUPATIONAL HEALTH NURSE

The human resources professional has the responsibility to collaborate with the occupational health nurse in the development of a program to manage disability and be proactive in facilitating the return to work of employees. The focus should be to consider both short- and long-term absences that are controllable and plan a corporate approach that minimizes absences due to illness and injury and maximizes attendance.

There are many ways that the human resources professional and the occupational health nurse complement each other's expertise. Without the continuing support of human resources personnel, it is extremely difficult to provide effective disability management, and without the expertise of an occupational health nurse, it is impossible to provide case management, interpret medical information relating to the return to work for management and supervisors, and monitor employees.

## Measuring, Monitoring and Co-ordinating

The first step of any plan begins with determining what information is useful. Collecting the information in a meaningful way assists in identifying an emerging or growing workplace problem or the development of a pattern that requires further investigation.

Reporting procedures, record keeping and data analysis interpretation provide decision-makers with meaningful information. Statistics such as frequency and occurrence of absence data are key to disability management. It has been reported in numerous studies that over a five-year period approximately 10 per cent of employees account for 50 per cent of all injury or illness absences and up to 80 per cent of the costs. The identification and management of these "costly few" and the development of a strategy for each case minimizes the impact on both the employees and the organization.

A timely, proactive referral to the occupational health nurse can be initiated to facilitate resolution. The resolution can take the form of a safe and timely return to work, determination of total disability, or re-education or retraining for another job that matches the abilities of the affected employee.

The tracking system is more effective when it is linked with payroll and human resources. Absence patterns and trends become evident and problems are identified. Automatic triggers can be built into the system to alert managers when disability management is required. There needs to be a comprehensive, co-ordinated approach. Short-term disability, long-term disability, and workers' compensation disability claims must all be handled together.

## Sick Leave Policy Practices

The sick leave policy, if poorly written and administrated, may in fact have the potential to foster misuse and abuse of the system. The nature of the policy and the collective agreement as well as how it is monitored and communicated contributes to the effectiveness of disability management.

When absence due to illness or injury is viewed as an entitlement rather than insurance, it can lead to abuse of the system and subsequently make disability management very difficult. Employees may be less inclined to participate in a return-to-work program initiated by the occupational health nurse or the immediate manager or supervisor. The policy should emphasize prevention of disability, modified duties and a safe and timely return to work. There should be provision for referral to the occupational health nurse for more difficult cases and the requirement for participation in rehabilitation for the purpose of returning to work.

## Health and Safety Problems

Disability management costs can be effectively reduced by ensuring that appropriate selection criteria are used on hiring. The occupational health nurse assists the human resources professional by developing a pre-placement assessment tool specific for the workforce.

Baseline information is established for each prospective employee to determine fitness for the job. Without this information, an employer assumes that the candidate is fit for the job and takes on the total responsibility for any subsequent health and safety costs. Attempting to prove that a condition is not a direct result of the workplace is very difficult and costly.

There is more and more health and safety as well as labour legislation regarding an individual's fitness for work and medical requirements of the hiring process. Many companies have responded to these changes by establishing well-defined protocols for a pre-placement health assessment. A pre-placement health assessment differs from a pre-employment health assessment. It is performed after it has been determined that the candidate possesses the qualifications for the position. It is usually at the point of the selection process where the job offer is forthcoming. The results are properly conveyed to human resources to enhance optimal job placement.

The pre-placement health assessment determines whether the individual can meet the demands of the job. A pre-employment health assessment is not specific to any particular job and generally looks at overall employability. The terms "pre-placement" and "pre-employment" are often used interchangeably. The pre-placement assessment is not considered to be a complete evaluation of the health of a prospective employee. Its purpose is to detect physical conditions that would not allow the individual to perform the essential components of the job for which the applicant is being considered. To accomplish this purpose, the examination should be job specific and performed by an occupational health nurse knowledgeable about the work tasks and health and safety hazards of the particular job.

The pre-placement assessment places individuals in the appropriate job based on their own physical and emotional capabilities, as well as the physical, psychosocial and environmental demands of the job. Recommendations are made to human resources personnel regarding the conditions under which the prospective employee may function safely and effectively. Government regulations are complied with and neither the individual nor co-workers are put at health and safety risks. A baseline of relevant health data is collected that can be used as a comparison that may be required later.

Previously unrecognized or inadequately managed health problems are identified and proper follow-up is established. Health related conditions that may be aggravated by the job duties or that may affect the health and safety of co-workers are identified. Pre-existing work injuries and exposures are documented for use with possible future workers' compensation claims during the course of employment.

A job demand analysis is completed for each job to establish the *bona fide* occupational requirements prior to establishing the pre-placement health assessment tool. This assists in determining the physical requirements for the job and provides the opportunity to match the best qualified candidate to the position. The job demand analysis is a systematic approach to collecting the data to determine the biological, chemical, ergonomic, physical, and psychosocial hazards associated with the job. Potential and actual work related hazards that employees may be exposed to are included. The physical requirements of the job are defined, especially the strength and mobility needed by the employee. The analysis should be conducted regularly, usually annually.

The job demand analysis describes exactly what the employee does, how often and for what length of time. It is an exact definition of the work to be performed. It includes the employer's expectations with respect to performance, physical activity, reliability, availability, productivity, expected duration of service, and any other criteria associated with job qualification and suitability. A sufficiently detailed job demand analysis provides the basis on which a determination can be made of the kind of information required in order to assess an employee's health in respect to the demands of the job.

The same information is used to accommodate employees returning to the workplace following an absence due to illness or injury. Modified duties, alternate work, transitional duties and return-to-work programs are established using this valuable data base.

With respect to employability, the occupational health nurse gathers information by asking questions of whether or not the documentation supports the conclusion that the employee's medical condition precludes the employee from travel to and from the workplace, being at work, performing assigned tasks and duties, and, in the case of declining job performance, whether or not the medical condition contributed to the decline. The occupational health nurse continues the assessment and collaborates with the manager or supervisor and human resources until there is resolution. This process takes into consideration the employee's motivation to work.

The job demand analysis is a useful tool for human resources to include within their job description. These descriptions would be helpful not only to the HR department but also to the worker's medical practitioners when determining return-to-work prognosis.

## Workplace Wellness

Workplace wellness programs are increasingly regarded as an effective tool for preventing absenteeism and managing disability, particularly in stressful work environments. The rationale being that an employee who has achieved a high level of wellness is less likely to have a problem with absenteeism and disability. There is a positive correlation between a healthy workforce, job performance, employee turnover, and morale in the workplace. The elements of workplace wellness programs are not as important as the commitment of a company to have healthy employees.

Other terms for wellness programs are health promotion programs and fitness programs. Regardless of what a company decides to call the program, the purpose of the program is to demonstrate that the company is interested in its employees' health and safety and in the prevention of illness.

Through a health risk assessment, lifestyle risks that threaten an employee's health and wellbeing can be identified. The occupational health nurse conducts the needs assessment and then plans, implements and evaluates the programs. The needs and funds may be prioritized and the programs gradually increased or changed to support a healthy lifestyle. On a health/illness continuum, the programs enhance high level wellness and reduce costs associated with absence and illness or injury.

A healthy workplace is encouraged by education and a positive attitude toward health. Rising disability costs and company trends in poor health, such as recurring back injuries, conditions related to repetitive strain, stressful work environment, infectious diseases and seasonal colds, flu and bronchitis are reduced. A culture is created in which employees are empowered to take responsibility for their own health and wellbeing.

There are many programs that can be offered. Typically, these include education on such topics as nutrition or weight loss, smoking cessation, stress management, prevention or rehabilitation of back injuries, accident prevention at work and home, cardiopulmonary resuscitation (CPR) and first aid, seat belt use, and group or age specific topics.

Stress reduction programs teach employees about managing worksite and personal stressors. Levels of control, commitment and challenge represent employee hardiness for coping when dealing with responsibilities and stress, leading to development of more successful coping mechanisms. Managing time, conflict resolution, developing better communication skills, managing anxiety, and building self-esteem are tools that provide employees with resources to help manage life stressors. Blood pressure clinics and follow up, cholesterol screening and control, and aerobic fitness testing may be of value to emphasize overall fitness.

Included under the wellness program umbrella is an employee assistance program (EAP) for those who may be experiencing problems that are affecting their wellbeing or their ability to perform their job. An EAP provides employees, managers and supervisors with a resource to use before problems escalate to a point where progressive discipline may need to be initiated.

Often the EAP is offered to both employees and their immediate family members to provide assistance to those who are experiencing difficulties in their marriage or relationship, family problems, legal or financial troubles, and alcohol and substance abuse problems. The occupational health nurse assists managers, supervisors and employees to identify when the EAP should be offered and assists the employees in the workplace or when returning to work.

A broader and more comprehensive approach to employee health integrates job demands, employee characteristics, the work environment, and other internal and external organizational and home influences. Linking existing workplace health and human resource initiatives and services better targets interventions for high-risk groups of employees. These interventions can be translated into disability management, reduced costs, reduced health risks and increased company valuation of employees.

## Flexibility of the Workplace to Accommodate Employees

The most fundamental, and perhaps most difficult, step that any company can take to improve its attendance management and disability management program is to expand the role of managers or supervisors in job retention for employees absent from the workplace due to disabilities from illness or injury. The question is not "whether the employee is returning to work" but rather "how is the employee returning to work".

Even when employees receive the best of rehabilitation services, not all will be fully capable of working in their former jobs. If a disability management program is to achieve the best possible results, then companies must assist employees to become productive workers even when they have a temporary or permanent impairment that precludes them from returning to their usual job duties. The program is based on "abilities" not "disabilities" of the affected employee.

Assisting the injured or ill employee to return to work is the primary focus. The employee may require auxilliary devices, modification of the work environment, modification of the job itself, changes to the work process, transitional work opportunities, graduated return-to-work schedules, work hardening or endurance at the workplace or outside the workplace, alternative jobs, or permanent job changes. Each employee's need is assessed individually, but there are sequential phases that must be explored when determining return-to-work options. Return-to-work plans stem from the option chosen by the employer and the employee's individual situation.

Possibilities for suitable job options are identified through personal knowledge or existing job descriptions. Managers or supervisors, with the assistance of human resources and the occupational health nurse, identify positions throughout the company with duties that would be suitable to accommodate employees who are determined to be able to safely return to work.

The provisions of the collective agreement should support these positions and how to access them, including seniority and payment issues. Positions do not need to be created for these purposes. The occupational health nurse provides an ongoing evaluation of the employee's progress, what barriers are encountered, and indicates when regular duties are anticipated or when further decisions are required in relation to the potential for return to full duties. The employer must offer meaningful and productive work and accept the employee into the workplace. Manager or supervisor and co-worker understanding of the return-to-work arrangement is essential. The occupational health nurse assists in matching the abilities of the employee to the duties when there is difficulty interpreting the abilities or other clarification is required.

The rehabilitation and reintegration of the employee into the workforce is based on the principle of returning the ill or injured employee to the workplace in a safe and timely manner. Retraining and re-education may be needed if it appears unlikely that the employee can return to his or her former position.

The process involves the following five sequential phases of employment exploration:

1. same employer, same job;
2. same employer, new job;
3. same industry, related job;
4. any industry, any job using existing skills; and
5. retraining.

## Return to Work to the Same Job with the Same Employer

All efforts are made to help the employee return to the same job with the same employer. The employee returns to a known environment, maintains seniority and company benefits, remains in the same union, and keeps existing friendships and co-worker support. Sometimes this is possible without any modification to the job or work environment. The employee may require medical assistance or physical conditioning, but it is expected that the employee will return to full duties. The occupational health nurse coordinates the case management and works with the employee and the treating practitioner to ensure progress or to identify barriers affecting the return.

In some instances there may be a requirement to accommodate job modification. The employee returns to the same job but there are minor restrictions or modifications. There may be a need to modify the work environment or provide a device to help perform certain tasks or some type of job sharing.

### Return to Work to a Different Job with the Same Employer

Where the employee cannot return to the same job, the employer is encouraged to accommodate job modification or alternate in-service placement. The employee still benefits from the employment relationship. The employee may still require medical assistance and physical conditioning, but in addition, may also need worksite or job modification and supplementary skill development involving on-the-job or formal training. A different job without any changes may allow the employee a safe and timely return. It may be appropriate for the employer to create a new job.

### Return to Work to the Same/Similar Job with a Different Employer

Where the employer is unable to accommodate the employee in any capacity, vocational exploration will progress to suitable occupational options in the same or in a related industrial sector, capitalizing on the employee's directly transferable skills. The employee returns to a known or related industry which best utilizes existing skills to optimize occupational potential. This may also allow the employee to retain union status where applicable. This is not a preferred option in most cases because of the difficulties of adjusting to a new workplace or relocating to a new city. Costs are usually higher when relocation, retraining and any job accommodations are necessary.

### Return to Work to Any Industry to Any Job Using Existing Skills

Where the employee is unable to return to alternate employment in the same or related industry, vocational assessment, recognizing the worker's transferable skills, aptitudes and interests, will provide information to determine suitable occupational opportunities in all industries. The employee returns to suitable employment in a different industry which best utilizes existing skills to optimize occupational potential.

## Development of New Occupational Skills

Where existing skills are insufficient to restore the employee to suitable employment, the development of new occupational skills should be considered. The employee may prefer to market a particular skill or expertise if return to a former job is not possible. This requires training and counselling to develop self-employment or alternate employment options suited to the abilities of the employee. The human resources department may be able to provide this assistance. If not, an outside agency would be used.

## PROGRAM IMPLEMENTATION STRATEGY

The occupational health nurse is the key support co-ordinator between the employee, the manager and supervisor, and the employee's physician. The occupational health nurse has the overall responsibility for managing the medical aspects to ensure that appropriate rehabilitation programs are in place and that the medical information is interpreted to the manager and the supervisor in relation to rehabilitation and return to work. This interpretation relates medical findings to the employer's decision about the disability and the eventual possibility of return to work for the employee concerned. Questions are asked regarding the diagnosis, reasonable treatment and prognosis in relation to the employee's ability to perform work-related functions. Efforts are made to establish better communication with the medical community so that physicians understand how medical findings relate to the return to work of the employee.

## Process

Disability management has usually focused on workers' compensation costs and attendance. The occupational health nurse model extends the approach to provide processes and procedures that minimize the immense costs associated with all absences from the workplace due to illness or injury and enhance disability management.

## Review Existing Case Information

The occupational health nurse collects all the existing information from the source of referral (*i.e.*, supervisor, manager). The procedure should require that the employee notify the supervisor and the supervisor report the incident to the occupational health nurse within 24 hours.

The information collected for review may include copies of: occupational fitness assessment form(s), letter documenting the reason for the referral, previous absences or accident information, reports from other health practitioners and a job demand analysis.

## Contact the Employee and Arrange a Meeting if Possible

The occupational health nurse contacts their employee to determine the health status and ensures that the employee understands the company program as well as available benefits and his/her involvement in the program. The meeting is arranged as soon as possible. The purpose of the meeting is to develop rapport, put the employee at ease, instill confidence in the process, obtain the employee's perception of his/her injury/illness situation, outline and clarify roles and responsibilities and obtain or arrange for completion of consent for release of confidential medical information. Often the employee is unable to come in to the office in which case a telephone contact is made or in some instances a home visit is offered.

## More Information Required

All of the available information sources are reviewed regarding the employee's health condition, capabilities and job requirements to determine if there is enough information to determine fitness for work status or proceed with a fitness assessment.

## Complete Release of Information Form

When further medical information is or may be required to clarify return-to-work status, the occupational health nurse explains the process and information required to the employee and arranges for the release of information form to be signed. The consent for release of information should include:

- a description of the specific health information to be disclosed;
- the purpose for which the information is requested;
- the name of the person or institution intended to release the information; and
- the time-frame for which the consent is valid.

The release is signed by the employee and witnessed by another party.

## Request Additional Information

The occupational health nurse sends the release of information form along with a cover letter explaining the company disability program, outlining the specific information required and how it will be accessed (*i.e.*, telephone, fax, letter, copies of reports) as well as his or her role in the disability management process. In order to expedite and clarify the process, the occupational health nurse may wish to fax the consent and follow this immediately with a telephone call.

## Determine if Further Examination is Required

The occupational health nurse prepares the groundwork for a safe and timely return to work by ensuring that referrals are made as required to enhance early rehabilitation. He/she determines the type of examination that will provide the information required and arranges for the appropriate referral and follow up. This process is expedited because the occupational health nurse is involved from the initial illness/injury to return to work.

These examinations could include:

- independent medical examination;
- functional capacity evaluation;
- occupational work capacity evaluation;
- fitness for work examination.

## Co-ordinate Rehabilitation

In collaboration with the treating practitioner, the occupational health nurse co-ordinates the referral and follow up. The facilities used for rehabilitation are reviewed for appropriateness and quality of care.

The occupational health nurse educates the provider regarding company job descriptions and any job demand analysis completed for the position to facilitate the employee's successful return to work. A close working relationship is established to monitor the program, progress of the employee and quickly be alerted to concerns, problems or delays with the rehabilitation process. The supervisor is notified of the progress and anticipated date for return to work.

The occupational health nurse continuously communicates with all involved with the rehabilitation process and is responsible for the extensive documentation. All of the necessary forms are completed to assure a seamless transition from treatment to early rehabilitation and return to work. For the employee, this eliminates or minimizes the possibility of the interruption of benefits.

## Determine Fitness for Work Status

Once the employee is considered able to return to the workplace in some capacity, the occupational health nurse interprets this information for the supervisor in relation to the work available. A return-to-work plan is collaboratively developed with the occupational health nurse, supervisor and the employee. The occupational health nurse monitors the progress and meets regularly with the supervisor and employee. The treating practitioner is contacted as required.

## Available/Appropriate Work

All of the information is collected and reviewed by the occupational health nurse. Where it is determined that an employee could perform some useful or productive work within the limits of the current state of his/her disability as reviewed and approved by the treating physician, then possible positions within the company are discussed with the supervisor. The first consideration is can alternate work be found within the employees present work area. If there is no possibility of remaining with regular co-workers, then any area within the company is reviewed. Supervisors are collaborated with to clarify the duties that can be performed as part of the employee's regular work or alternate work availability that is not part of the employee's regular work.

## Determine Long-Term Options

When the employee is unable to return to the work available on a permanent basis, the occupational health nurse meets with the supervisor to discuss other options.

This could mean:

- vocational assessment;
- need for retraining;
- out placement opportunities;

- early retirement if employee warrants;
- long term disability benefits.

All options are considered and an action plan established. The occupational health nurse ensures that the necessary forms are completed and involved parties notified.

## Obstacles to Return to Work

Throughout the process, the occupational health nurse is aware of the many obstacles that can delay recovery while trying to return the employee to work.

These include:

- continuation of subjective pain symptoms without objective findings;
- prolonged use of medication;
- repeated postponement of the return-to-work date;
- employee blames the employer for the injury and becomes bitter;
- the injury is so serious that the employee is afraid to return to the workplace;
- the family becomes protective of the employee and distrustful of attempts to provide treatment/rehabilitation/return to work plans;
- the treating practitioner (treating physician, specialist, physiotherapist, *etc.*) becomes frustrated with the lack of progress;
- the attending physician becomes wary that the employer will not adhere to restrictions outlined in the return-to-work plan specifically related to the modified duties/alternate work offered;
- the manager/supervisor resists bringing the employee back and blocks availability of modified duties/alternate work;
- the employer human resources/payroll cause delays waiting for paperwork to clear channels;
- bed rest is prescribed by the treating physician for more than two to three days;
- reliance on pain medication at the end of 30 days;
- reliance on supports, braces and collars;
- no reduction in pain by the end of 30 days;
- no improvement in functional ability by the end of 30 days;
- unusual eagerness to illustrate pain and prove a disability;
- pain diaries;
- lack of general muscle strength and fitness;
- poor disability and claims history;

- spotty job history;
- job dissatisfaction;
- proximity to retirement;
- illiteracy;
- psychological factors;
- excessive stressful situation such as, recent birth, death, marital separation, unemployment;
- withdrawal from personal contact;
- history of substance abuse;
- impending litigation;
- awaiting some kind of pension decision.

The occupational health nurse uses these predictors for prolonging recovery to continually review, evaluate and prioritize action plans for employees and set realistic goals for return to work. He/she can identify difficult cases and work collaboratively with the manager/supervisor toward resolution.

The occupational health nurse facilitates the disability management process by using extensive communication and co-ordination skills. This occurs between the employee, the treating practitioner, rehabilitation specialists and the manager/supervisor. The focus is on employee individuality and how he/she will be returned to the workplace in a safe and timely manner.

## The Future-Combined Approach

It usually takes a combination of human resources and the occupational health nurse to complement each other's expertise and provide the initiative required to implement disability management. Organizational effectiveness is contingent upon people as the most valuable resource. Human resource initiatives, together with the education, documentation, and referral for assistance can be viewed as adding value to the company.

The importance of returning employees to the workplace is emphasized in the belief that people are better off at work; they can benefit in so many ways. Employees need to feel that they make a difference, that their work matters. Through work employees feel that they have more control or financial independence and can retain their self-esteem more easily. By providing a combination of programs to assist disability management, the employee is also assisted in a smooth transition from absence due to disability from illness or injury to return to work.

# Chapter 6

# PSYCHOSOCIAL FACTORS: BARRIERS TO RETURN-TO-WORK OF WORKERS DISABLED BY OCCUPATIONAL LOW BACK PAIN AND CHRONIC PAIN

MANJIT GREWAL

## INTRODUCTION

In today's competitive market place, employers need to ensure that the employees that they hire are not only productive but are at work and able to work. For employers, these non-productive employees increase their indirect costs associated with re-training, finding replacement employees, turnover, and decrease morale that are getting extremely expensive for businesses.

Many different medical conditions lead to employee absences. These absences are getting the attention of upper management primarily because of the impact on the bottom line. There seems to be an increase in interest in conditions such as Occupational Low Back Pain (OLBP) and Chronic Pain because most employees who are eventually disabled by chronic pain do not return to work. One of the most difficult challenges a return-to-work (RTW) program faces during the re-entry to the workplace of workers disabled by OLBP and chronic pain is the negativity among line managers. For example, most managers verbalize that it is not possible to rehabilitate employees with Low Back Pain (LBP), *i.e.*, "people with a bad back never come back to work". This is no longer the case if the worker's low back pain is addressed correctly. This is especially important when considering not only the hardship on employers but on disabled workers with OLBP and chronic pain. For example, the physical hardships of chronic pain often force workers to withdraw from friends and colleagues further compounding their feelings of isolation, frustration, and depression.

An entire chapter has been dedicated to discuss the barriers and challenges with workers disabled by OLBP and chronic pain. This will be done by looking at the intricacy of these conditions to better understand the conditions in order to look at what can be done to decrease incidences, be proactive, improve return-to-work (RTW) outcomes, to decrease chronicity, and to have the disabled worker back to their pre-disability life (work) as soon as possible.

## OVERVIEW OF OLBP AND CHRONIC PAIN

Low back pain is a universal and common occurrence among people. For example, it is usual for a person to experience at least one episode of backache per year. So eventually, we will all have experienced back pain at one time or another. However, we all do not develop chronic pain and the reasons for this will be examined in this chapter. First, it is important to understand how LBP, OLBP, and chronic pain are defined and their relationship to each other.

### Definition of Low Back Pain:

Low back pain is a pain and stiffness in the lower back. It is also known as "non-specific" low back pain.

### Definition of Occupational Low Back Pain:

Occupational Low Back Pain (OLBP) results from work or can be exacerbated by work.

### Definition of Chronic Pain:

Chronic pain is a persistent pain that tends to be constant rather than intermittent. This can evolve into a pattern of painful sensations continuing long after the initial injury.

### Relationship Between LBP and Chronic Pain

Chronic pain has a mutual relationship with Low Back Pain. For example, approximately 1/5 of the group of patients with non-specific low back pain is prone to developing chronic pain. Thus, low back pain can become a chronic condition, causing patients to develop occupational problems that are far more complex than the original diagnosis would lead one to expect.

## MEDICAL CHALLENGE

Although OLBP and chronic pain are both common medical conditions there is no "quick fix" to treat these conditions. The next section will discuss some of the medical challenges that health care professionals experience in addressing these conditions.

### Incidences of OLBP Increasing or Decreasing?

OLBP poses a very serious problem that has been rising steadily for the past two decades. It has continued to increase even in the presence of vast technical advances in diagnosis and therapy, in addition to lessened physical job demands. Fortunately, most people who develop OLBP are able to recover from it and continue to be productive members of society. Those that do not recover go on to become chronic OLBP sufferers which usually leads to lost earnings and employment difficulties; thus an altered lifestyle.

### Treatment Difficulty

The prevalence of OLBP has caused many professional health-related disciplines to focus on the cause, care, rehabilitation, and treatment of it. Even primary care physicians struggle to determine the best approach for the treatment of patients who suffer with low back pain. This could be because the majority of patients do not have complicated low back pain and that the identification of patients with an underlying malignancy or neurologic deficit is a difficult task which further complicates the approach to treat low back pain symptoms.

## Nature of OLBP and Chronic Pain

OLBP and chronic pain are difficult conditions since their nature is inherently subjective and there are no thoroughly reliable ways to measure it. This makes treatment of these conditions difficult. Because these conditions usually involve injuries to soft tissues, normal diagnostic methods including X-ray, MRI and other imaging techniques are not effective. OLBP and especially chronic pain can seldom be cured. Those who suffer from chronic pain also tend to avoid physical activities. However, because of the complexity of this condition, it cannot be understood by looking at the severity of pain caused by the injury and intolerance of physical activities. This means that one cannot develop a RTW plan based on how much pain a worker is in.

Indeed, it is possible that the *nature* of pain contributes to the dynamics of this multi-faceted condition. Among the most difficult challenges to health care professionals, for instance, is chronic musculoskeletal pain of "non-specific" origin. This type of pain is a growing problem for health-care professionals, insurance carriers, and employers.

## RE-ENTRY TO THE WORKPLACE

Now that the terms have been defined and there is a better understanding of the medical challenges, the workplace challenges will now be explored.

The transition back to the workplace of workers who have been away from the workplace due to OLBP and chronic pain are of a particular concern to employers since their RTW success rate is relatively low.

The difficulty is that 80 per cent of the population are likely to have had nonspecific back pain and are likely to improve regardless of treatment. However, about 20 per cent are prone to develop chronic back pain, presenting complex psychosocial and occupational problems. This poses not only a diagnosis problem for physicians, but also for employers who cannot be sure when or what accommodations needs to take place.

In order to effectively manage any disability management program case managers, RTW co-ordinators, and health care providers must gain further insight in order to assist in the facilitation of RTW.

## Current Situation

Currently, when a worker sustains a work-related injury, is diagnosed with OLBP or chronic pain, and has not returned to work within six months after the date of disability, the insurance carrier refers the injured worker to a pain clinic for treatment. The expectation on the part of the insurance company is that the pain clinic will not only treat the pain but also facilitate the transition of disabled workers from treatment to re-employment.

## Transition from Pain Clinic to Workplace

Currently, this group's transition from treatment to re-employment is effected through a Graduated Return-to-work (GRTW). A GRTW is a form of a RTW intervention used by the majority of pain clinics in British Columbia (BC) during the transition of workers disabled by OLBP and chronic pain from treatment to re-employment.

## Definition of GRTW

According to the Program Evaluation and Research Unit[1] at the Workers' Compensation Board (WCB of BC), GRTW solely consist of pre-arranged incremental exposure of disabled workers to physical activities associated with their jobs during the first four weeks of the job re-entry process.

## Effectiveness of GRTW

The structure of the GRTW process considerably detracts from its effectiveness as a RTW intervention. For example, GRTW has a success rate of 37 per cent of re-employing workers disabled by OLBP and chronic pain after treatment from a pain clinic.[2] Although, 37 per cent is

---

[1]  Program Evaluation and Research Unit (PERU), (2000). Leslie Petersen Rehabilitation Centre, Workers' Compensation Board of British Columbia, Vancouver, B.C.
[2]  Ibid.

better than a zero per cent success rate, there is still room for improvement.

Since pain clinics often use a GRTW to help facilitate disabled workers transition from the pain program to re-employment, the GRTW currently constitutes an important component of the RTW plan, in spite of the low success rate of this intervention.

The problem with GRTW is that once the disabled worker diagnosed with chronic pain has been referred to a pain clinic, there is often no involvement or input from the employer. The employer usually only becomes involved when it is time for the insurance carrier and the pain clinic to set up and support a GRTW for the disabled worker. Consequently, there is little communication between the pain treatment clinicians and the employer's Disability Management (DM) Committee.

The last section of this chapter "Strategies to Enhance GRTW and Improve RTW Outcomes" will discuss four possible solutions to improve RTW outcomes of workers that are disabled by OLBP and chronic pain.

## EARLY INTERVENTION

The next section will discuss the importance of early intervention followed by two examples of this related to workers disabled by OLBP and chronic pain.

When looking at improving RTW outcomes of workers disabled by OLBP and chronic pain, the earlier the intervention starts the better. In other words, the concept of early intervention is a key element in the disability management process. This concept is crucial when considering the definition and progression of low back pain to chronic pain. For example, the majority of back pain is brief and time-limited. As time goes on, more patients with back pain are recovered. Of those whose symptoms persist more than three to four months, the majority will continue to be disabled and unable to work at the end of the year, and the greatest number of these individuals will continue to be disabled after two years. By this time, the chances become very remote that a person will ever return to any type of productive employment. Thus, when considering RTW outcomes, early intervention is the key with the primary importance of an intervention being to prevent the progression of OLBP to chronic pain.

## Early Intervention Examples

Two early intervention strategies that relate to workers disabled by OLBP and chronic pain that are receiving treatment at a pain clinic are described below including the advantages and disadvantages of each. One would occur in a clinical setting and the other at the workplace.

### 1. Work Hardening

Work Hardening is an intervention used in a clinical setting such as a pain clinic. This intervention uses equipment at the site of the clinic in order to use real or simulated activities of the disabled employee's job duties that she/he is intended to return to. For example, if an employee's pre-disability job requires them to climb a ladder and stock grocery shelves, then the clinic would have the employee climb a similar ladder and stock those similar items on a shelf. In other words, the clinic would attempt, as much as possible, to create the same job duties as the workplace. The goal of work hardening is to have the employee perform the physical functions of the pre-disability job duties in a "controlled" environment with the hope of the same being replicated at the workplace.

### (a) Advantages of Work Hardening

There are many advantages of work hardening. For example, this method is appropriate to use when employees are anxious to return to the workplace as it allows them to focus on one task at a time. In addition, this is a great first step in cases where the workplace is a complicating factor that contributes to the worker's pain. Furthermore, this method does not require co-ordination with the workplace and the results are easily measured.

### (b) Disadvantages of Work Hardening

Despite the many advantages of work hardening there are also disadvantages to this type of method. For example, the "true" work environment is difficult to achieve in a clinical setting. This is especially true when considering the reality of such things as interruptions by co-workers and customers which is difficult to simulate in a clinical setting. Also, workplace dynamics are a reality such as the relationships the disabled worker has with their co-workers and supervisors. Further, just getting to work has its own challenges such as waking up, getting to work, being at work on time, seeing the workplace and working in it. The work hardening method promotes the disabled worker being disconnected with the workplace that does not allow them to keep up with the changes that are taking place such as new hires, re-organization of areas, and procedural changes.

## 2. GRTW

The GRTW is the second intervention that is commonly used in rehabilitating a worker which takes place at their place of employment. Please refer to the earlier section of this chapter for the definition of a GRTW.

### (a) Advantages of GRTW

Initiating a GRTW at the worker's place of employment has many advantages.

Injured workers can remain involved in the day-to-day routines of going to work and interacting with co-workers and supervisors. Also, injured workers are in a better position to be abreast of the changes that may take place at work. In addition, the employee makes "real" contributions in the workplace while doing work that would need to be done anyway. In return this usually makes an employee feel productive and valued versus just an "injured" employee. Often, relationships at the workplace are a big part of a worker's support system which would only help the employee through the transition of being away from work to being at work.

### (b) Disadvantages of GRTW

Of course, there are many disadvantages as well with the GRTW approach. For example, it may be too soon for the employee to be at work. The employee may need to increase their confidence before doing the "real" thing.

Both work hardening and GRTW strategies have a place in the disability management process. However, it is important that the selected approach is implemented as soon as possible because the more time that passes from the onset of disability the less effective it will be.

## EXPLORATION OF ABSENTEEISM — FALSE ASSUMPTIONS

Two common false assumptions of the cause of absenteeism are described below.

## Old Age — Make a Difference?

Employers are also becoming increasingly concerned about the absenteeism and reduced productivity as a result of an aging workforce. This trend is mainly the result of downsizing as a measure to cut operating costs. Employees that remain with the company after a downsizing event tend to be more senior, and hence older. Older, non-disabled workers oppose accepting the harder tasks of less senior (and often younger) disabled workers since they often feel that, by virtue of their seniority, lighter jobs should be assigned to them. The resulting tensions negatively affect the employer's RTW program and are often the cause of it to fail. Although age appears to be a variable, there is actually no direct correlation between back pain and age. Age cannot be the sole cause of extended absenteeism from work due to low back injuries.

## Disability Benefits — Make a Difference?

There are many beliefs of employees that are in receipt of disability benefits that make a difference in areas such as their extended absenteeism, duration of claim, and reluctance to attempt coming back to work. Unfortunately, this is not clear-cut as some disabled workers for whom disability benefits would represent a net economic gain still continue to work. This means that the answer in improving RTW outcomes of workers disabled by OLBP and chronic pain needs to go beyond the monetary factor, hence the further exploration below.

## EXPLORATION OF HIGH GRTW FAILURE RATE

There are many reasons why GRTW(s) fail. However, only the two most relevant to the RTW transitions from treatment to re-employment of workers disabled by OLBP and chronic pain are addressed in the next part of the chapter. They are: 1) the negative influence of psychosocial factors on the job-worker relationship; and 2) emotional distress as a consequence of disabled workers' concerns about re-employment barriers posed by psychosocial factors.

## Definition of Psychosocial Factors

Psychosocial factors are features of a workplace and/or a home environment that result in psychologically stressful situations experienced by the worker who is exposed to them.[3] Tense relationships between the worker and their supervisor are one of many examples of a psychosocial factor.

It is important to look at psychosocial factors because there is an abundance of evidence that points to a wide variety of these factors that cause much of the disability related to OLBP and chronic pain.

## Definition of Emotional Distress

Emotional distress that is the consequence of job-worker interactions is also thought to lead to activity avoidance, work or not work related, and, thus, affect RTW outcomes.[4][5]

## Exploring the Psychosocial Factor Link — Beyond the Physical Factor

In addition to the uncertainty surrounding a serious chronic problem, a number of other variables can affect the length of work absenteeism due to low back pain. For example, psychological factors can influence how an employee responds to physical treatments and, in this way, extend the length of time they may be off work.

Back pain is a common occurrence among workers and yet there is no clear answer on how to prevent back pain from occurring. The matter is further complicated by the fact that once a worker is disabled by OLBP, the employer's focus on reducing physical risk factors has not usually provided successful RTW outcomes. In efforts to prevent back injuries, there have been many studies suggesting refined ways to lift, twist, bend, and perform other physical risk factors. However, only a small percentage of all back pain can be linked to related physical risk factors. It appears as if the disabled worker with OLBP or chronic pain may have reasons other than pain and discomfort to explain the RTW failures. This may mean that the cause of OLBP may or may not be due to the

[3] D. Shrey, *Worksite Disability Management and Industrial Rehabilitation: An Overview — Principles and Practices of Disability Management in Industry* (Winter Park, Fla: GR Press Inc., 1995) at 4-53.

[4] J.D. Loeser, *Perspectives on Pain* (1980) in W.E. Fordyce, ed., *Task Force on Pain in the Workplace* (Seattle: IASP Press).

[5] W.E. Fordyce, *Back Pain in the Workplace* (Seattle: IASP Press, 1995).

physical demands imposed at work. Further to this, the majority of workers who report themselves disabled continue to work. This leads to the question as to why some disabled workers that are suffering with OLBP and chronic pain continue to work while others do not?

## Who is More Likely to Develop OLBP and Chronic Pain?

The next paragraph looks further into who is more likely to develop OLBP and chronic pain. It would only be logical to first look at the initial injury that an employee suffered in conjunction with the type of work performed. However, there is little association between the severity of an injury and the type of work performed.

Certainly, a more open-minded approach is needed to understand the back pain experience such as the recognition of the influence of a range of psychological and workplace variables. The science of bio-mechanics may help to explain (some) initial injury mechanisms, it currently offers little in way of explanation for persistent trouble; management strategies may be better guided by an understanding of the nature of pain and its relation with disability.[6] Thus, chronic disabilities still elude modern science.

It is important to keep in mind that it is normal to experience some discomfort and pain when working. Although, these transient symptoms may be a normal consequence of life, if the worker erroneously believes that the job is to blame, there is the potential for psychosocial factors to intervene.[7]

## PSYCHOLOGICAL VERSUS PHYSICAL INTERVENTION

The idea that pain and chronic problems can be avoided by psychologically helping the worker is slowly being examined by other researchers and will be explored below.

### Psychological Influence

Psychosocial factors have the potential to influence an acute musculoskeletal pain problem at three distinct phases: the onset of pain;

---

[6] K. Burton, "Spine Update Back Injury and Work Loss: Biomechanical and Psychosocial Influences" (1997) 21 *Spine*, 22, 2575-2580.
[7] *Ibid.*

the seeking and receiving of health care and income support; and the development of chronic pain-related disability and work loss.[8] This implies that psychosocial factors are more important than the pain itself. Thus if someone does not like their job because they cannot keep up with the pace, then it may affect the amount of pain they are willing to tolerate.

There are five brief examples provided below in different work areas to primarily illustrate how psychosocial factors can influence how much pain a worker will experience.

## 1. Example One — Predicting Work Disability

The first example by Yelin, Nevitt, and Epstein's[9] study talks about work disability of workers with rheumatoid arthritis. Work disability for people with rheumatoid arthritis was predicted by social characteristics of the work place more than by any other factors, including the medical and physical demands of the job. Control over the pace of work was found to be especially important. Implied in this study is a suggestion that those who control the pace of work, or have flexible schedules of work, are more satisfied with their jobs and are, therefore, more willing to tolerate pain. This further implies that unhappy workers are more likely to become disabled.

The main message of this study is that, in addition to medical treatment, more attention should be paid to the social characteristics of the workplace.

## 2. Example Two — Factors Associated With a History of Back Pain

The second example addresses common factors in the workplace that are associated with back pain. For instance, Svensson and Andersson[10] surveyed a number of work environments and found a number of factors within them to have an association with a history of back pain. These factors were monotonous or boring work, diminished work satisfaction, decreased potential to influence the work situation, and less demand on concentration.

---

[8] G. Kendall, "Prediction of Pain Rehabilitation Outcomes" (1999) 16 *Disability Rehabilitation* at 21-25.

[9] E. Yelin, M. Nevitt & W. Epstein, "Toward an Epidemiology of Work Disability" (1980) 58 *Milbank Memorial Fund Quarterly/Health and Society* at 386-415.

[10] H. Svensson & G. Anderson, "Low Back Pain in Forty to Forty Seven Year Old Men: Work History and Environmental Factors" (1983) 8 *Spine* at 272-276.

## 3. Example Three — Factors That Exacerbate LBP and Chronic Pain

The third example looks at a wide variety of psychosocial factors which may exacerbate chronic pain and non-specific low back pain. Farrell, Knowlton, & Taylor[11] and Feurestein[12] [13] have enumerated a number of variables that are commonly encountered in *clinical practice* with chronic pain patients. The variables include poor working conditions with increased risk for exacerbation or re-injury on return to current job, mismatches between patients' physical capabilities and day-to-day work demands (particularly in medium to heavy-labour jobs), an inability to offer lighter-duty positions to accommodate patients' early return to work and residual functional capacity, a lack of transferable skills, negative attitudes from co-workers and employers toward patients with a history of work disability, and the viability of the job market at the time patients attempt to return to work. Given the number and range of these potential factors, it is not difficult to see that even the best and most effective clinical management of highly motivated chronic pain patients, as well as those afflicted by Non-Specific Low Back Pain (NSLBP), may not be sufficient to accomplish a return to work, since the employment environment may not be receptive to this particular outcome.

## 4. Example Four — Factors that Contribute to Developing Chronic Pain

The fourth example looks further at work environment factors that contribute to developing chronic pain by Valat, Goupille, and Vedere.[14] For example, they provide occupational factors such as for blue collar jobs that are important: workers with heavy labour jobs that require efforts beyond their physical capabilities, with poor job satisfaction, with poor working conditions, with many new people at their job, or with workers not well rated by their supervisors, are more likely to develop chronic pain.

---

[11] G.P. Farrell, S.K. Knowlton & M.C. Taylor, *Second Chance: Rehabilitating the American Worker* (Minneapolis: Northwestern National Life Insurance Company, 1989).

[12] M. Feurstein, "A Multidisciplinary Approach to Prevention, Evaluation and Management of Work Disability" (1991) 1 Journal of Occupational Rehabilitation at 5-12.

[13] M. Feurstein, "More Than Meets the Eye: It is Not Simply an Image Problem: Challenges Facing Chronic Pain Management Clinics" (1994) 4 APS Bulletin at 1-3.

[14] J. Valat, P. Goupille & V. Vedere, "Low Back Pain: Risk Factors for Chronicity" (1997) 3 *Rev. Rhum*, 64 at 189-194.

## 5. *Example Five — Factors that Influence Work Loss Due to LBP*

The fifth example, a study by Magnusson, Pope, Wilder, and Areskoug[15] specifically looking at the role of driving a truck in its relation to back, neck, and shoulder pain found that work loss from low back pain was influenced by perceived job stress. This is explained further by a more specific study on transit operators that found the relation to psychosocial factors with back or neck pain to include extended uninterrupted driving periods, frequency of job problems, high psychological demands, high job dissatisfaction, and low supervisory support.[16] These studies not only support the argument that OLBP and chronic pain are likely to be present at a workplace but there are a number of work-related factors that could hinder a successful GRTW of the disabled worker.

Thus, there are many reasons that could contribute to the high number of GRTW failures. The way GRTW(s) are presently used as a RTW intervention from treatment to re-employment is simply ineffective. The focus of the GRTW intervention presently is primarily on a progressive increase of physical activities and hours of the disabled worker until they reach their pre-disability job capabilities. This clearly does not recognize other factors that may need to be addressed or taken into consideration such as the presence of work related psychosocial factors and the relationship of on-the-job worker relationships. There is a great demand for interventions that address both physical aspects of a worker's job together with the psychosocial factors that are unique to the disabled worker's job-worker relationship.

## EMOTIONAL DISTRESS — THE CONNECTION TO FEELING PAIN

The next section explores the relationship between emotional distress and LBP. Knowing that patients respond very differently to LBP and that patients report a wide variety of symptoms would lead one to believe that the symptoms are a substitute for emotional difficulties. This would make the detection of emotional distress crucial and worth exploring further.

---

[15] M. Magnusson, M. Pope & D. Wilder *et al.*, "Are Occupational Drivers at an Increased Risk for Developing Musculoskeletal Disorders?" (1996) 6 *Spine*, 21 at 710-717.

[16] N. Krause, D. Ragland & B. Greiner *et al.*, "Psychosocial Factors Associated with Back and Neck Pain in Public Transit Operators" (1997) 23 *Scand. J. Work Environ. Health* at 179-186.

It is possible that emotional suffering, regardless of cause, results in pain.[17] People who suffer, from any cause, often use the language of pain to describe their feelings. In cases where suffering is associated with a specific activity, it leads to activity intolerance.[18] However, the more active patients become, the less pain they will report. This places the person disabled by pain in a dilemma, since in order to reduce their pain they must perform an activity that they often associate with being the very cause of their pain.

The suffering that workers feel may also develop as an expression of emotional distress which may arise as a consequence of negative job-worker interactions.[19] Thus, emotional distress may mediate the relationship between pain (from any cause) and avoidance of physical activity. This statement implies that negative job-worker interactions are important factors to take into consideration with OLBP and chronic pain workers.

### Can You Predict Who Will Develop Back Pain?

The next section will explore further from what has been discussed so far if it can be predicted who will develop LBP. It is the interesting symptoms of psychological (emotional) distress in individuals without back pain that predicted the subsequent onset of new episodes of LBP.[20]

More importantly, improvements in physical function and decreased psychological distress meant that psychological adjustments normalize with improvement in physical activity.[21] The fact that improvement in a patient's psychological profile matches improvement in physical activity is of tremendous importance to a RTW intervention such as the GRTW. It also supports the current treatment trend towards the prescription of exercise rather than rest for LBP.[22]

Although there is no perfect solution for the suffering, emotional distress and activity intolerance associated with workers disabled by

---

17   *Supra*, note 4.
18   *Supra*, note 4.
19   *Supra*, note 5.
20   P. Croft, A. Papageorgiou & S. Ferry *et al.*, "Psychological Distress and Low Back Pain: Evidence from a Prospective Study in the General Population" (1995) 20 *Spine* at 2731-2737.
21   F. Keefe, L. Bradley & J. Crisson, "Behavioural Assessment of Low Back Pain: Identification of Pain Behavioural Subgroups" (1990) 40 *Pain* at 153-160.
22   B. Naliboff, M. Cohen & G. Swanson *et al.*, "Comprehensive Assessment of Chronic Low Pain Patients and Controls: Physical Abilities, Level of Activity, Psychological Adjustment and Pain Perception" (1985) 23 *Pain* at 121-134.

OLBP and chronic pain, there is always room for improvement. There are several possible solutions to not only improve RTW outcomes but also to reduce the suffering that is caused by OLBP and chronic pain. One approach may be to reduce emotional distress (thus pain and suffering), especially in workers who can identify psychosocial factors at the workplace that may cause them distress. If this would lead to higher activity tolerance, then it would be worthwhile to pursue it as part of a potential solution.

## STRATEGIES TO ENHANCE GRTW AND IMPROVE RTW OUTCOMES

This chapter has several implications for RTW efforts. These include strategies that complement the GRTW aimed at co-workers, supervisors, union representatives and other stakeholders. Described below are four key examples.

### Joint Effort Between Pain Clinic and Employer

The first strategy indicates that a joint effort between the pain clinic and the employer should start at the floor of the pain clinic prior to the disabled worker's transition from the pain clinic to job re-entry. This would ensure that the disabled worker can contact the appropriate people as situations come up. For example, if the disabled worker is concerned about performing their job duties, they could contact the pain clinic's occupational therapist. The supervisor at the work site could then advise the occupational therapist on what can and cannot happen. The Disability Management (DM) committee could also assist in the co-ordination of the clinicians' efforts. In doing so, it would fulfil its DM mandate which calls for an employer-centered, proactive process of co-ordinating the activities of labour, management, insurance carriers, health care providers and rehabilitation professionals for the purpose of minimizing the impact of injury, disability or disease on a worker's capacity to successfully perform their job.[23] Implementation of the DM mandate would help prevent the disabled worker from leaving the job, which is what currently occurs when the worker first experiences discomfort or pain after returning to work.

---

[23] *Supra*, note 3.

## Supervised GRTW

The second strategy indicates that a lack of supervised RTW interventions contributes to the current high rate of GRTW failures. Supervision of GRTW would increase the RTW outcomes by addressing the dynamics of the job-worker relationships. Consequently, a supervised transition from treatment to re-employment would have to consider all of the job-worker psychosocial factors. If overseen by the pain clinic and insurers such as WCB, such supervision could trigger the proper co-ordination of job re-entries and GRTW with the employer.

In addition, by the time an injured worker is eventually referred to a pain clinic, more than six months may have elapsed from the date of disability, sometimes as high as two years. This fact, compounded by the poor RTW success rate, has made employers and insurers anxious to find alternative, potentially cheaper ways of helping disabled workers recover.

## Development of RTW Tools and Customized Interventions

One of many possible answers to poor RTW outcomes involving workers disabled by OLBP and chronic pain may be the development of practical RTW tools and interventions capable of producing evidence that attests to their effectiveness. In order to ensure efficacy, these RTW tools and interventions need to have both, the sensitivity to the individual disabled worker's job re-integration needs and the flexibility to adapt quickly to the demands of the work place environment.

It is important to discuss common issues and to create strategies for dealing with problems associated with the job-worker relationship especially at each workplace. As work dynamics differ, so too do the common psychosocial factors in a particular occupation and/or company. A homogeneous study of the above-mentioned variety would allow the employer to have standard interventions in place that become standard practice; this could be done, for instance, by having a standing order for nurses to administer certain treatment based on certain criteria. The true test of the effectiveness of such a tool/strategy would be the long-term results, meaning that follow-up studies at three, six, and 12-month intervals should be done to explore what is and is not working.

In this regard, the conflict resolution theory may provide the necessary framework for the creation of future RTW interventions. From the perspective of the workplace, and because of so many competing and conflicting interests, conflict between labour/ management, employer/ insurance carrier, employer/treatment programs is a common occurrence.

The existence of the conflicts is detrimental not only to the parties mentioned above but also to the disabled worker who is inadvertently caught in the middle. DM committees are the most likely bodies within employer organizations to address such conflict especially when it arises from the disabled worker's re-employment issues. According to Mills,[24] both union and employers falsely believe that rehabilitation services and compensation systems could solve disabled workers' problems. The change in such beliefs is imperative and the RTW results demonstrated to date only serve to accentuate this need. In addition, according to Mills, labour and management have the sole responsibility for creating disability management policies and interventions. The different DM committees could be the leaders of these discussions. If such discussions were to take place, conflict resolution techniques could be incorporated into these policies and interventions, which in turn would create a better potential for re-employment of disabled workers.

Tools that have the capability to recognize and assess the importance and the extent of a disabled person's response to OLBP and chronic pain are of great value. It is also important for studies to focus on the needs of "able" workers as well in order to provide a bridge between the disabled workers and their co-workers. Thus, there remains a need for interventions that help disabled people develop strategies that enable them to address RTW issues such as hostility and discrimination at the workplace. This is crucial in facilitating successful transitions from dependency to independence.

Further exploration of the RTW intervention, other than GRTW, are necessary for bridging the gap between treatment centres and the workplace. The following points below describe what the RTW tool needs to take into consideration:

- The use of the RTW tool would need to take place early in the pain treatment program (as a record of the presence and the level of emotional distress resulting from the disabled workers' concerns about re-employment barriers posed by the presence of psychosocial factors at the workplace), could result in participation in, rather than avoidance of, physical activities that are very much a part of the pain program treatment modalities.
- The RTW tool needs to be able to set objectives/goals for the transition of disabled workers from treatment to employment. It would

---

[24]  D. Mills, "Building Joint Labor-Management Initiatives for Worksite Disability Management" (1995) *Principles and Practices of Disability Management* (Winter Park, FLA).

do that by enabling the vocational rehabilitation professionals in the pain programs to identify strategies required for the removal of re-employment barriers caused by the different psychosocial factors. This in turn would highlight the need for supervision of these transitions. Supervised GRTW, as suggested earlier, could lead to better RTW outcomes, a development that, undoubtedly, would be welcomed by all parties involved.

- The RTW tool would need to be able to identify injured workers who are at higher risk of developing chronic pain because it focuses or targets on issues that are uncomfortable and awkward to bring up. It is currently impossible to assess each disabled worker with respect to psychosocial factors due to limited time, efficiency, workload, and resources. In addition, each ill or injured worker's condition is unique to their form of chronic pain. Because of this, there are no formulaic answers.
- The RTW tool would need to provide a potential answer to this problem by at least allowing each RTW action plan to be customized for each individual. This customization would assist rehabilitation professionals in maximizing their resources for the best results; they could thus become more proactive instead of merely reactive. For example, rather than making workers with chronic pain wait for over six months, the workers could be enrolled in a comprehensive pain-management program as soon as it becomes apparent that their condition is not improving, even as early as in the first month of their injury. Aggressive pain management strategies during this sub-acute phase would diminish the probability of chronic pain and the resultant disability.

## Educating Non-Disabled Workers

Lastly, a more detailed exploration of the perceptions on the part of non-disabled workers, management and union representatives and their views as they relate to the uniqueness of workers afflicted by OLBP and chronic pain, would be useful.

Education of both non-disabled and disabled workers is one possible solution for reducing chronic pain. For example, if future studies demonstrate that education is a good approach to deal with psychosocial factors, and show that education actually decreases emotional distress, it could have a significant impact on improving RTW outcomes. Education of this sort could affect the workforce by changing the work environment to keep more people happy, keep people staying in their jobs longer, and put more pressure on employers to discuss and face the psychosocial issues that may exist. This would also promote solutions to many of the psychosocial issues. A useful comparison is "duty to accommodate". It is currently law that an employer has an obligation to actively demonstrate that they have exhausted every possibility to the extent of "undue hardship" before they can legally claim that they cannot accommodate a permanently disabled employee. If they fail to demonstrate this, they are possibly at risk of dealing with the Labour Relations Board and with Human Rights and with receiving a human rights complaint. However, it must also be taken into account that ill or injured workers need to be very active participants in their own recovery while the employer facilitates the process. This may mean that ill or injured workers may choose to quit their jobs or seek alternative occupations. Helping all employees at the job site understand the factors that impact on OLBP and chronic pain will improve the company's and injured worker's return to work outcomes. This will improve the injured worker's quality of life and the company's bottom line.

## FUTURE IMPLICATIONS

It is known that problems associated with OLBP and chronic pain cannot be entirely attributed to either problems with workers or problems with work. It is possible, though, that these problems may reside, partly, in job-worker relationship. Literature does not provide a clear picture of the problem. This may be due to the fact that biomechanical (physical) factors are seldom examined together with the psychosocial factors.[25] Instead, only the bio-mechanical (physical) risk factors are well-measured. Consequently, this trend makes it difficult to gain insight into how both factors, acting simultaneously, affect the job-worker relationship. Therefore, it would be logical to suggest that future research studies should include into their design provisions that allow for simultaneous exploration of both bio-mechanical (physical) and psychosocial factors.

The natural history of OLBP varies from person to person. This makes it necessary to differentiate risk factors that leads to the occurrence of OLBP for each individual. It also suggests the need for an individualized approach to RTW interventions.

---

[25] J. Frank, I. Puleins & M. Kerr et al., "Occupational Back Pain an Unhelpful Polemic" (1995) 21 Scand. J. Work Environ. Health at 3-14.

Another problem is that the chronic pain disabling the worker may only be the "tip of the iceberg". Chronic pain can often hide underlying issues requiring proper, but different, care.

Employers and insurance carriers who fail to recognize this and only pay for 'medical care' are ultimately confronted with greater costs when medical attempts to handle non-medical issues fail. Although the worker may be forced to go back to work on the basis of an independent medical evaluation, the underlying issues, which can have many different forms including psychiatric, are not usually addressed and will surface in another way or injury.[26]

---

[26] G. Hubbard, G. Tracy & S. Morgan *et al.*, "Outcome Measures of Chronic Pain Program" (1996) 12 *The Clinical Journal of Pain* at 101-109.

# Part 2

# THE INSURANCE PROCESS

# Chapter 7

# THE INSURANCE PROCESS

ANN LECKIE AND SUE JORDAN

## THE CLAIMS PROCESS

Employers, employees and unions are often mystified at the decisions an insurance company makes on disability claims. Employers may not fully understand the plan that they purchased, its limitations and exclusion and other limiting factors. Employers are excluded from the medical facts of the case, so they might not understand why an employee who doesn't "seem" that ill is given benefits and another employee who "seems" to be very ill is denied. For many employees, now claimants, the process works smoothly and a secure income flow occurs during the course of the disability. For others, the paperwork required and the claims process itself is a mystery that they feel excluded from. Further, unions who are often asked to represent their members, may be excluded from the process. The purpose of this and subsequent chapters is to clarify the roles and responsibilities of experts in the insurance companies and outline common errors made by claimants.

The claims process described in this chapter is a simplified version of general claims processing. The chapter outlines the various experts and steps to processing a short- or-long-term disability claim. Within each step are problem-solving tips to ease communication between the employer, the employee and the insurance company. The process is purposely very general in order to allow for differences between various insurance companies.

## Role of the Insurance Company

The insurance company is the middleman in the disability chain: the employer or trust pays the appropriate premiums to the insurance company, and the insurance company either administers the policy (administration services only) or underwrites the benefits. Please see Chapter 11 for a more detailed description of funding mechanisms. The insurance company is then responsible for seeing that the agreed-upon benefits are delivered to the employees. Insurance companies use the resources of key experts in the field to provide the services. The central decision-maker on the validity and duration of claims is the case manager.

The insurance company's case manager processes the disability claims. The insurance company is responsible for ensuring that the medical documentation submitted on behalf of the employee clearly supports total disability as defined by the terms of the policy before a claim is approved. The insurance company must also outline any medically-based limitations to the employee's ability to perform his or her job, so that the employer can make an appropriate RTW plan.

## Advantages of Using the Insurance Company

The following points emphasize the advantages of using an insurance company to administer your disability plan.

The insurance company makes objective decisions regarding the validity and duration of the claims, and may facilitate the return to work of the employee, either to his or her own job (sometimes with modification), to a different job with the same employer that is more suited to the employee's limitations, or to a job with a different employer.

The insurance company can provide professional decisions about claims because it has access to experts in the field that an individual employer often does not have access to.

Medical data remains confidential because the data is kept out of the workplace. Confidentiality can be extremely important for claims such as AIDS or mental illness.

Insurance companies can offer financial flexibility when a plan is designed to suit the employer's needs.

## Role of the Case Manager

The case manager is the facilitator of the insurance process and is responsible for compiling and organizing the original data submitted by the employer, the employee, medical professionals, other insurers and the union where appropriate. The first step for the case manager is to review the data and determine whether the employee is eligible for insurance coverage. The next step for the case manager may include the following: interview the employee over the telephone to determine, for example, the employee's perception of his or her abilities, their level of daily activities and motivation to return to work. The case manager may also interview the employer to identify any barriers at the workplace that may hinder a return to work, and to determine how the employer can accommodate the employee with his or her current limitations.

The case manager obtains a medical opinion from the insurance company's medical consultant if clarification of medical data is necessary, or to determine what information is missing, and to verify that the treatment plan and/or prognosis is appropriate. The case manager or medical consultant may recommend an Independent Medical Examination (IME) by a specialist, a multi-disciplinary assessment if more than one diagnosis is indicated, or a functional capacity evaluation. These can help clarify the employee's limitations, or determine the best possible treatment plan for the employee. The medical consultant is a licensed physician hired by the insurance company to provide objective and fair opinions to assist the case manager in making decisions. Please see Chapter 8 for a more detailed description of the role of the medical consultant.

If further medical data is required, the case manager will write to the attending physician, or have the medical consultant call the attending physician or specialist. Another method to gather more information is to have the insurance company's rehabilitation specialist visit the employee. Please see Chapter 9 for a more detailed description of the role of and current theories about vocational rehabilitation specialists.

Once the case manager has sufficient medical data on file a decision is made. If the claim is approved the case manager will monitor the employee's medical status. A rehabilitation consultant will arrange a visit if one has not already been done, unless this is inappropriate due to the prognosis and/or other limiting factors such as the employee's age.

The case manager and the rehabilitation specialist will then formulate a disability management plan. For example, they may arrange a physical re-conditioning program for the employee, followed by a functional capacity evaluation, a worksite visit, and a graduated return-to-work plan. The disability management plan is approved by the medical professionals, as necessary, involved in the employee's care before it is executed.

Early intervention is essential because the longer the employee is absent from work, the more difficult it can become for him or her to return to the workplace.

As the disability management plan is executed, the case manager and the rehabilitation specialist maintain contact with the medical professionals, the employer and the employee so that all attempts are made to remove barriers to a successful return to work. Clear and open communication between all parties is essential if the plan is to succeed.

If the medical documentation clearly does not support total disability from the employee's occupation as outlined in the policy, the case manager denies the claim. The decline letter states the reason for denial and includes an outline of what documentation the employee should submit if he or she wants to appeal the decision.

Poor documentation of the initial illness is often the reason for initial declines. For example, if the claimant submits an attending physician's statement with vague documentation of the condition, or the duration of recovery recommended in the statement seems lengthy compared to medical standards, the claim might be denied. Objective medical data such as clinical test results, consultation reports, and physiotherapy progress reports (if applicable) can help clarify the reasons for the employee's prolonged absence from work and result in an earlier acceptance of the claim.

## Benefit — Funding Mechanism

There are two kinds of claims payments — taxable and non-taxable benefits. For example, the employees may pay premiums for short-term disability, in which case the benefits recieved would be non-taxable. If the employer pays premiums for long-term disability, then the benefits received are taxable.

## Short-Term and Long-Term Disability Claims

Typically insurance companies define claims according to whether they are short-term or long-term. Qualifying periods apply to both kinds of claims.

## Short-Term Disability Claims

The qualifying period for short-term disability claims is typically three to seven days, except in the case of an accident, when there is usually no waiting period. The length of the short-term disability plan can vary, and is typically from 15 weeks to 52 weeks.

A common definition of disability in a short-term disability policy states that to qualify for benefits the claimant must be unable to perform the essential duties of his or her own occupation (not just his or her own job) due to a medical illness or accident. For example, if an employee suffers from an anxiety-related disorder stemming from conflict at the workplace, the employee may be unable to return to his or her own job but, depending on the severity of the condition, may be able to return to work at a different location or with a different employer. If this is the case, the employee would not be considered totally disabled from the duties of his or her own occupation as defined by the terms of the policy.

## Long-Term Disability Claims

Many claims are resolved in the short-term disability period. If the claim moves into long-term disability due to the nature of the illness, the transition from short-term disability should be as smooth as possible. If there is sufficient current medical data on file prior to completion of the long-term disability claim, the attending physician's statement portion can be omitted.

The typical qualifying period for long-term disability claims is from 15 to 52 weeks. The employee usually receives income replacement during this qualifying period by either employment insurance or a short-term disability or salary continuance plan.

Once the employee satisfies the qualifying period for long-term disability benefits, usually, during an initial period the employee must continue to be unable to perform the essential duties of his or her own occupation due to a medical illness in order to receive benefits. This is followed by a longer period during which the employee must be unable to perform any occupation for which he or she is reasonably suited by education, training or experience, in order to continue receiving benefits. The most common length of the initial "own occupation" period for long-term disability is 24 months. Once the employee qualifies for benefits in the "any occupation" period, the typical maximum benefit date is the employee's 65th birthday.

If the short-term disability claim already provides sufficient medical evidence of total disability, the attending physician's statement portion of the long-term disability claim can be omitted. Otherwise, after the case manager compiles and organizes the original medical documentation provided, the same steps described earlier in this chapter under the section "Role of the Case Manager" are followed.

Medical conditions can change so that an individual's limitations fluctuate, making the return to work more of a challenge as time passes. Often an independent medical examination or a functional capacity evaluation is done well into a claim if, for example, there is conflicting information on file, if the level of treatment appears to be waning or if permanent accommodation is being considered.

## Summary: Claims Flow Chart

The case manager operates within the framework of the insurance company's processes. These processes can vary from insurance company to insurance company. The following list charts the generalized procedure of adjudicating a claim. The steps are explained individually after the list.

1. Claim is received and coded;
2. Eligibility is determined:
    (a) eligibility requirements are reviewed according to the insurance contract, and
    (b) claim is accepted or rejected on the basis of eligibility;
3. Limitations or Exclusions are determined:
    (a) limitation,
    (b) exclusions,
    (c) pre-existing conditions,
    (d) pregnancy, maternity or parental leaves,
    (e) specialized clauses by contract;
4. medical profile is assessed:
    (a) existing medical information is reviewed;
    (b) resources for review of claim are utilized:
        i) medical consultant,
        ii) independent medical examiner,
        iii) function capacity examination, and
        iv) rehabilitation;
    (c) claim is accepted or rejected, or more detailed information is requested;

5. approval for a specific time;
6. creation of a management strategy; and
7. closing the file:
   (a) appeal,
   (b) close, and
   (c) return to work.

## ADJUDICATION OF THE DISABILITY CLAIM

### Claim is Received and Coded

All claims, once they are received by the insurance company, are encoded with a policy number and a number specific to the claim. All correspondence that is received in regard to that claim is coded with the same number and a specific code. This ensures that all correspondence (mail, fax, courier or other electronic means of communication) is recorded, processed and stored in one location.

### Problem Solving

When dealing with an insurance company by phone or letter, it will speed the processing of the claim if the claimant or policyholder provides the individual's claim number and policyholder number. The claim number is the number given to the specific claim and the policyholder number is given to all the individuals covered under the insurance policy. This will help the examiner quickly find the specific file. Examiners can find the information without these numbers but it is easier for all parties if they are provided. There are many Jane Smiths in an insurance company's files but only one Jane Smith, Policy Number 24444, Claim Number 666 777 888.

### Determination of Eligibility is Performed

Eligibility requirements are reviewed according to the contract between the insurance company and the policyholder (usually the employer, the union or an association). Not every employee of every company is automatically eligible for disability benefits. Employees may not be eligible for benefits if:

1. they have not worked at the company for a sufficient length of time;
2. they only work part-time;

3. the disability began before the policy was in force; and
4. in a flexible benefits plan the employee may not have selected the benefit.

There are any number of reasons why an employee may not be eligible for benefits. Determination of acceptance or rejection is made on the basis of eligibility. This information may be given over the phone to the employee who was applying for benefits, but must always be followed with a letter explaining why the employee was not eligible.

## Problem Solving

It is important to always review the employee handbook to determine eligibility. If it is believed the employee is eligible for benefits, but he or she was not on the insurance company's system and thus declined, the human resources department can make inquiries to determine the employee's eligibility.

## Limitations or Exclusions are Determined

### 1. Limitations

Limitations occur when the employee is eligible for benefits, such as those outlined above, but cannot receive payments for a specific reason, such as being on a leave of absence. A list of of limitations is provided in the STD/LTD contract.

### 2. Exclusions

Exclusions occur when the employee is eligible for benefits but cannot receive payment because the illness or injury resulted from a situation not covered by the plan. Thus, an employee who committed a robbery cannot claim benefits from the gunshot wound he received during the course of the robbery. A list of of limitations is provided in the STD/LTD contract.

### 3. Pre-existing Conditions

Pre-existing conditions are defined in the insurance contract and these conditions occur when the employee is eligible for benefits but cannot receive payment because the illness or injury is the result of a previous illness or injury.

There are limits on pre-existing condition clauses imposed by law. A common limitation is that if the employee were able to work for one year with the given condition (*e.g.*, diabetes), then payment would be made if he or she became ill due to complications after the year at work and the waiting period was completed. However, had the employee filed a claim within the year, there is a possibility this claim would fall under this limitation and he or she may not be eligible for benefits. This usually applies to long-term disability cases.

Not all contracts contain a pre-existing condition clause.

### 4. Pregnancy, Maternity or Parental leaves

Pregnancy is, of itself, not a compensable illness or injury. However, complications of pregnancy may be covered under the contract. Many pregnant women work until their due date. Periods of leave for maternity or parental leave are generally not covered. (This law is in a state of flux, please contact a specialist in your province to review current legislation).[1]

### 5. Specialized Clauses

The policyholder can place additional exclusions in the contract. For instance, one policyholder with employees in western Canada excluded all injuries that resulted from voluntary participation in the rodeo. Many employees in this area participated in a local rodeo every summer and suffered from broken arms and twisted backs. The employer did not feel that it was appropriate for these employees to receive benefits for participating and becoming injured in this voluntary sport.

## Problem Solving

If an employee is declined benefits based on a limitation or exclusion, the reason must be clearly stated in the denial letter. This letter should be checked against the contract to ensure that the examiner's decision follows the guidelines. If an employee feels that the limitations or exclusions were improperly applied, a written reply to the insurance company will ensure that the examiner re-evaluates his or her decision.

---

[1]  For further information, read Chapter 8, The Insurance Medical Consultant, Pregnancy.

## Medical Profile is Assessed

### 1. Review Existing Medical Information

Each insurance company provides its policyholders with a form to collect medical information on the employee who is applying for benefits. There may be a charge for collecting this information and the terms of the contract will determine who is responsible for this fee. The importance of the information collected on this form cannot be understated. More claims are denied on the first attempt due to poorly filled out forms than any other reason. For example, the insurance company cannot accept a form that states that the nature of the illness is pregnancy. If this same employee is suffering from severe nausea due to pregnancy and is undergoing treatment, but the insurance company is unaware of this, then payment will be denied even though the employee is medically disabled.

### 2. Utilize Resources for Review of Claim

If the medical information is not clear, or if the return-to-work date is outside of generally accepted norms for the stated disability, the insurance company can utilize many resources to determine the severity of the illness or injury. Some of these resources are listed below:

1. Medical consultant;[2]
2. Independent medical examiner, who provides a third-party objective assessment of the illness or injury;
3. Functional capacity examination;[3] and
4. Rehabilitation.[4]

## Claim is Accepted or Rejected, or More Detailed Information is Requested

A determination is made to accept or reject the claim based on the examination of employee eligibility, limitations, exclusions, unique clauses in the contract and existing medical information provided on the application for benefits. Should more detailed information be required

---

[2]   See Chapter 8, The Insurance Medical Consultant.
[3]   See Chapter 13, Physical Rehabilitation.
[4]   See Chapter 9, Vocational Rehabilitation in Disability Management.

prior to making this determination, the employer, employee and physician will be advised by letter detailing the necessary requirements.

## Problem Solving

If the claim is denied for lack of medical information, the employee must ensure on the appeal that there is complete, legible and sufficient medical information supplied to the insurance company.

## Approval for a Specific Time

Payments are usually approved for a specific period of time. The time is determined by the medical information supplied and the normal duration of absence for that particular condition and by the time-limits set out in the contract. If the employee does not return to work once this pre-determined period is complete, payment will be suspended and there will be a request for further medical information.

## Problem Solving

Many claims are halted in the middle of the illness or injury because the employee has failed to submit further medical information. The insurance company should request this information in advance, by letter or on the cheque stub. The insurance company must ensure that its claimants are aware of the significance of this request and that failure to submit the required medical information could jeopardize timely payments of benefits in the future.

## Creation of a Return-to-Work Strategy

A return-to-work strategy is the crucial step in any well thought-out disability management program. In this step, all the resources of the insurance company, the employer and the employee, and if appropriate the union, unite to help the employee return to work. First, a clear medical plan must be in place listing all the needs of the employee. Following this, a rehabilitation plan can be created to ensure that the employee has all the necessary support to return to work in a safe manner. Early intervention of claims, a key component of disability management, is brought into play in this portion of the program. A good management strategy must be created as soon as possible so that everyone involved in the claim can work toward the same goals.

### Communication

Communication with all parties in the disability program must be clear and precise at this point. Written claims management plans must be clearly documented. If there is a change in the medical condition of the employee, new plans must be created.

A problem in early intervention can arise if the employee does not understand why he or she is involved in a return-to-work program when he or she is still disabled. All participants of the disability management program must work to educate the employee on the importance of early intervention. It is critical to keep the employee focused, not only on the current situation, but on the fact that some day he or she will return to the workforce and the plan will help achieve this goal.

## CLOSING THE FILE

The insurance company process of closing a file is outlined below.

### Appeal

Each insurance company has its own appeal procedures. Generally, an appeal requires the employee to submit more detailed medical information to support the claim. This information should come from the employee's treating physician. If there are any concerns about the information that the insurance company wants, the employee should contact his or her case manager to clarify the outstanding issues.

### Close

A file is closed when the employee successfully returns to work or accepts the decision of the claims examiner.

### Return to Work

The employee's return to work is the ideal resolution of a claim. When an employee returns to work at the earliest possible time in a medically safe manner, the program of disability management is working.

## Conclusion

The claims examination process is multi-faceted. It utilizes the resources of many specialists to determine the best possible method to help the employee return to work in a medically-safe manner. Despite the involvement of numerous specialists, this process should be straightforward and simple for the employee, provided the following people fulfil their requirements:

1. The employee should:
   (a) thoroughly complete the application form and provide all required information; and
   (b) provide information when requested, in particular, timely and complete medical updates.
2. The employer should:
   (a) provide all necessary information in a legible and timely manner; and
   (b) correctly fill out all forms.
3. The physician should:
   (a) thoroughly fill out all required information in a timely manner.
   (b) ensure to write out all complications and reasons why this claim is unique.

## FUTURE

Communication is the key to a successful claims process and will only expand in the future. If all players in the process perform their function, the eligible employee will receive payment in a timely manner. If there is a problem, all parties should feel comfortable in talking to their case manager to resolve or at least fully understand the concerns in their particular files.

# Chapter 8

# THE INSURANCE MEDICAL CONSULTANT

DR. ERROL FERGUSON AND DR. DONALD BUTT

## WHO IS THE MEDICAL CONSULTANT?

The medical consultant is a licensed physician whose expertise is sought by the insurance company to advise on matters pertaining to insurance medicine, including disability. The physician's specialty is commonly in family medicine, but can be in any of the major specialties including psychiatry. The physician may have had special training in insurance medicine and may have attended an intensive course sponsored by the American Academy of Insurance Medicine. At the very least, the physician will have attended special meetings and conferences on insurance medicine. The physician may have expertise in occupational medicine or in medico-legal matters as well, but most important is the knowledge and experience derived from clinical practice. The medical consultant may likely be familiar with many of the attending physicians of the claimants. This is an advantage when a telephone call is necessary.

In advising on cases for adjudication, the medical consultant should be objective, accurate and fair. The final decision is not made by the medical consultant, but by the claims adjudicator. The medical consultant is one member of the team who provides information to enable the claims adjudicator to make a fair and proper decision.

## DISABILITY PHILOSOPHY

An insurance company's disability claims policy is to pay all legitimate claims quickly and to help the disabled return to a healthy and purposeful lifestyle, which includes returning to work, if possible.

## DISABILITY ADJUDICATION STAFF

Disability claims are adjudicated by a disability claims examiner. This person is responsible for processing the claim, deciding what information needs to be gathered and whether the claimant should be interviewed, sent a questionnaire or receive a home visit to gather more information. The examiner also decides if the file should be reviewed by the medical consultant, who reviews the file and interprets all medical treatment and investigation information sent by the treating physicians. Often the medical consultant offers opinions regarding what further information is needed, whether the claim of total disability is medically supported, and if so, when an update should be requested from the treating physician(s).

If the claim information supports total disability, the file is often referred to a rehabilitation specialist. The specialist conducts a home visit with the claimant and visits the employer to establish return-to-work accommodations and reviews the job description in the workplace. Often a visit to the attending physician is necessary to obtain details about the treatment plan and possible return-to-work date and give the physician information regarding employer accommodations. Each disability claims examiner reports to a supervisor who has experience with difficult claims. This is particularly important as the frequency of difficult claims is increasing. The supervisor oversees the entire process to make sure correct decisions are being made, and monitors the examiner's workload so as to allow for quick and accurate claim processing.

Another member of the adjudication staff is the litigation claims specialist who reviews claims that are going to litigation. These specialists have experience with all aspects of the claims process and court proceedings.

## MEDICAL CONSULTANT'S ROLE

The medical consultant performs many other functions beyond what has been mentioned above. They often help with specific medical wording and detail design of questionnaires and disability forms being sent to claimants and attending physicians.

The medical consultant is often asked to phone attending physicians to uncover a more complete picture of the disabling condition, and to discuss the disability contract so that the attending physician understands how the claim has been adjudicated.

The medical consultant often interacts with the employer's occupational physician to get further details of the job, the disability and accommodations available. This is often very useful for early return-to-work initiatives.

The medical consultant also educates the claims staff regarding various medical conditions through presentations or one-to-one dialogue of specific cases. Often the medical consultant is called upon to give expert advice to the underwriter, lawyer or the sales staff.

Medicine is not an exact science, as is mathematics or physics. There are many exceptions to the "rule" and that is what makes analysis of medical conditions and human behaviour so challenging. For instance, a person may not fulfil the strict medical definition of a particular mental illness, but that person may well feel "sick" nonetheless. Furthermore, the attending physician may well agree that the person is sick, or at least not well, and be actively supportive of a disability claim. Often this situation results from stressful circumstances either arising out of seemingly unresolvable conflicts at home or in the workplace. Such a situation may lead to a prolonged mental illness if remedial action is not taken — usually a temporary removal from the stressors. Therefore, there may be justification for a limited period of "disability" on a medical basis in order to stop a process toward mental illness.

Allowing for this flexibility often has long-term beneficial results in preventing prolonged absences from work. Such limited time away from work should be in conjunction with a counselling program designed to enhance coping skills and raise self-esteem.

## DISABILITY, IMPAIRMENT AND HANDICAP

Understanding the difference between disability, impairment and handicap is very important in rendering disability claims decisions.

Impairment may be defined as an alteration in a person's health, whether psychological, physiological or anatomical, that is measured by medical means. Most people have impairments that do not affect their ability to work. Examples of common impairments would be heart problems or arthritis.

Handicap is defined as a barrier or obstacle to functional activity. Examples of handicaps would be someone who stutters or is deaf or has lost a limb. It is amazing what some individuals accomplish in spite of handicaps.

Disability is an alteration in a person's health that is measured by medical and non-medical means and relates to an individual's capacity to meet personal, social and occupational demands. In considering disability, adjudicators must measure and understand the impairment and take into consideration the job demands. They must also be alert to other factors such as motivation and compliance with treatment.

## SOME COMMON CONDITIONS

### Psychiatric Conditions

Mental and nervous conditions currently make up 20 to 30 per cent of the reasons for long-term disability (greater than six months away from work), and for short-term absence and decreased productivity the percentage is greater than 50 and is increasing annually. The efficient management of these conditions is therefore critical to the overall performance and profitability of any company. The prevention, early detection and follow-up management of susceptible employees require efficient attendance policies and management training. These conditions used to be roughly thought of in three major categories: neuroses, psychoses and personality disorders. The personality disorders should not be the prime reason for absence from work as they are long-term in their development. They do, however, often play an important role where there is work stress and conflict.

### DSM

The American Psychiatric Society developed a document called "The Diagnostic and Statistical Manual of Mental and Nervous Diseases and Disorders" (DSM as it is popularly known). This has greatly clarified understanding of the field of mental and nervous disorders by providing criteria that must be met for each psychiatric diagnosis. This is a most useful book and it, or one of its handbooks, should be a part of the library in every office where claims adjudication takes place. In determining whether a person is eligible for disability benefits for mental or nervous conditions, it is important to first establish if diagnostic criteria are met. DSM is indispensable in this process. For instance, "stress" is not a diagnosis in DSM, but "Major Depression" is, and criteria are clearly spelled out in order for this diagnosis to be made.

Once a diagnosis is established, the next step is to determine the impairment, and if there are factors in the person's life that need addressing, such as workplace issues. DSM is helpful here too with the "Multiaxial Assessment". This involves an assessment on five axes as follows:

Axis I      The primary psychiatric diagnosis or other conditions that may be a focus of clinical attention
Axis II     Personality Disorders or Mental Retardation
Axix III    General medical conditions, such as asthma
Axis IV     Psychosocial and environmental problems (such as work issues)
Axis V      Global Assessment of Functioning (GAF)

The GAF or Axis V provides a numerical value on a scale of 0 to 100 as to how the person is functioning in his or her daily activities, and gives a quick reference as to how the disease impacts on the patient. Levels of over 80 are considered normal functioning. At a level of 60 people may begin to drop out of the workplace and below 50 most are unable to continue working in a productive way.

The following is a brief outline of a few of the most common conditions.

## Depression

Along with general anxiety disorder, depression is the most common reason for absence from work. Depression is defined as a mood change lasting at least two weeks and characterized by a loss of interest in nearly all activities. The mood may be either irritability or sadness and may include changes in appetite or weight, sleep and energy level (vegetative signs). Patients may experience feelings of worthlessness or guilt, difficulty with concentration and even recurrent thoughts of death. Some individuals complain of bodily aches and pains rather than sadness but often their facial expression and demeanor indicate otherwise.

The degree of impairment varies from person to person with depression. There must be significant distress or interference in social or occupational areas of functioning in order to make the diagnosis and differentiate depression from the sadness that everyone experiences from time to time. Sadness and joy are part of the fabric of everyday life and should be differentiated from true depression and mania. Transient depressive periods are a universal human response to disappointment, defeat or other adverse situations. These can range from depression associated with certain memories on holidays or significant anniversaries, maternity or menstrual blues to more severe symptoms with grief and bereavement. Depression, stress reactions and illness behaviour are often very difficult and sometimes impossible to distinguish.

Major depression is diagnosed when the symptoms are severe and last for a longer period than most people experience in similar situations. As well, true depression is often recurrent and there may be a strong family history. It is clinically useful to distinguish between bipolar (having depression and elated or excited periods) and unipolar (depressions only) mood disorders. Unipolar depression usually lasts six to nine months, though periods may last longer than two years in 15 to 20 per cent of cases. The period of depression is very dependent on optimal drug choice and dosage.

Another condition called dysthymia is a low-grade depression that usually begins insidiously in childhood or adolescence and lasts for many years or decades. These individuals may have episodes of severe depression superimposed on the dysthymia. There is very effective drug therapy for major depression and this is why it is important for managers and co-workers to help identify and direct these individuals to appropriate caregivers for treatment. The medications used to treat depression often bring about a dramatic change in four to six weeks once the right drug and dose are determined. Because of the high rate of recurrence, these individuals need regular support.

## Post-Traumatic Stress Disorder

The essential feature of this condition is the development of characteristic symptoms following exposure to an extreme traumatic stressor (*e.g.*, near-death experience). The characteristic symptoms are persistent avoidance of all stimuli that remind patients of the unpleasant event, as well as agitation. Disturbances of appetite, sleep and ability to concentrate, and therefore, work are often seen. Flashbacks and nightmares about the event are common. Post-traumatic stress disorder refers to conditions involving death or threat of death such as in a severe motor vehicle accident.

Each situation must be evaluated on its own merits and the length of time to recover should be reasonable for both employee and employer. It is important for such patients to be encouraged to face gradually the areas that are particularly painful to them. With understanding and support from supervisors and co-workers, these individuals can return to their previous productive lives. They will need support, professional counselling and often medications for severe and lengthy cases.

## Anxiety Disorder

Anxiety disorders and panic reactions are those characterized by overbreathing, rapid heartbeat, sweating and complaints of "butterflies in the stomach". Weakness and dizziness are very common with this disorder. A sense of "air hunger" and loss of contact with people and objects may occur. The patient may complain of numbness and tingling of his or her hands and feet. These attacks may be precipitated by conscious external painful events, but often are caused by subconscious inner conflicts relating to sexual, aggressive or dependency needs. The attacks may be sudden and last only minutes or be less intense and occur over a longer duration, even days or weeks.

Insight counselling (to help a person understand his or her behaviour and its consequences), relaxation techniques, meditation, as well as the careful administration of relaxants or antidepressants are used to treat this condition. These drugs should be used along with counselling to avoid dependency and overuse.

This disorder like the others we have discussed are often managed efficiently with support and understanding from managers and co-workers.

## Psychotic Conditions

Major alterations in mental function and severe disturbances in thought and perceptual processes characterize these conditions. Such changes are of a biochemical nature. There are often unrealistic beliefs (delusions) and false sensory perceptions (hallucinations).

Two main types of psychotic disorders are severe bipolar affective disorder and schizophrenia. Both of these conditions can be effectively treated and although these individuals will have recurrent problems, many of them maintain good work attendance and offer employers a great deal of loyalty and dedication.

## Alcohol and Drug Abuse

A single definition for drug dependence is neither desirable nor possible. Abuse is definable only in terms of societal disapproval and involves different types of behaviour:

1. Experimental and recreational use of drugs;
2. Unwarranted use of psychotherapeutic drugs to relieve problems or symptoms; and
3. The use of drugs for the above reasons at first and then development of dependence and continuation at least partially to prevent symptoms and discomfort of withdrawal.

Drug and alcohol abuse usually follows the course of psychological dependence followed by physical dependence characterized by tolerance and withdrawal symptoms when the drug or alcohol is discontinued.

## Alcohol Abuse

About 10 per cent of the adult population of North America abuses alcohol, with the incidence being significantly higher in those under age 35. Alcohol misuse is implicated in a significant number of accidents, homicides and suicides. The excessive use of alcohol is also associated with psychiatric disability and disorders of the gastrointestinal, nervous and cardiovascular systems. Individuals may frequently use alcohol in large amounts yet not be alcoholics, *i.e.*, addicted to alcohol. The non-addicted drinker generally is able to reduce or stop the use of alcohol when it affects health, social relationships or job performance.

Alcoholism is a disease characterized by pre-occupation with alcohol and loss of self-control in its consumption. It is typically an illness of denial on the part of the individual, and evidence of alcoholism is also frequently minimized by family, friends and medical sources, who unwittingly become enablers.

Very effective programs are available to help these individuals with withdrawal and long-term counselling. A team approach involving family, employer and friends as well as specially trained medical personnel is required to get these people to admit to their problem and to comply with short- and-long term treatment programs.

The early identification and reporting of these individuals often falls to managers and co-workers and should be encouraged by workplace educational programs.

## Drug Abuse

Drug abuse is defined as the use of drugs to obtain a sense of pleasure and to avoid discomfort and includes the non-medical use of drugs as well as those prescribed for medical reasons.

Drug abuse is often associated with psychological and physical dependence. Psychological dependence is a compulsion to continue use of the drug despite adverse consequences (social, financial and occupational), whereas physical dependence or addiction means that the individual will experience withdrawal symptoms if use of the drug is discontinued. Addiction is usually associated with tolerance, *i.e.*, the need to use increasing amounts of the drug in order to produce the desired effect. An overdose may be fatal, and there is an increased incidence of all forms of violent death (accidents, suicide and homicide) in the drug-abusing population. Intravenous injection of drugs is associated with infectious diseases, *e.g.*, heart valve infections, hepatitis and AIDS. Complications of chronic drug abuse include disorders of the liver, cardiovascular system, lungs and nervous system.

As with alcohol abuse, drug abuse requires professional help, family and friends and sometimes employers to help these people address their problem and return to normal functioning.

## SUBJECTIVE CONDITIONS

Subjective conditions are defined as those where there are no objective measurable findings to establish a diagnosis or measure the degree of impairment. We will discuss six of the most common conditions of this type but there are many more. Controversy rages over whether some of these conditions actually exist or whether they are manifestations of stress and burnout, and if they do exist how they should be managed.

It is generally accepted that these conditions are at least related in part to some form of stress in the claimant's life, and although not pleasant experiences, they should seldom, if ever, be totally disabling or cause prolonged absence from work. It is important, however, for managers to understand these conditions and help these employees cope with their workload and stressful situations encountered at work. Many of the symptoms seen in these disorders can be alleviated by understanding and good supervision from the manager if the employee is co-operative and motivated.

## Fibromyalgia

Fibromyalgia (FM) condition gets its name from the fact that there is a complaint of fibrous tissue and muscular pain and tenderness that must be present for at least three months. The pain and tenderness is generalized involving all four quadrants of the body. Eighteen anatomical sites are tested for tenderness and 11 must be positive in order to make a diagnosis of fibromyalgia. Pressing on the site with the examiner's finger, or using an instrument called a dolorimeter that standardizes pressure when applied to the site is how tenderness testing is performed.

There is no known specific cause for this condition, but stress induced by work pressures and conflicts, traumatic events such as a motor vehicle accident, illness, or unhappy family events may precipitate this condition. As well as the generalized muscular pain and tenderness, there is usually associated fatigue, sleep disturbance and emotional upset. When the physician examines the patient there are no abnormalities except tenderness.

These patients should be treated with re-assurance about the fact that this is not a serious life threatening condition and is best coped with by staying at work, resolving all conflicts and engaging in a graduated exercise program. This program should be primarily stretching and aerobic exercises such as walking, cycling and swimming and not formal physiotherapy.

These patients often benefit from long-term counselling, helping them to learn to cope with stress, maintain good nutrition and continue with their exercise program, as well as in the development of good work management skills. The early detection of these susceptible individuals is very important, and managers should be watching and refer these employees to appropriate caregivers. They should also help the employee maintain sensible workloads and deadlines.

This condition should not usually prevent employees from working but may require job description changes and a temporary decrease in hours for a few weeks.


## Chronic Fatigue Syndrome

Chronic fatigue syndrome (CFS) has many names such as chronic fatigue immune deficiency syndrome (CFIDS) and myalgia encephalomyelitis (ME), but because there has not been any proven immune problem or inflammation of the brain or spinal cord the preferred term is chronic fatigue syndrome. For some reason the incidence of this condition seems to be decreasing.

This condition is diagnosed by excluding other medical conditions that could cause this degree of fatigue, and therefore a thorough medical history and investigation should be carried out before a diagnosis of CFS is made. There must be fatigue that limits individuals to 50 per cent of their activity and the fatigue must have been present for at least six months. All medical and psychiatric causes of fatigue must be eliminated. Chronic fatigue syndrome, like FM is much more common in females than in males.

There is no known specific cause for this condition, but stress induced by work pressures and conflicts, traumatic events, illness, or unhappy family situations may precipitate this condition.

There are usually sleep disturbances and emotional distress associated with the fatigue. When the physician examines these patients, there are no abnormal findings. All laboratory testing is also normal.

The treatment is the same as that for FM and consists of re-assurance about the fact that this is not a serious life threatening condition, and it is best coped with by staying at work, resolving all conflicts and engaging in a graduated exercise program. This program should be primarily aerobic exercises such as walking, cycling and swimming. The exercises may need to be even more gradual than in FM because the main symptom in this condition is fatigue rather than pain.

These patients often benefit from long-term counselling helping them to learn to cope with stress, maintain good nutrition and continue with a regular exercise program, as well as developing good work management skills.

Like FM, the early detection of these susceptible individuals is very important, and managers should be watching and refer these employees to appropriate caregivers.

This condition should not usually prevent employees from working but may require job description changes and a temporary decrease in hours for a few weeks.

Although some physicians and support groups differentiate between FM and CFS, there is very little difference from a functional point of view or in managing these individuals.

## Multiple Chemical Sensitivity

Multiple chemical sensitivity (MCS) has also been called environmental illness or twentieth century syndrome. There is a great deal of controversy about the existence of this condition. It is stated to be a chronic condition lasting at least three months and characterized by recurrent symptoms occurring in response to various foods and environmental irritants.

The symptoms vary from "cold-like symptoms" to difficulties with breathing and thinking but may present in many other forms. To qualify for this diagnosis, the symptoms should recur and abate in response to exposure and removal of specific irritants.

There have been cases of respiratory difficulty associated with a buildup of bacteria in poorly ventilated buildings, but this is not the syndrome that is described here.

The difficulty with this condition is the severity of the symptoms that these individuals claim, and the symptoms do not disappear when they are removed from the environment that caused the problem. The condition has been used by some patients and physicians to explain psychological and personality abnormalities.

There are no physical findings on examination and all tests are normal. There are some strong advocates of this condition who report testing abnormalities, but the existence of multiple chemical sensitivity as a diagnostic entity is not generally accepted by the medical profession.

Treatment consists of re-assurance and removal of the precipitant if identified.

This condition should not be totally disabling. Note that total disability in the context of insurance refers to disability such that a person is unable to perform the essential duties of his or her occupation.

## Repetitive Strain Injury

Like the other subjective disorders, there are many names for repetitive strain injury (RSI), such as cumulative trauma disorder and occupational cervical brachial syndrome and many others, but the most descriptive term is RSI. This condition is characterized by chronic pain and numbness of the arm(s) and is caused by both physical and emotional factors which vary from case to case.

The symptoms usually involve both arms. Rest does not decrease the symptoms and these patients usually do not respond to conventional treatment methods. These people are often overachievers and perfectionists.

It is important that this condition be distinguished from carpal tunnel syndrome where there is objective evidence of nerve impairment at the wrist and therefore effective specific treatment.

The treatment for RSI requires a multi-disciplinary team approach. Individuals need to be empowered to manage their symptoms of physical discomfort and emotional stress. The treatment is vocationally directed and emphasizes maintaining regular work. Although there is controversy as to the usefulness of ergonomic assessment and workplace changes, these often motivate the employee and show employer interest. Stretching and aerobic exercises as well as good posture and relaxation techniques are important, while purely strengthening programs should be avoided. Splints should usually be avoided with these patients as they tend to make individuals feel RSI is primarily physical. Also splints can cause muscular weakness if they are used for too long a period of time.

Successful outcomes with individuals who have RSI will occur when the whole individual is treated and when they take responsibility for their physical and emotional welfare.

## Migraine Headaches

Migraine is a common type of headache that affects approximately five per cent of men and 15 per cent of women. Its cause remains unclear and it is diagnosed by a specific history coupled with a normal neurological physical exam. The headache is usually on one side of the head but may be on both sides and is often associated with distortions of vision and stomach upset. Migraines can last several hours or even days, but it is unusual for them to last for weeks and therefore, migraines should not commonly be a reason for prolonged absence from work. The headaches are often precipitated by specific triggers like sleep deprivation, weather changes, stress and menstrual periods.

Drug therapy is commonly used to treat migraine symptoms. Lifestyle changes, relaxation training, yoga and acupuncture have been used, but there is very little data establishing these techniques as efficacious. The drugs used vary from ASA or acetaminophen in milder cases to non-steroidal anti-inflammatory drugs in the more moderate cases to Ergotamine preparations in more severe cases. Sumatropan, although expensive, is very effective in cases of frequent migraine and relieves 70 per cent of cases within one hour.

There are also a number of medications that can be used preventatively for patients who experience headaches on a weekly basis. Sometimes dietary changes can be helpful in the prevention of these bothersome headaches.

## Vertigo and Dizziness

Dizziness has been rated as the third most common complaint, after chest pain and fatigue, taking people to their physicians. There is often a wide gap between what physicians mean by dizziness and what patients mean. Physicians use this term to describe a condition where the patients or surroundings are felt to be in motion. Patients often use this term to describe a general sense of loss of equilibrium or lightheadedness.

There are many causes of dizziness and this complaint requires a detailed history and careful neurological exam. The most common causes are related to short-lived inner ear inflammations or psychological disorders. Serious causes make up 10 per cent of the cases and must be ruled out if symptoms last for longer than two months.

Dizziness is discussed under the subjective disorders because psychological problems make up about 33 per cent of the cases, but 50 per cent of these cases of dizziness are caused by minor ear problems. These two major causes of dizziness can be differentiated by careful neurological exam.

The treatment for the dizziness is determined by the cause. Minor ear problems get better in a few weeks and require little or no treatment, but the psychological causes often require stress relief and counselling.

## MUSCULOSKELETAL CONDITIONS

### Myofascial Pain Syndrome

This term describes the syndrome that commonly follows a documented injury, *e.g.*, whiplash. It is most often seen following a car accident in which one was rear-ended. The amount of damage to the vehicle does not always correlate to the severity of symptoms, however The Quebec Whiplash-Associated Disorders Cohort Study (Spine Vol. 20, #8S 1995) refers to a simple classification where outcome may be predicted:

Grade 0 — No complaint about the neck. No physical signs
Grade I — Neck complaint of pain, stiffness, or tenderness only. No physical signs
Grade II — Neck complaint AND Musculoskeletal signs
Grade III — Neck complaint AND neurological signs
Grade IV — Neck complaint AND fracture or dislocation.

Symptoms and disorders that can be manifested in all grades include deafness, dizziness, tinnitus, headache, memory loss, dysphagia, and temporomandibular joint pain.

The physical findings on early examination are often minimal, but as the days and weeks progress, muscle spasm and restricted range of movement is reported to greater degrees. The injury is to soft tissues around joints, e.g., ligaments and muscles. As there are a multitude of small joints in the neck, and the head can oscillate quite violently in a rear end car accident, there may be extensive straining of these ligaments and muscles. This straining may produce prolonged pain in the neck and shoulders and radiate down the arms.

The treatment usually prescribed is physiotherapy and anti-inflammatory medication. As with so many chronic painful conditions, narcotic drugs, e.g., codeine compounds, should be avoided for fear of addiction. At times, a mild dosage of an antidepressant is used to raise the pain threshold or aid sleep, but this should not be interpreted to mean the patient is necessarily depressed. After a brief period of physiotherapy and/or other passive treatment, patients are encouraged to be more active in their exercise. This may increase the symptoms initially, but persistence will benefit the patient.

Unfortunately, myofascial pain syndrome may be associated with secondary gain, both financial and emotional. The secondary gain factor has the effect of prolonging and making more severe the reported symptoms. Attending physicians in their role as patient advocate often find this secondary gain factor difficult to deal with. On the one hand, the physicians are doing everything they can to help the patient recover, but on the other are encumbered with forms and letters for medico-legal purposes which dwell on the severity of the condition.

In some cases, evaluation of the degree of impairment cannot rely solely on patient or physician reports. There may be a requirement for more objective information in the prolonged cases that have outlived a reasonable predicted duration of disability. The information includes an independent medical examination (IME) or a careful assessment of what the individual actually does by questionnaire or surveillance.

## Low Back Pain Syndromes

The low back is the hinge around which most of the low back movements are made. We refer to the lumbar and sacral sections of the spine in this area. These joints carry all the weight of the body and are susceptible to very large forces when a person bends, twists and carries a weight. The low back, like the upper back and neck, are composed of vertebrae with joints between each of them. The vertebrae are separated by shock absorbers which consist of tough fibrous discs, stabilizing joints known as facet joints that extend backwards, and strong ligaments and muscles. Each of these areas is susceptible to injury and often more than one area is involved.

## 1. Acute Back Strain

Acute back strain is a common diagnosis in an otherwise healthy individual who has placed too much physical demand on the muscles and other soft tissue. Patients are often deconditioning or out of shape. There is a soft tissue injury to ligaments or muscles and this results in pain when patients move their backs. The physical examination reveals an individual who is quite limited with all back movements, *e.g.*, twisting and bending forward, backward or sideways. X-rays, if taken, fail to reveal any significant pathology.

Treatment consists of rest and anti-inflammatory drugs for a brief period followed by a structured exercise program and mobilization. Too long at rest will increase and prolong the symptoms and the disability. Most of these individuals should be back at work in their usual capacity within two or three weeks.

## 2. Sciatica

In the low back there are canals at each level through which nerves branch to the legs and pelvis. As the nerves course through these narrow tunnels, they may encounter certain obstacles. The most common obstacle is the disc that is herniated or out of position and squeezes against one of the sciatic nerve branches in the narrow canal. When a nerve is squeezed or irritated, it results in pain, muscle weakness or numbness along the route it takes. If the root of the nerve close to its origin in the spinal cord in the lumbar or sacral areas is involved, this is known as sciatica.

Depending on the severity of the damage to the nerve root and the area of symptoms, surgery may be considered to decompress the nerve and restore its function. The majority of cases are treated with rest and modified activities, followed by structured physiotherapy and a work hardening or exercise program. It may not be possible for some of these individuals to resume heavy work again. These patients are usually under the care of an orthopedic surgeon or neurosurgeon as well as their family physician.

## Inflammatory Arthritis

The hallmark of this condition is inflammation in the joints and their surrounding joint capsules. The joints of the hands and feet are often involved as well as the larger joints of the arms and legs. Inflammation is characterized by redness, pain, swelling, heat and loss of function. Therefore, there are usually identifiable physical signs and positive laboratory tests making the diagnosis more definitive. The most familiar condition in this category is rheumatoid arthritis, although there are a number of other related conditions that behave in a similar fashion.

There is a wide range of severity. The pain can be only mildly symptomatic to downright disabling. There may be few outwardly obvious physical signs, especially in the earlier stages, but as the disease progresses the appearance becomes more marked with the obvious deformities of the hands and feet.

Fortunately, there are many new medications and other physical treatments available to slow the progression and ease the suffering. However, there is no cure as yet. Rheumatoid arthritis has been identified in the mummies of Egypt, so it is not a new condition.

The degree of impairment varies from person to person. Disability depends on the specific impairments and the job description. The employer carefully assesses the specific impairments and relate these to the actual job requirements. A diagnosis of arthritis does not necessarily mean disability. In fact, some individuals with advanced and obvious deformities continue to be quite productive in the home and at work.

## Carpal Tunnel Syndrome

The nerves entering the hand on the thumb and index finger side must go through a tunnel in the wrist known as the carpal tunnel, named after the carpal bones in close proximity, together with the tendons to the fingers. This tunnel is covered by a tough unyielding fibrous band the size of a postage stamp. Under some conditions of repetitive use, the tissues in the tunnel sometimes become inflamed and swell up squeezing the nerves and causing the characteristic numbness, pain and weakness in the hand. Keyboard operators are particularly at risk for this, especially when the workstation is not properly designed. In the more extreme cases, muscle wasting in the hand can be seen.

The condition is diagnosed by the symptoms and the physical signs. At times, a test to detect a blockage in the nerve impulses is used (EMG).

This test will not always be positive in the milder or intermittent forms of carpal tunnel syndrome.

Treatment is designed to relieve the pressure in the tunnel. This can be done with anti-inflammatory medication and resting the hand. Other treatments include physiotherapy and splinting. In more extreme cases, surgery is required to relieve the pressure in a tight canal especially where there is evidence of muscle wasting. At times, diuretics are used to remove excess fluid if the condition is caused by general fluid retention.

This condition can be stubborn to treat and disabling for those who must use their hands in the repetitive manner. Most, however, do respond to treatment, but when they are exposed to the same set of work conditions, the symptoms may quickly return. Therefore, it is important to address the ergonomic issues at the workstation.

## CARDIAC CONDITIONS

Most of the heart conditions encountered in disability are in males over 50 years of age; the majority of these are due to coronary artery disease. Risk factors include family history or personal prior history of coronary artery disease, diabetes, overweight, lack of exercise and smoking. But others can be affected by coronary artery disease, including young individuals and females.

In susceptible individuals, the small arteries that course around the heart and supply blood to the heart muscle gradually become narrowed. At a critical moment when too much demand is put on the heart, as in strenuous effort, insufficient oxygen reaches the heart muscle and it cries out in pain, so to speak. This is angina. The pain resolves when the demand on the heart muscle eases or the individual takes something such as nitroglycerine that dilates the coronary arteries allowing more blood flow.

If a blood clot forms it stops the blood flow in the coronary artery. Permanent damage can then occur to the heart muscle and this is called a "heart attack". The most dangerous disease occurs in the anterior descending artery that supplies the important left ventricle, the part of the heart that pumps blood to most of the body.

Modern treatment for an acute heart attack, where there is complete blockage of the blood flow, includes an emergency injection of a substance that dissolves the clot restoring blood flow. This must be done immediately after the arrival of the ambulance at the hospital. It can prevent or minimize heart muscle damage. Treatment is highly individualized and may include drugs to relax the muscles in the coronary artery walls, *e.g.*, calcium channel blockers, beta adrenergic blockers, or drugs to open up the arteries, *e.g.*, nitroglycerine, and others to reduce cholesterol and attempt to prevent further coronary artery narrowing. Balloon angioplasty, where a catheter is threaded up inside an artery in the groin to the blocked coronary artery and inflated, or bypass surgery can be performed. If treatment is successful and no permanent damage to the heart muscle has been sustained, these individuals can return to normal functioning.

Impairment largely hinges on two factors:

1. In the case of arteries that are partially blocked and the individual experiences angina with a predictable amount of effort, heavy work is probably not possible. The degree of impairment can be measured objectively by a treadmill or stress test. An individual is hooked up to a cardiograph machine and walks on a graded pace and effort on a treadmill. When the ECG shows changes typical of insufficient blood supply to meet the demand, the physician can calculate how much effort the person is capable of. A variation of this includes a similar exercise test, but with the use of a radioactive substance to show the blood supply impairment, *e.g.*, thallium stress test.

2. If the heart muscle has been permanently damaged, it is replaced by a large area of scar and this part of the heart does not function like the normal healthy muscle does. As a result, the heart loses part of its ability to pump. The degree of loss is measured by assessing the degree of muscle loss and by measuring the amount of blood that is pumped out of the heart relative to that arriving to the heart. This is measured by either ultrasound or the injection of a radioactive substance. Normally, the heart pumps out at least 60 per cent of the blood flowing to it with each beat. When a large amount of muscle is lost, this figure can drop to 15 to 20 per cent. Such individuals are significantly impaired and have little stamina; they may be very short of breath and tire easily. There is no treatment that will restore lost muscle other than a heart transplant.

Most individuals with an impairment from coronary artery disease can carry on a lifestyle that is quite functional. But individuals are advised to carry out activities consistent with what is demonstrated in the tests. Regular exercise is helpful in restoring function.

One other factor that should be mentioned is stress. Stress, if sufficiently severe, can bring on angina. This type of angina likely has to do with adrenaline production and the increase of the heart rate. The effect of stress is more difficult to evaluate objectively. However, it can be done to a degree with a 24-hour Holter monitor, a pager-sized portable ECG worn by the individual while normal tasks are undertaken. This monitor can show ECG changes typical of those seen in angina that may coincide with documented stress.

## LUNG CONDITIONS

The more common lung diseases encountered are asthma and chronic obstructive pulmonary disease (COPD). They fundamentally differ in a number of aspects, but are similar in that there is obstruction of the airways with coughing and shortness of breath.

### Asthma

This is a reversible obstruction characterized by wheezing and coughing. The underlying problem is inflammation of the lining of the bronchial tree. Diagnosis is by symptoms and physical findings. Treatment is aimed at reducing the muscle spasm in the walls of the bronchial tubes, and more importantly, reducing the inflammation. Puffers are the main mode of treatment now, but some individuals must take oral medication as well.

Asthma can be brought on by exposure to allergens and irritants, including certain fumes and dust, or it can occur in susceptible individuals in response to infections or exercise. It is important to try to identify the precipitating factors in order to avoid them. Similarly, it is important to know what triggers in the workplace the individual is not sensitive to so that the individual does not avoid some areas unnecessarily. Asthma may lead to COPD when it is chronic and if uncontrolled, but usually it can be controlled and should not be disabling.

### Chronic Obstructive Lung Disease

Chronic obstructive lung disease is a condition where the lung tissue is permanently affected. A form of it is also known as emphysema. Chronic obstructive lung disease results from smoking and a variety of other contributing factors. It is diagnosed by symptoms and history, but also by pulmonary function testing or spirometry. These tests measure the rate at which a person can exhale air during the various phases of breathing. The result is compared with what is expected in a normal person of similar age and gender. This test provides a good objective measure of the degree of impairment and should be sought in all cases of COPD for adjudication.

Treatment may improve the readings, as there is often a reversible component to the disease, but does not cure it. These individuals are usually capable of performing sedentary or light work, but depending on the severity, an individual may not be capable of heavier work.

## PREGNANCY

With the workforce made up of nearly 40 per cent of women, disability in pregnancy is becoming more common. In the past, pregnancy was viewed as a normal condition and would not under normal conditions be a basis for disability, but more and more often insurers see claims for disability in pregnancy.

There are four types of claims arising from pregnancy:

1. Those claims related to the pregnancy itself;
2. Medical or surgical conditions occurring during a pregnancy;
3. High risk situations when the person is pregnant; and
4. Occupation exposure hazards.

It has been stated that a woman having a normal uncomplicated pregnancy working at a job that represents no more than the normal hazards of daily life should be able to work until labour; however, the definition of "high-risk" pregnancy has been expanded greatly in recent years.

Traditionally, employers and the Employment Insurance Commission have allowed wage replacement for two weeks prior to delivery and until six weeks postpartum.

An Alberta court judgment[1] has ruled, however, that women on maternity leave should receive the same benefits as employees collecting sick or disability benefits for the period of their pregnancy and after delivery where there is some health-related problem. Duration is determined on a case-by-case basis rather than setting the duration of disability at six weeks. Some progressive employers are already changing

---

[1] *Alberta Hospital Assn. v. Parcels* (1992), 1 Alta. L.R. (3d) 332 (Q.B.).

their plans to include pregnancy in their disability policies. In Ontario, discrimination based on sex is prohibited in the workplace; however, it is not viewed as discrimination to exclude employees from short- or long-term disability benefits while they are on maternity or parental leave.

Some complications commonly seen in pregnancy which require a few weeks off work and require reassessment to determine the safe time of return to work are as follow:

1. Nausea and vomiting due to pregnancy;
2. Threat of miscarriage; and
3. Anemia.

In each of these conditions the symptoms must be regularly reassessed by the physician and a return-to-work safely planned when the condition is under control. The usual time is two to six weeks for these conditions, but there is some variability.

There are other conditions where there is obvious total disability. Such conditions are:

1. Ruptured membranes;
2. Bleeding in the last three months;
3. Premature labour with hospitalization; and
4. High blood pressure and fluid accumulation with protein in the urine.

There are medical conditions during pregnancy which require individual consideration. Some examples are:

1. Asthma;
2. Heart problems;
3. Diabetes;
4. Seizures; and
5. Low back pain.

There are many surgical conditions which may require immediate treatment during pregnancy, but others where the individual can rest until after delivery and then have the surgery. An example of the former is acute appendicitis, and an example of the latter may be gallstones without obstruction.

There is a long list of conditions where the pregnancy from the beginning is considered high risk and a plan must be worked out with the employer and physician to decide the appropriate job description changes and when the patient should stop working. Examples of such conditions are:

1. Sickle cell trait;
2. Uterine structural abnormality with previous loss of pregnancy; and
3. Multiple pregnancies.

Finally, there are workplace environmental factors which are not conducive to the pregnant worker. Some factors are:

1. Heavy metal exposure;
2. Chemical exposure, such as organic solvents;
3. Radiation exposure; and
4. Physical demands, *e.g.*, climbing.

In conclusion, it can be quickly seen that work issues and pregnancy need to be carefully evaluated in conference with employee, employer and the treating physician.

## FUTURE TRENDS IN DISABILITY MANAGEMENT

Over the last decade there has been a marked increase in the incidence of claimed psychiatric and subjective disorders, which have been discussed above. This trend is likely to continue because it is driven by the economy and demographics. Baby boomers, the largest group of our population, are reaching the age of highest incidence of claimed disability. This, together with the aging population and more women in the workplace, adds up to tremendous stress on working families, and thus a higher incidence of claims for disability.

Workers' compensation boards, together with insurers, are tightening up their adjudication processes to be sure that only those truly disabled and motivated to return to work receive benefits.

Government provincial health care payers are demanding more accountability from physicians and other care givers in regard to investigations and the treatments they order. Various forms of combined health systems are being explored where patients would be treated by a specific group of physicians in order to be more integrated and avoid costly duplication and overuse.

This next decade will be characterized by unprecedented change that will occur very quickly. Everyone must join to help preserve the best health care.

# Chapter 9

# VOCATIONAL REHABILITATION IN DISABILITY MANAGEMENT

MARGARET BELLMAN

## WHAT IS DISABILITY MANAGEMENT?

Disability management can be thought of as the services, people, resources and materials used to:

- prevent disability;
- encourage rehabilitation and return to work for employees with disabilities; and
- minimize the impact and the costs of disability on the individual and the organization.(Schwartz, Watson, Galvin 1989).

While disability management certainly includes the delivery of rehabilitative services to individual employees, it is important to realize that it is also an organizational strategy that includes the development of:

- policies which reflect the organization's commitment to assist disabled employees to successfully return to work;
- procedures outlining the various player's roles and responsibilities;
- supportive benefit plans to encourage an early return to work;
- training programs which educate employees and managers;
- resources to provide rehabilitation services;
- individual rehabilitation plans; and
- a system to evaluate program results.

Disability management, therefore, can be looked upon both as a service for individuals with disabilities and also as an approach taken by organizations.

In the late 1990s several authors differentiated the two forms of DM by assigning new names. The NARPPS Disability Management Advisory Board White Paper referred to the provision of individual services as "Little DM" and services for the organization as "Big DM". Hall labels the two forms of DM as MICRO and MACRO while Rochelle Habeck calls them Organizational and Individual DM.

MACRO or Organizational DM can be considered proactive in that it is focused on preventing disabilities and improving the organizational response to disabilities. MICRO or individual DM, on the other hand, is reactive in that it is a specific response to an individual's needs once that person has become disabled.

Preventing disabilities from occurring is the ideal. But despite the best intentions and the best programs, some people unfortunately will still become disabled. The remainder of this chapter will focus on the processes involved in the delivery of INDIVIDUAL DM services.

## WHAT IS REHABILITATION?

As identified above, rehabilitation is an integral component of DM. Rehabilitation is a term that many people use but it has different meanings to different people. Technically speaking, rehabilitation is a "progressive, dynamic, goal-oriented, and time limited process aimed at enabling a person with an impairment to reach his or her optimal mental, physical, cognitive and/or social functional level". (Rehabilitation Services Inventory and Quality Project)

In this general definition of rehabilitation, the emphasis is on function. When functional impairments specifically relate to work, vocational rehabilitation (VR) is necessary.

## WHAT IS VOCATIONAL REHABILITATION?

Using the above definition of rehabilitation, VR can be thought of as a progressive, dynamic, goal-oriented and time-limited process aimed at restoring individuals with impairments to their optimal vocational level. In other words, it is all of the activities necessary to bring the individual to a "work-ready" level.

Although medical and psychological rehabilitation differ from VR, they are often critical elements of it. The goal of medical rehabilitation is optimal physical functioning. The goal of psychological rehabilitation is optimal emotional functioning. In order for an individual to return to work, he/she must be able to function at physical and emotional levels that are compatible with the person's job tasks and demands.

Often nurses have been involved in the medical rehabilitation phase while vocational rehabilitation experts took over once the disabled individual was deemed to have reached maximum medical recovery. Today, many people realize that efforts focused on the return to work process overlap with medical rehabilitation and both can often take place concurrently. For this reason a new role that requires the professional to co-ordinate medical as well as vocational rehab plans has evolved.

## WHO IS QUALIFIED TO PROVIDE DISABILITY MANAGEMENT?

Disability management uses a case management approach that incorporates medical and vocational rehabilitation. In the United States there are several accredited certification organizations under the umbrella of the National Commission for Certifying Agencies that certify professionals involved in DM. These include the:

- Certification of Disability Management Specialist Commission;
- Commission for Case Management Certification;
- Commission of Rehabilitation Counselor Certification.

In Canada there is currently no specific accreditation process for DM practitioners. Professionals from a number of different educational backgrounds provide DM. The most common professional backgrounds include nursing, occupational and physical therapy, vocational counselling and social work.

The Canadian Association for Rehabilitation Professionals (CARP) accredits rehabilitation professionals based on educational background and experience. While not a universal requirement for practice, more and more rehabilitation professionals are writing the examinations necessary to qualify for their Canadian Certified Rehabilitation Consultant (CCRC) designation. This designation ensures clients that the rehabilitation provider has the essential knowledge of rehabilitation theory and practice.

The authors of the Code of Practice for Disability Management believe that DM requires unique competencies. A sample of the recommended skills and competencies include:

- Knowledge of disability management theory and practice;

- The ability to apply legislation and benefit programs;
- Labour/management relations;
- Utilize communication and problem-solving skills;
- Disability case management;
- Return-to-work co-ordination;
- Health, psychosocial, prevention and functional aspects of disability;
- Development of program management and evaluation activities; and
- Demonstrate ethical and professional conduct.

They stress that because there are limited formal DM training opportunities in Canada that emphasize workplace-based disability management activities. They also indicate that formal training in areas such as occupational health nursing, physiotherapy and occupational therapy without experience in workplace settings was insufficient to prepare these healthcare professionals for the practice of DM.

## WHEN IS INDIVIDUAL DISABILITY MANAGEMENT PROVIDED?

Individual DM can be provided whenever there is a gap between a disabled person's ability to perform work and the work demands. Regardless of the cause of disability (occupational or non-occupational illness or accident, motor vehicle accident *etc.*), the process is the same. The only differences in approach rest with the contractual obligation to provide rehabilitation. For example, while Workers' Compensation legislation mandates rehabilitation assistance, the same obligation does not exist in insured STD or LTD contracts.

Rehabilitation provisions exist in many Short-Term Disability (STD) and Long-Term Disability (LTD) policies. In most cases, these provisions spell out how earnings received during rehabilitation employment (such as a graduated return to work) are integrated with disability benefits. Usually these provisions are void of any contractual obligation for the insurer to provide rehabilitation assistance. Nevertheless, most insurers recognize the value of rehabilitation in shortening the duration of disability claims and have, as a result, either built in-house DM departments or out-sourced this function to external firms. In the context of group disability insurance then, the focus is a return to employability.

## THE INDIVIDUAL DISABILITY MANAGEMENT PROCESS

Although a positive organizational impact results from successful DM, the focus of rehabilitation is always on the person with the disability. For this reason, DM is client-centred. It is not something done to an employee, but a process in which the person is an active participant. At the same time, DM practitioners must not forget the ultimate goal — the employee's return to work. Although their primary focus is on the participant, they must not lose sight of the organizational context to which the client will return.

Frequently, (DM) practitioners use a case management approach. Case management, a concept "borrowed" from social services, is a broad term and is used by many people to mean different things. From a DM perspective it refers to the structuring and sequencing of activities and resources to meet an individual's health needs in an efficient and cost-effective way.

## CASE MANAGEMENT IN DISABILITY MANAGEMENT

Case management in DM involves the following steps:

1. early identification of cases and early intervention;
2. assessment;
3. analysis and plan development;
4. co-ordination and implementation; and
5. evaluation.

### Early Identification and Early Intervention

#### 1. Early Identification

Case management can be expensive but when done well is worth every penny. Because case management is expensive it makes sense to use this approach in situations where the benefits clearly outweigh the costs. For straightforward cases or uncomplicated return-to-work situations, case management is unnecessary.

Various authors have identified markers or "red flags" that tend to signal a long, difficult return-to-work process. When these markers are identified, a comprehensive case management approach is recommended. Some of the markers frequently cited are:

- a high rate of absenteeism prior to disability;
- performance problems or disciplinary actions in the year prior to the disability;
- pending litigation;
- an expected duration of disability to exceed two months;

- delays in expected return-to-work date;
- disorders that lack observable clinical evidence such as psychiatric conditions, repetitive strain injuries, fibromyalgia, sick building syndrome, multiple chemical sensitivities, *etc.*;
- multiple diagnoses;
- a pattern of "doctor shopping";
- non-compliance with treatment plans.

## 2. Early Intervention

Studies clearly demonstrate that the longer a disabled employee is away from work, the less likely the chance of ever returning to the work force. Consider these statistics:

- only 50 per cent of employees disabled for six months ever return to work;
- after one year, only 10-15 per cent of disabled employees ever return to work ( Bigos, Spengler, Martin *et al.*).

Psychosocial changes begin to occur between the third and the sixth month of a person's disability. Because of the impact of disability on the individual's life, he/she may become psychologically distressed. There is often a drop in self-esteem and self-confidence levels. Often a secondary depression occurs. Regardless of the degree of psychological side effects, altered social interactions frequently occur. The result is that the person must deal with the functional limitations caused by their accident or illness, as well as face the resulting psychological and social stressors. Intervening prior to the onset of a "disability mentality" has been demonstrated to shorten the disability duration.

Although most people in Canada who require medical rehabilitation receive it, the same cannot always be said about vocational rehabilitation. Until recently only a few employees with non-occupational disabilities have had access to VR services prior to the approval of their LTD benefits. In many cases this meant that at least six months (a common waiting period for LTD benefits) passed before VR was offered. The impact of delayed intervention was disability claims of longer duration. This translated to a direct financial burden to employers. In response, many employers have started to consider early intervention programs.

## Assessment

In the past, the medical model was used to assess disability. The belief was that disability stemmed primarily from a biological perspective. In other words, the focus was on the physical causes of disability. Today, DM practitioners recognize that while biological factors are important, psychosocial factors play significant roles in the development and maintenance of disability.

In contrast to the medical assessment the DM assessment includes the medical aspects of the disability as well as the psychosocial aspects of the person's life. These include an examination of factors such as the home situation, work, financial status, belief systems, cultural factors, and personal supports and stresses. An appropriate DM plan requires the identification of the drivers of disability and the barriers to a successful return to work.

During the assessment, the DM practitioner examines the disabled person's work, and the person's work experience. Pre-disability work performance is a critical factor in predicting return-to-work success. Employees with good work records return to work at a higher rate than those employees deemed to be poor performers (Gamborg, Elliott & Curtis, 1992).

Frequently, as part of the assessment phase, the VR practitioner also meets with the employer (often the supervisor) to gain a better understanding of the employee's pre-disability level of functioning, and determine if there are any identifiable barriers to the return to work. Barriers may be physical or attitudinal. In the latter case, poor pre-disability performance may result in a supervisor or co-workers being less than enthusiastic about enabling an employee's early return to work.

In addition, the DM practitioner also gathers information about the person's educational experience (formal and informal). This is important information for the practitioner to know should the person become unable to return to his/her own job.

## Analysis and Plan Development

After considering all the information collected during the assessment phase, the DM practitioner identifies the barriers to a successful return to work. These are considered when working with the employee to develop a personalized rehabilitation action plan.

The sequencing of rehabilitation steps is critical to the entire rehabilitation process. For example, if a person is unable to walk as a result of an accident, medical rehabilitation in the form of gait re-education would be necessary before considering a work-hardening program aimed at increasing their walking tolerance. It is the DM practitioner's role to ensure effective sequencing of the rehabilitation steps so the rehabilitation process is successful.

### Co-ordination and Implementation

The "project team" always includes the employee and the employer, and often involves such health care professionals as physicians and therapists. The DM is the project manager when it comes to the return-to-work process. He/she must be able to define the employee's goal for all team members and encourage them to articulate their plans for enabling the employee to reach the stated goal(s).

The case manager regularly monitors the return-to-work progress. If it appears that the plan is veering off course, he/she helps to get the plan back in the right direction by re-assessing the situation and modifying the plan as required.

### Evaluation

Since the goal of DM is returning a disabled individual to a level of employability, success is determined by whether or not the employee is deemed to be employable at the end of the process. Other performance measures include employee satisfaction with the process, cost effectiveness and efficiency of the process. For an employer, success measures might include the number of employees who return to the organization, the average duration of disability, and indirect measures of absence/disability costs.

## DISABILITY MANAGEMENT TOOLS

### Functional Abilities Evaluation

From a DM perspective, the functional abilities evaluation (FAE) is an important tool. The FAE is an objective way of assessing a person's physical abilities and identifying physical limitations they might have.

Occupational therapists, physical therapists and kinesiologists usually conduct FAEs. They measure elements such as lifting, pulling, pushing, walking tolerance and standing tolerance to name only a few job tasks.

## Job Analysis

The job analysis combined with the FAE provide a critical piece of information in deciding whether an individual is capable of performing a specific job. As the name suggests, a job analysis is simply an examination of the various components of the person's job. Usually the emphasis is on identifying the physical demands of the job, but attention is also put on the physical environment in which the job is performed. More recently, there has been a move towards focusing on the psychological or emotional aspects of the job as well.

## Matching Job Demand with Ability

After a DM practitioner understands a disabled employee's physical abilities and limitations as well as the disabled employee's job demands, he/she is able to look at any job to see if the person's abilities match the job demands. This process is simple if there is just one job in question. If, however, the challenge is to identify a number of jobs that the person might be capable of performing, the task becomes more complex. For this reason there have been various attempts to develop software to assist with this process. For example, a software program developed by the City of Toronto's Employee Assistance and Rehabilitation Department quickly searches a job analysis data bank for jobs that individual employees are capable of performing.

## Work Hardening

Employees who have become disabled are often physically de-conditioned. The activities of work are like exercise: if you stop exercising you become less fit. When employees stop working they become less fit for work and for the daily activities of life.

In some ways, work hardening is an extension of the physical rehabilitation process since it continues to try to improve the employee's physical tolerance in an applied manner. Rather than doing specific exercises, the employee performs the specific job-related activities required for the job. Sometimes this work-simulation takes place in a clinical setting. Ideally, however, it occurs in the workplace. By conducting work hardening in the workplace, the employee also becomes re-conditioned to the social aspects of the workplace such as punctuality and appropriate attire.

During work hardening, the assigned work is usually of lower priority and intensity. Typically it is work for which the organization would not hire additional staff. Productivity is not the goal of the activity — rather an increased tolerance to activity is desired. The employee, in essence, returns to a "sheltered-workshop" climate.

While the employee is participating in the work-hardening program the disability benefit continues providing that ongoing medical information supports the disability. This approach allows employees to return to the workforce without fear of jeopardizing their benefits.

Like all other aspects of rehabilitation work hardening is goal-oriented and usually fairly short term. In other words, specific goals are set. Work hardening ends either when the goals are met and/or the pre-determined maximum time is reached.

## Transitional Work

Transitional work is a way of enabling the employee to reintegrate into the workplace when he/she is able to perform some but not all of the duties of the job. In other words, the employee returns to work on a graduated basis.

Transitional work is not "make work". Instead, experienced employees perform meaningful work. The employer can therefore expect the same work-quality standard as received from other employees. For the employee it is a means of easing back into the workplace without the physical and emotional fatigue that often accompanies a full-time return to work. The result is that transitional work provides benefits to both the employer and the employee.

Because the employee is performing meaningful work he/she is compensated at their normal rate for work actually performed. During the transition period, disability benefits continue as a "top up" until the employee returns to full duties. As with other forms of rehabilitation, transitional work is goal-oriented and time-limited.

## Vocational Assessment

Unfortunately, some employees are unable to return to their own jobs. In this case, a vocational assessment is done to help the person identify some appropriate job options.

The vocational assessment often has several parts:

1. Interest testing — an objective way of finding out what kind of work an employee likes to perform (e.g., Strong Campbell Interest Inventory);

2. Aptitude testing — a way of predicting future job performance (*e.g.*, General Aptitude Test Battery (GATB)); and
3. Situational assessment — a way of evaluating how an employee performs in a work-simulation (*e.g.*, Valpar).

## Retraining/Skill Upgrading

In DM a work hierarchy exists:

1. a return to one's own job;
2. a return to the same work but with some modifications;
3. a return to the same employer but to different work (alternative duties); or
4. a return to different work with a different employer.

When an employee is returning to the work force but in a different job capacity, re-training or skill upgrading may be necessary. In some cases on-the-job training may suffice, but in other instances, formal re-training may be required. Due to the nature of LTD contracts, DM may be time-limited. For example, sometimes a rehabilitation plan cannot extend past the "own occupation" period of disability.

As with all other rehabilitation processes, retraining should be goal-oriented. The vocational assessment will assist the employee and the DM practitioner in determining appropriate vocational goals. Retraining should be job-specific rather than general. For example, if an employee seeks a clerical job requiring computer skills, taking a word processing course instead of a computer science degree may be more appropriate.

## PROVISION OF DISABILITY MANAGEMENT SERVICES

### Internal vs. External

Some large organizations provide vocational rehabilitation using internal personnel. Some advantages of in-house DM programs include:

- knowledge of the return-to-work options;
- knowledge and understanding of the corporate culture; and
- an understanding of the reporting structure and key contacts within the organization.

In contrast, some organizations that previously provided in-house DM are now considering out-sourcing this function because it is considered a non-core business. In other organizations, there is a movement towards out-sourcing because of a perception that the in-house personnel cannot be as objective as an external party. As well, there is a belief that external resources who service a wide variety of organizations may have a broader perspective of the job market. Another frequently given reason for out-sourcing DM in large and small organizations alike is the high cost associated with having in-house DM professionals.

## Vendor Selection

If an organization decides to out-source its DM function, it is important to carefully select the service providers. The following are a number of factors to consider when choosing an external provider:

- Cultural fit;
- Shared vision;
- Staff qualifications, *e.g.*, professional credentials and certifications;
- Specific areas of expertise, *e.g.*, psychological disabilities;
- Location of the firm and consultants, *e.g.*, travel, long distance telephone, fax and/or mail costs;
- Service standards, *e.g.*, timeliness of reports;
- Quality assurance standards;
- Fees;
- References;
- Business history; and
- Outcome measures, *e.g.*, how do they define success in terms of rehabilitation, average cost to savings per case, client satisfaction surveys.

## THE FUTURE OF DISABILITY MANAGEMENT: WHERE DO WE GO FROM HERE?

To understand where we are going, it's helpful to understand where we have been. According to some, we are now entering the third wave of disability management (Habeck, 1997). In the first wave, rehabilitation happened outside the workplace. Generally only physically disabled people received rehabilitation. Return to work was only possible when they were 100 per cent fit to return to work.

In the second wave the financial impact of rehabilitation became evident. Disability management was held out as the miracle cure for organizations. The belief was that early intervention would return everyone to work.

In the third wave, there is the recognition that we were overly enthusiastic in the second wave. Since the early 1990s there has been a steady increase in the complexity of disabilities. Psychiatric diagnoses and other conditions such as fibromyalgia are on the rise. A growing body of knowledge is demonstrating that organizational factors as well as individual factors affect these complex disabilities. For example, management style (*i.e.*, participative vs. autocratic) has been shown to be related to disability incidence within organizations (Habeck *et al.* & Moran *et al.*).

Traditionally, rehabilitation focused almost entirely on the disabled individual, *i.e.*, "Little" or Micro DM. While there will always be a need for Micro DM, there are signs that an increasing number of organizations are also beginning to see the value of "Big" or Macro DM. Practitioners who wish to be a part of this movement will need to possess strong clinical skills and an understanding of organizational behaviour. They will need to understand the business reasons for DM and be able to demonstrate a return on the investment for companies. They must also appreciate the culture of the organization into which the disabled employee will be returning and will often need to educate the workplace on matters relating to disability and its relationship to productivity. In short, Macro DM practitioners will need to assume an organizational development perspective.

## BIBLIOGRAPHY

Schwartz, G., Watson, D., Galvin, D., Lipoff, E. The Disability Management Sourcebook, 1. Washington, D.C. Washington Business Group on Health, 1989.

NARRPS Disability Management Advisory Board White Paper. (Presented at the NARRPS 1999 Conference and Exposition March 14, 1999).

Hall, R., The integrated disability management landscape, Disability Management News, Summer 2000.

Habeck, R., Job Retention through Disability Management, Rehabilitation Counselling Bulletin, June, 1999.

Rehabilitation Services Inventory & Quality Project, Phase One Report, Institute for Work and Health, 1995.

Code of Practice for Disability Management, Describing Effective Benchmarks for the Creation of Workplace-based Disability Management Programs, National Institute for Disability Management and Research, 2000.

Bigos, S.J., Spengler, D.M., Martin, N.A. *et al.* "Low Back Pain in Industry: A Retrospective Study" 111 Employee factors (1989) 11 Spine 252-56.

Gamborg, B., Elliott, W., Curtis, K. "Chronic Disability Syndrome" Rehab and Community Care Management. June. 19-23, 1992.

Habeck, Rochelle, "Evolution of DM: Current Challenges for Practice. Speech presented at the 3rd National Disability Manager's Training Conference" Michigan State University, July 13-15, 1997.

Habeck, R., Leahy, M., Hunt, A., Chan, F., Welch, E. "Employer Factors Related to Worker's Compensation Claims and Disability Management" (1991), 34 Rehabilitation Counselling Bulletin 210-26.

Moran, S.K., Wolff, S.C., & Green, J.E. "Workers' Compensation and Occupational Stress: Gaining Control. In L.R. Murphy, J.J. Hurrell, Jr., S.L. Sauter, & G.P. Keita (Eds), *Job Stress Interventions* Washington, DC:American Psychological Association 1995: 355-68.

## Chapter 10

# COMMUNICATION STRATEGIES TO IMPROVE RESULTS FOR THE ILL OR INJURED WORKER

*ALYSON MACDONALD*

## COMMUNICATION

Communication is defined in the Oxford Dictionary as "the science and practice of transmitting information". As it relates to disability management, it is the collaboration with all stakeholders to assess, plan, co-ordinate, implement, monitor, and evaluate the resources required to meet the desired outcome. Effective communication is crucial to achieving successful and durable results.

Often, this communication involves each of the following stakeholders:

- Client;
- Physician;
- Employer — Union/Management;
- Rehabilitation providers/treatment team;
- Sponsoring parties (Insurance, WCB, *etc.*).

This chapter will provide an overview of communication strategies amongst stakeholders, specifically as it relates to disability management, and the return-to-work process.

## CLIENT-CENTRED COMMUNICATION

Establishing rapport and an environment of trust and open communication is the first step in the process. Clients develop trust when they feel they are being truly listened to, and understood, and when expectations are clear.

Throughout the rehabilitation process, from injury reporting to treatment to return-to-work planning, it is vital to encourage self-responsibility in the client. Being an active participant in their own treatment, goal setting and return-to work planning decreases resistance dramatically and fosters an attitude of "ownership" ("I have control over my rehabilitation/wellness"). Without this ownership, there is usually a fatalistic or passive stance ("there's nothing anyone can do").

### Communication through Assessment and Treatment

Throughout the assessment, rapport is built and information is gathered through active listening techniques. A good rehabilitation assessment will review the following with the client:

- Mechanism of injury;
- Medical management to date;
- Brief medical history;
- Current subjective complaints;
- Current job status;
- Job duties/demands/activities of daily living.

These are all subjective findings, as reported by the client. The rehabilitation professional(s) will then take the client through a variety of tests, which will include:

- Neurological screen;
- Objective functional testing/measurements;
- Psychological/behavioural testing.

Once the interview and testing process is complete, recommendations and prognosis will be developed. It is at this time, that all other stakeholders are contacted, to review findings, recommendations, to discuss any identified barriers to successful recovery, and to confirm job demands.

At the commencement of rehabilitative treatment, the client is oriented to the treatment team, and the course of treatment is explained. The purpose of the orientation is to outline expectations, and instil confidence in the client, by reviewing:

- Treatment objectives/anticipated duration/attendance;
- Emphasis on client responsibility/empowerment;
- Emphasis on the importance of education in their treatment;
- Client awareness of our communication with doctor, sponsor and employer;
- Goal-setting process;
- Anticipated return-to-work date.

It is important that the client understands that the rehabilitation process has been designed with their specific needs in mind, that all stakeholders are involved to ensure that the goal of a safe and successful return to work is met.

## Education

Education is vital in the prevention and management of an injury, as it encourages empowerment, self-efficacy, and independence. Throughout the rehabilitation management process, the client should receive education regarding such principles as hurt versus harm and the nature of the injury and healing process. Ongoing, the client should be instructed in the proper use of body mechanics in order to avoid injury, and in coping strategies to manage symptom "flare-ups".

Educational materials can also be developed specific to the client's occupation, and can be provided on an ongoing basis in association with intervention strategies and training of new employees. This preventative approach may include education specific to high-risk job tasks, and stretching and strengthening techniques that can be performed at the worksite.

## Goal Setting

Intentions are a key predictor of behaviour. A client's outcome and efficacy beliefs concerning their ability to succeed are critical. By making informed decisions, the client participates in planning a course of action, and making a commitment to it, increasing the likelihood of success through their opportunity to provide input.

In goal setting, consider the following framework:

- Measurable/specific;
- Achievable/realistic;
- Client participation;
- Progressive.

Then, more specifically, the following:

1. Goals related to the progression of treatment (exercise, functional gains, and education);
2. Establishment of anticipated return-to-work date, return to activities of daily living;
3. Personal goals related to the client's recovery (client-generated);
4. Weekly team meetings to review progress;
5. Return-to-work planning.

Return-to-work planning may involve a variety of options, depending on factors such as the client's current physical capabilities, their critical job demands, length of time missed from work, and the employer's ability to accommodate. It is important to establish a return-to-work plan early in the treatment/recovery management process, and have the client demonstrate their commitment by signing the plan.

Goal setting also involves the other stakeholders: the physician, employer, and sponsor. Gaining consensus amongst all parties will keep the client focused on the objective, and ensure a cohesive team approach to the attainment of common goals.

## Team Meetings

Team meetings are held weekly with the client in order to review progress, maintain focus with respect to return-to-work planning, and review interim goals set in that regard. All stakeholders are involved in the process (either through attendance, or by way of verbal or written communication), which will include:

- Review of treatment plan;
- Establishing new weekly goals (treatment progression, functional gains, work tolerance);
- Review progress to date;
- Confirm return-to-work date/expectations.

### Cross-Cultural Communication

We are responsible for managing the care of unique individuals of varying ages, gender, and cultures. It is therefore necessary to be aware of how these differences impact communication.

Verbal language can present an obvious barrier if there is little or no understanding between parties. In such cases, family members or an independent interpreter can be accessed to assist in the communication process.

Non-verbal language can present an equal barrier. Being sensitive to cultural/gender issues will enhance your ability to effectively communicate, and avoid issues such as resistance/fear, which could result in early termination of treatment.

General things to consider when communicating:

- Personal space/privacy issues;
- Clothing/apparel;
- Gender (client and rehabilitation professional);
- Eye contact;
- Tone/volume of speech.

This open, ongoing communication with the client throughout the rehabilitation management process establishes trust and confidence, and enables the client to actively participate in their rehabilitation and return-to-work process, optimizing the success rate.

### THE STAKEHOLDERS

When organizing treatment services and return-to-work planning, it is important to remember that you may be dealing with a variety of stakeholders, who may have a variety of expectations and differing issues. For example, a physician may be most interested in pain-related issues, while the employer may have limitations surrounding a transitional return-to-work or regulations, and the sponsor may have time/cost/compensable limitations. Facilitation of consensus in reasonable goal setting and expectations will eliminate "surprises" and is paramount to the ultimate achievement of a return-to-work goal.

## PHYSICIAN INVOLVEMENT

Physicians have the primary relationship with the client and as such are an extremely important factor in the outcome. It is important that the physician, through early and regular communication, is made to feel an integral part of the "rehabilitation management" team, which in turn enables him/her to make informed decisions regarding their patient.

According to a physician survey conducted by CBI Health, the number one factor in selecting a provider of rehabilitation services for their patients was the results achieved in restoring function. Further, they indicated a desire to be involved not only in patient care issues, but also in the return-to-work planning. Based on the provision of objective information, the physician is in the best position to support a safe and effective return-to-work plan.

Communication with the physician throughout treatment should include:

- Confirmation of client referral and ensure that there are no contraindications to treatment;
- Discussion with respect to client's current symptoms;
- Recommendations, prognosis, and identified barriers;
- Medical input into treatment;
- Clarification of job demands;
- Ongoing objective data regarding client's functional ability;
- Confirmation of physician support of client treatment/progress;
- Early discussion/consultation of tentative return-to-work date and plan;
- Establish physician commitment to rehab/return-to-work plan.

By providing the physician with objective functional data, he/she is able to provide support and encouragement to the client, and assist in handling pain-related concerns in the return-to-work process.

There may be instances where more than one physician is involved in the rehabilitation process. For example:

- Further investigations are required;
- Outstanding medical diagnosis;
- Client requires specific medical treatment or post-surgical care.

In such cases, facilitation of a consensus regarding medical issues is vital in order that medical closure is obtained. Resolving diagnostic, treatment and return-to-work issues serves an important role in progressing the client through the disability management process with full medical support and confidence.

## THE EMPLOYER

When communicating with the employer, it is important to immediately establish whether or not the work environment has union involvement. If so, all appropriate parties (labour/management) must be involved in communication in order that a return-to-work plan is fully supported, and complies with any collective agreements and regulations. For the sake of this section, it will be understood that reference to "the employer" will include all such parties (including Human Resources and Health and Safety, if appropriate).

Although many employers may already have an established disability management model, some may not. It is important to establish that there are supportive policies and procedures in place to manage clients through the return-to-work process.

Regular and ongoing communication with the employer will assist in return-to-work planning and increase the likelihood of a durable return to employment.

This communication begins with:

- Confirmation of job duties;
- Physical demands analysis/survey;
- Job site visit to
  (a) assess job environment/workplace barriers;
  (b) assess ergonomic issues;
  (c) assist in developing appropriate work simulation activities in treatment;
  (d) confirm/facilitate the employer's support of the return-to-work.

Ongoing, it includes:

Return-to-work planning and expectations:

- Job availability;
- Transitional or modified work accommodations;

- Work return date setting;
- Updates regarding client's progression to return-to-work goal;
- Recommendations regarding "work style" or ergonomic issues;
- Expectations for success.

This communication will help ensure that the employer is informed and capable of providing the proper support to the client throughout the return-to-work process. It also ensures that the employer will have realistic expectations of the client, especially through a transitional return. Employers may have apprehensions surrounding the return of an employee, especially if the employee had previously failed in an attempt to return to work. Keeping them well informed of progress, expectations and functional abilities helps alleviate these fears.

Assisting the employer in understanding issues such as pacing and hurt versus harm will assist them in supporting the client through the return to work. Their thorough understanding of the return-to-work schedule (graduated or modified) and information regarding how they can support the plan will increase the likelihood of success. It is most helpful if the client is included in this communication, as expectations will be understood and agreed upon by all parties.

Education may also be provided to the employer and/or other employees. This may be necessary in situations where the work environment may be resistant to the return of the employee (for safety fears, *etc.*), or where there are non-constructive employee/employer relations.

A proactive approach to follow-up with the employer will assist in ensuring that recommendations have been implemented, and provide support to both the employer and employee through any difficulties they may experience in the return-to-work plan. This may include job coaching to ensure the client is utilizing the skills they have learned regarding body mechanics while allowing the client to maintain the required and agreed upon level of productivity safely.

## THE SPONSOR

As the party responsible for funding the client's treatment, and possibly wage-loss, the sponsor must be kept well informed of status and progress of the client throughout treatment and the return-to-work process. Expectations must be clear in order that all parties understand the parameters in which they will participate.

According to a sponsor satisfaction survey conducted by CBI Health, sponsors report that the two most important factors in client rehabilitation are cost and outcome. That is, provision of a timely, successful and durable return-to-work that is cost-effective.

Communication with the sponsor begins with reporting the assessment findings, and discussing recommendations. Once recommendations have been agreed upon, communication continues as follows:

- Discussion regarding goals for treatment;
- Discussion regarding compliance to treatment;
- Updates regarding client progress, functional gains;
- Updates regarding any changes in treatment direction;
- Involvement in team meetings, if appropriate;
- Assistance in the return-to-work process;
- Discussion surrounding any barriers to return-to-work.

Keeping the sponsor well-informed, and providing an organized, progressive treatment and return-to-work plan will optimize success as it is defined by the sponsor: timely, cost-effective service with a positive outcome.

This can sometimes present a challenge to those facilitating a return-to-work where there may be barriers present that are not injury-related. For example, poor employee/employer relations may present an obstacle in obtaining support of a return-to-work, but this is not directly related to the physical injury. It is important that the sponsor is aware of these issues, and that an understanding is achieved surrounding how these types of issues impact success, and what can be done (within the appropriate parameters) to overcome them. By involving all stakeholders in these discussions, a solution may be found that satisfies the needs and requirements of all involved and supports the client through the process.

In situations where the employer is the sponsor, the goal is to ensure that the client/employees view the disability management program as a benefit, while at the same time producing a measurable cost-savings to the employer that exceeds the investment required to implement the program. This mutual support of the program will assist in ensuring its effectiveness.

## THE FUTURE

Regular communication with all stakeholders ensures that all parties work cohesively toward establishing and achieving a common goal, and is crucial to achieving a successful return-to-work outcome. It is, simply, what differentiates an excellent disability management program from others. The need for high quality communication will only expand over time.

# Part 3

# THIRD PARTY PROVIDERS OF SERVICE IN DISABILITY MANAGEMENT

# Chapter 11

# THE ROLE OF THE CONSULTANT IN DISABILITY MANAGEMENT

SANDRA PELLEGRINI AND PATRICIA MONTEATH[*]

## INTRODUCTION

Numerous specialists devote their career to the development, implementation, and analysis of disability management. Given that disabilities themselves have become more complex and more costly, there has emerged a compelling need for additional specialists to help employers manage their disability programs. The title "consultant" is often given to these specialists. With the broad spectrum of disabilities and different management strategies, it stands to reason that the background, experience and role for consultants in disAbility management is diverse. This chapter will describe the role of the consultant, the different types of consulting services and the practical application of consultant expertise. The purpose of this chapter is to share information with all consultants working within the infrastructure of an insured disability program. In providing a framework of the environment in which consultants operate, the goal is to improve the level of service delivered to those in need in a more cost-effective manner.

---

[*]  Edited from the original chapter by Joan Fitch and Marilee Mark.

## TYPES OF CONSULTANTS IN DISABILITY MANAGEMENT

There are many different types of consulting services. The following list of providers looks at the ones most commonly utilized but is not exhaustive.

### Consulting Firms

Consulting firms engage in disability management strategies and solutions that orchestrate the broader scope of practice in the continuum of disability. Their clients are the employers, and ultimately the policyholders. Clients employ consulting firms not only to create a strategy for management and cost containment of disability and related issues, but to design and develop a best practices model that reflects the company's vision, mission and philosophies.

There is a broad range of consulting firms offering human resources, actuarial, employee benefits and other disability management needs. These firms range from one-person companies[1] to multi-national corporations with thousands of employees. A company may prefer the "one stop shopping" approach or find that combining the expertise of several firms works best. For the former choice, a large full-service firm will best suit the company's needs; for the latter, either specialty or full-service firms could be used.

### Brokers/Agents

Brokers and agents play a role in one aspect of a disability management program, that of placing insurance coverage for benefits including disability with the most appropriate insurer. Similar services are also provided by many consulting firms which provide benefits services. Brokers and agents may also assist with the design of the employee benefits plan. While it is difficult to generalize, smaller plan sponsors seeking only to place benefits coverage with an insurance company would use a broker or agent. Larger organizations seeking a more customized approach are more likely to use a full-service consulting firm.

---

[1] See Independents below.

## Independents

In the field of disability management, there are many specialized practitioners. These practitioners attempt to meet specific needs of employers, insurers, or unions and are sometimes thought to be more flexible in the administration and design of their contracts. The challenge is to locate these individuals and gather sufficient confidence in their abilities and services when their reputation is less widely-known. Word of mouth and references play a large role in selecting independent consultants.

## Insurance Companies

For the most part, long-term disability (LTD) insurance and the associated administration of the claims are managed, adjudicated and paid by an insurance company. This can also be true for many short-term disability (STD) programs. Insurance companies employ claims adjudicators and often adjunct professionals including but not limited to medical consultants, medical and vocational rehabilitation professionals and account management, actuarial and underwriting specialists. Some insurers have aligned themselves with Early Intervention and/or EAP providers, either within the cost of the rates for disability benefits or on a fee-for-service basis.

## HOW ARE CONSULTANTS PAID?

Once a company has decided to use external help for a disability management program and is ready to select a consultant, there are several payment options. No particular option is better or worse than any other — it is just a question of knowing the cost of services, method of payment and expectations for the dollars spent. Once again, this section discusses only a few of the alternatives which may be used alone or in combination.

## Commissions

Payment by means of commission may be an option if a company has hired a consultant to place disability benefits coverage with an insurer. The commission, payable to the consultant or broker, is included in the rates for insurance. Commissions are a reasonable alternative for companies who do not have a budget for consulting fees. The sponsor of the benefits program does not have to budget additional funds for the services of the consultant. In situations where employees pay a portion of the premiums, the employees share in the cost of the consulting services. However, some organizations are uncomfortable with commissions paid directly by the insurance company to an external resource. This can be resolved by asking the consultant, broker or agent to disclose the amount of commissions on an annual or more frequent basis. The organization can then assess whether the commissions received by the consultants match the value of the services they provide. Commissions paid by the insurer may not cover all of the consulting services required for a company's disability management program.

## Fees

A fee-for-service arrangement is another option for payment. The company is billed for services as these services are provided, or may be subject to a contracted amount agreed to by the consultant and the client. The costs of these services may fluctuate with client needs, thus requiring a flexible budget. Often consultants working on a fee-for-service account are asked to project fees, allowing the client to budget accordingly. In Canada, fees are subject to the goods and services tax (GST), whereas commissions are not.

Alternatively, a "fee-offset" arrangement can be used, combining the features of a commission-based payment agreement with a fee-for-service approach. In a fee-offset arrangement, commissions received by the consultant from the insurer are balanced against the fees incurred. The remainder is invoiced to the client.

## Retainers

A retainer arrangement involves a flat regular payment to the consultant, in exchange for performance of a list of agreed services. In some cases, the retainer is subject to a year-end review, with excess time spent above the amount of retainer reimbursed to the advisor, or the excess retainer applied to the next time period. Other retainer arrangements are fixed, regardless of the time actually spent to provide the service.

The selection of the most appropriate payment structure is based on a combination of several factors. In a situation where employees pay for all or part of the disability benefits premiums, the company may wish to share the cost of consulting services with employees. This is more easily achieved in a commission type of arrangement. If a fee-for-service arrangement appeals most to a company, then the company needs to balance the control gained in defining the exact services management is willing to pay for with the resulting fluctuations in cost. A fee-for-service arrangement simplifies the allocation of consulting costs to different divisions in the organization. A retainer arrangement simplifies budgeting for consulting services. Regardless of the type of funding arrangement, it is essential to have a written agreement outlining the services to be delivered and the associated costs.

## SELECTING A CONSULTANT

The choices of external service providers available to assist a company with its disability management program are numerous and varied. There are many different types of vendors offering expertise in the field, with credible references and impressive *curriculum vitae*. Whether the project is big or small, picking the right firm or person for the job to make the best use of time and money is the desired outcome. This section examines five key considerations in selecting an external consulting provider.

### Philosophy, Vision and Relationship

Above all else, the consultant must understand the needs of their client. An appreciation of the client's philosophical approach to disability management and overall vision will enable a productive relationship based on trust and a common perspective to develop.

Provided that a company has asked only reputable disability management consulting firms to bid on the project and assuming their credentials are very similar, then the company probably wants to work with someone management feels comfortable with. A portion of the due diligence for selection of a Disability Management Consultant(s) may include personal and candid presentations from finalists. Ideally, the presenters are the same people with whom the company will be working on a regular basis.

### Cost

Once a decision is made on a method of remuneration, the company still needs to assess the real cost of receiving consulting services. This can be very difficult. A firm with higher hourly rates may still be the best choice if they have the required expertise and provide the best value for the allocated budget. An independent or small vendor may be less expensive on a per-hour basis, but the project could be at risk if the principal consultant does not have all the expertise or back-up required or is unable to complete the project within the preferred time line.

Regardless of cost, a company needs to weigh whether the outcome will meet their needs and whether they will be satisfied with the deliverables. Balancing costs with benefits is one of the more interesting challenges in the selection process and further supports the importance of chemistry or trust in the consultant's capabilities.

## Technical Expertise

There are a number of ways of testing technical expertise, although none is foolproof. The checking of references is a good first step to take. However, a company needs to ensure that the projects successfully undertaken by the consultant parallel the challenges of the company's project. A consultant is only likely to give positive references. A company should ask about projects undertaken that were not successful or obtain references from former clients. Much can be learned about the consultant through careful reference checks. Reviewing specific educational credentials is also helpful, although their relevance to the project might be limited. In some cases, a company may consider assessing the capabilities of a potential consultant by a pilot project.

## Reputation

To assess a consultant or firm's reputation, a company should access its personal and professional network. Input can be gathered on whether the firm is well-respected, completes projects on time and within the budget. The reputation and business practices of the firm should be assessed to see if they fit the organization's, particularly if the consultant could be representing the organization in the community.

## National versus Regional Focus

The decision to select a specific consultant or firm may be based in part on whether the consultant needs to be involved on a national or more local basis. An ongoing role with a national focus requires both the availability of resources and the current knowledge of national issues, applicable legislations and characteristics of the different jurisdictions involved. While a national mandate may not preclude local firms, it may result in additional challenges or costs associated with activities outside of the primary delivery location. Factors to assess include the firm's resources or established partnerships on a national basis, their ability to provide standardized services and communication capabilities.

Other factors for consideration in the selection of a consultant include the ability to access additional resources (*e.g.*, legal, financial or medical services), the length of time in business, business ethics, and contributions to the field of disability management through articles or presentations.

Having outlined a process for the selection of a consultant, we will now move on to the scope of the consultant's role in disability management, beginning with the development of an organization's disability management strategy.

## THE CONSULTANT'S ROLE IN STRATEGY

Consultants with expertise in the field of disability management and experience in the entire continuum of disability management offer an external, objective perspective in the review or development of a company's disability management strategy. A strategy is a plan of action to attain an ultimate goal. Most organizations today have developed and communicated a high-level mission statement with associated objectives. The challenge for the consultant is to create a disability management strategy in line with the corporate objectives.

These objectives form the basis of the business plan which outlines in more detail exactly how the organization's mission is to be achieved within a specified time period. The business plan, in turn, requires the right people resources. The human resources objectives are in turn supported by the cash compensation philosophy, employee benefits, performance management and the disability management strategy. Included in the disability management strategy for the purposes of this discussion are the organization's occupational health and safety programs, wellness initiatives, absence management, disability benefits and Employee and Family Assistance Program (EFAP).

To be truly successful, an organization's approach to disability management must be well aligned with the organizational and human resource objectives and philosophy. The diagram below illustrates the relationship between the organization's mission statement and disability management:

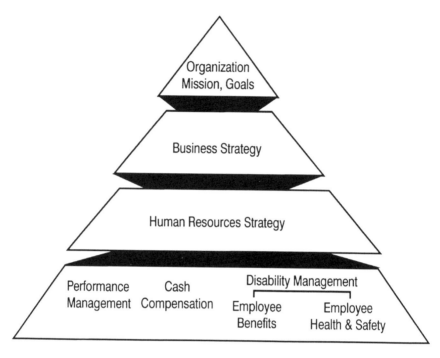

Barriers can develop when the disability management strategy is not supported fully by the organization. For example, a program objective to return absent employees to the workplace early and safely is less likely to be achieved if there is no support or process to bring employees back to work unless they can perform 100 per cent of their job duties. Evidence that the organization supports this objective could include relief in the staffing budget if modified duties or hours are required for a limited period of time.

An organization may also set aggressive objectives for increased revenue requiring greater productivity with no increase in staff. A disability management strategy which focuses on identifying employees who may be at risk for injury or absence and dealing with those issues early before individual productivity is compromised can contribute to that objective.

The consultant may gather information on the organizational objectives and philosophy from a variety of sources, including written policies, corporate communications, the annual report, interviews, and focus groups with internal stakeholders.

## ONGOING ROLE OF THE CONSULTANT

Once a disability management program is in place, there are many services consultants can provide to help an organization manage the ongoing operation of their plan. A disability management plan needs to be monitored, measured and adapted based on employer needs, trends, or legislation changes. Consultants are keenly aware of the marketplace and are well positioned to provide advice to organizations on how to strengthen their disability management plan.

### Broaden scope of analysis

Consultant firms can bring in various other specialized consultants to look at entire continuum of benefits and analyze how each can have a direct impact on each other. Changes to extended health benefits or drug plans may impact disability management outcomes and costs. New drug therapies may shorten the length of disability but health care system delays for medical treatment may have an adverse effect. As well, an in-depth analysis of an organization's overall plan may present opportunities to focus on preventative strategies, which promote health and reduce disability incidence and cost.

### Training and Coaching to In-house Disability Management Administrators

Given the complexity of disability contracts, employers often need assistance in understanding and applying the different provisions. Consultants can offer training to in-house disability management administrators so that the organization can build internal expertise around the application of the contract. They are also available to answer questions and give advice should an employer need clarification of a provision or encounter an unusual scenario.

### Employee Education Opportunities

Through employee surveys or other feedback mechanisms, an organization may discover that there is a need to provide their employees with more information about disability management. A consultant could be used to partner with the organization in preparing a seminar for employees explaining the details of the plan and the corporate philosophy towards disability management.

## Emerging Trends and Marketplace Changes

With strong business networks, consultants are knowledgeable of new initiatives or programs offered by other organizations and their outcomes. Consultants can make sure an organization's disability plan is competitive in the marketplace and does not become a roadblock to retention and recruitment.

## Assessing the Impact of Legislation Changes

Changes in legislation and court rulings on relevant legal cases require an organization to review their disability management plan. Consultants can give advice on whether an organization needs to make any changes to their disability management plan and practices in order to comply with the law or avoid potential legal embarrassment.

## Executing Ad Hoc Research Projects

Very often someone within an organization sees a need or has an idea for a specific initiative to improve or enhance the disability management plan. Many organizations find that consultants are suited to carry out the activities leading to the validation and/or implementation of the new idea. Recognizing lack of internal resources or time, some organizations may even approach a consultant to develop and implement a project plan. Sometimes an organization will decide that a consultant is better positioned to prepare and execute a new idea — especially if there is concern that employees may not be receptive to the change.

## Advice Prior to Purchasing Vendor Services

Many vendors offering promising services approach organizations. A relationship with a trusted consultant is helpful to gain an objective perspective and a third-party opinion on the services offered by another vendor. For example, an organization may see value in purchasing a health promotion service from an identified vendor. A known and respected consultant will give an impartial opinion to ensure the service being purchased is right for the organization.

## Role in Program Measurement

The design of a new disability management program, or modification of an existing one, involves the establishment and measurement of program objectives. Advances in technology, particularly in the ability of employers to track data relating to employee health and attendance, allow for more objective program measurement. The consultant is involved in designing program measures, particularly those that allow comparison with other organizations.

## Ongoing Measurement and Assessment

The consistent collection, interpretation and sharing of information related to program measurement is frequently an issue for organizations who lack the internal resources. The consultant may assist in selecting the most appropriate methods of program measurement and in developing the measurement tools and reports. Measurements, if done on an objective basis, allows comparison of results with other external organizations and the creation of industry benchmarks.

## Vendor Audits

In some cases, ongoing measurement may extend to a deeper examination of program results and outcomes with an audit of the vendor. Audits are an effective tool for both the organization and the vendor to ask the question — what can we do better? Up front, the consultant must establish the purpose of the audit and specific areas that need to be explored. Formalized audits of insurer, for example, can include a review and commentary about the application of the technical provisions and philosophy direction of the plan. As the facilitator, the consultant can help both parties to work towards effective changes. Sometimes, an audit will uncover quality concerns or philosophical differences. In this case, the consultant would take a stronger position in advocating the organization's concerns to the vendor or, when problems are irreconcilable, recommend vendor changes.

## Claims Review for Self-insured Groups

Some consultants offer hands-on claims management services that provide objective, third-party opinion where a significant period in the disability continuum is self-managed by the employer. Managing claims has become very specialized and some self-managed employers may wish to get a second opinion on their adjudication decisions.

## EFAP Analysis

Consultants have a big picture view of an organization. In examining EFAP data, consultants can study utilization trends and establish possible correlations to disability experience. Pro-active recommendations can be made before trends escalate into larger, more costly problems. Moreover, they can make sure that the organization realizes the most value from the EFAP provider. For organizations that do not use EFAP services, consultants are able to analyze if such services would benefit an organization and assist in determining which provider to use.

## REVIEWING THE ORGANIZATION'S DISABILITY MANAGEMENT PROGRAM

Many organizations have elements of a disability management strategy. Many are interested in measuring the program's effectiveness or determining the need for program changes or enhancements. Evaluation of the program by a consultant may involve a strategic analysis of the organization's approach to preventing and managing health-related issues that impact on productivity and attendance, or may be limited to specific program elements such as the disability benefits design or return-to-work policy.

The need for a program review may be precipitated by dissatisfaction with current service providers or with the results of the program. Why might the company be disappointed with the results of their disability management strategy? The program design may be flawed or may not have been administered according to the original design. Although the reasons for disappointing results can be quite varied and unique, some common trends emerge. Some of the known contributors to dissatisfaction in an existing Disability Management Program are as follow:

1. Lack of a defined or properly executed communication strategy to explain the program to all stakeholders;
2. A benefits plan design (such as supplementary health, STD or LTD) that fails to support the objectives of the disability management program (*i.e.*, lack of financial encouragement for return-to-work initiatives);

3. Lack of a defined model or approach to disability management resulting in several separate or *ad hoc* initiatives that may be working at cross purposes and fail to demonstrate non-discriminatory practices;
4. Absence of senior management commitment to the program which results in mixed messages to managers or lack of financial support for the program;
5. Fragmented programs that operate in isolation from each other or have different reporting structures, *e.g.*, the management of non-occupational disabilities may be totally separate from that of occupational disabilities;
6. Poor co-ordination between the short-term and long-term periods of disability;
7. Absent or poorly defined stakeholders' roles in the program. This results in role overlap and confusion, loss of efficiency and frustration by all involved;
8. Poorly understood and followed policies or routines associated with the program;
9. Programs that take a punitive approach such as managing absence as opposed to promoting health and productivity; and
10. Presence of organizational barriers to returning absent employees to work.

It is always difficult for an internal stakeholder to be truly objective and critically evaluate both the strengths and the weaknesses of the company's own disability management program. However, an external consultant can bring an unbiased perspective to the program review. By comparing the results of the company's program with the best practices of other organizations, the consultant can assist in the program evaluation and communication to senior management. Evaluation of the current program, taking into account the needs of the organization and its employees, is often the first step in promoting change. Such an evaluation may include the following five elements:

## Review of the Disability Management Program Model and Associated Processes

Mapping out the current program and processes, according to how they operate, provides a clearer picture of how the program functions. A visual picture or map can clarify who is involved in the program, when they get involved, what the various decision points are, and the actions that take place. It may indicate when actions or accountabilities overlap or when too much effort is expended in a low-risk area of the program at the expense of an element considered to be really important. Facilitating the process mapping and the review of results is a common role for consultants. The findings may be discussed with the internal stakeholders as the starting point to identify potential areas of focus for change or development.

## Clarifying Roles and Responsibilities

All stakeholders in the disability management program must have a good understanding of their roles in the program as well as the roles of others who may be resources to them. Key stakeholders vary according to the scope and nature of the program. The list may include employees, union representatives, managers, occupational health and safety professionals, human resources personnel and benefits representatives. External stakeholders should also be identified as they contribute to the results of the disability management program. These external stakeholders may include, for example, EFAP service provider, insurer, external rehabilitation resources, external occupational health and safety providers.

Organizations that have implemented successful disability management programs also recognize the importance of including the union as a key stakeholder by inviting union representatives to participate in program development and evaluation. Failure to do so can result in delays in program implementation or resistance to specific elements such as benefit design or return-to-work programs. Certain collective agreements include statements about the "mismanagement of disabled members". These must be understood and accommodated.

It is interesting to note that, although most organizations would name the supervisor and employee as key stakeholders, their roles are often ill-defined and training to perform their role is insufficient. If the entire program is designed to revolve around the employee and involve the supervisor in a meaningful way, then the program must strive to maintain that important relationship when an absence occurs. A breakdown in that relationship can destroy that important bond between the employee and the workplace, a critical element for a successful return to work.

The consultant gathers information on current roles from a variety of sources including the review of program documentation, existing position descriptions and various communication pieces. Information is also gathered through interviews and focus groups. The consultant may then recommend the addition of new roles or modifications to existing roles.

## Availability and Use of Resources

The ability to assist employees and managers access the most appropriate disability management resources in a timely and cost-efficient manner is another area of program review and gap analysis. These resources may include internal/external occupational health and safety services, the EFAP and human resources personnel. The consultant may assist in the identification of the current resources and additional external resources, such as a treatment provider that could be considered as beneficial to the overall program. The consultant explores links between the existing programs, such as the EFAP with the disability management program.

## Benefits Program Design

There are consultants who specialize in the design, implementation and evaluation of benefits programs. Benefits programs are often the most visible and influential element of a disability management strategy and warrant a more in-depth discussion.[2] A comprehensive review considers the relationship of benefits such as a salary continuance program, STD, LTD, supplementary health, dental and EFAP with the objectives of the disability management program. Benefit design should support the objectives of the organization's disability management strategy as opposed to being viewed as simply the cost of attracting and retaining employees. However, benefits programs that are covered under a collective agreement are difficult to modify. This is another reason why union support is critical to a successful program.

An employer's retirement program may also be reviewed in relation to the disability management program. The pension plan may include a disability retirement pension. In addition, the provision of lifestyle counselling may be a common element of both retirement planning and disability management.

## Program Measurement and Reporting

To rationalize the importance and success of a disability management program, the goals, outcomes, and benchmarks along with the ongoing performance measurements must be understood and managed. The consultant is able to play a critical role in the development and

---

[2] See Disability Benefits Plan Design below.

implementation of ongoing evaluation and reporting, and may assist in the collection of information and the ensuing analysis.

Benchmarks may include the incidence and duration of employee absence, statistics relating to utilization of benefits such as disability, workers' compensation (WC) or health, and measures of internal hazards or occupational health and safety risks. The consultant not only looks at the methods and appropriateness of measurement in comparison to program objectives, but also the means of communicating the results to the key stakeholders including employees and senior management.

Not all evaluation occurs with the external assistance of a consultant. There are elements of program evaluation that should be done within the organization in order to identify issues as they arise. Internal evaluation can occur on an ongoing basis using such means as employee satisfaction surveys, internal audits of occupational health case management, and analysis of program measures. Built into the internal evaluation process must be a method to "red flag" problems.

An external review is beneficial if the program is felt to require significant changes or if the corporation decides to outsource the program. Consultants can also provide an independent review to measure the quality of services delivered from other external providers or vendors.

## DESIGNING A NEW DISABILITY MANAGEMENT PROGRAM

Organizations launching a new program or making significant changes to an existing disability management program may require the services of a consultant to assist in the program design. Comprehensive services are provided by consulting firms, as described earlier in this chapter. This assistance may include researching the various disability management models implemented by other employers, performing due diligence on potential providers to evaluate the match between their services and the organization's needs, facilitating a working group to design the program, and determining the required budget for the program. The steps that are undertaken in program design include:

1. Environmental scan;
2. Setting objectives;
3. Designing the most appropriate program model;
4. Identifying roles and responsibilities for key stakeholders;

5. Integrating the program with benefits design and human resources policy;
6. Identifying resources (internal and external);
7. Developing operational procedures;
8. Determining methods of communication; and
9. Communicating the program philosophy, design, and procedures to the stakeholders.

For the remainder of this chapter, we will examine in more depth the consultant's role in the environmental scan, disability benefits plan design, disability management program implementation and measurement.

## ENVIRONMENTAL SCAN

The first step in designing a disability management program is the environmental scan. An alternate way of describing this first step is to describe it as a thorough assessment of current practices, programs and delivery. In order to design the most appropriate disability program and associated employee benefits, it is worthwhile to spend some time at the outset to gather input from employees, determine the objectives of management, consider internal constraints and the impact of the external environment.

### Employee Needs

The demographics of the employee population, their current health status and that of their dependents, and their expectations are all factors to be considered when assessing employee needs. Employees' expectations of disability benefits such as STD and LTD are sometimes unrealistic in terms of wage loss replacement. Some employees see a disability plan as an early retirement program or an unemployment insurance scheme, but disability plans are neither. Some employees may expect the plan to fully replace their income, whereas most plans replace only part of the employees' income.

To assess the expectations and needs of employees, the following strategies can be used. First, a carefully worded employee survey, perhaps as part of an overall review of the entire benefits package, can give invaluable feedback, while at the same time clarifying the purpose of the disability plans. Second, focus groups can be used in conjunction with an employee survey or alone. Consultants are often used to assess employees' needs and opinions in this way. Sometimes "outsiders" are more accepted and employees express opinions more freely if they perceive a low risk of repercussions.

## Management Objectives

Organizations have a unique culture and this culture influences programs and policies including the disability management program and associated employee benefits. A paternalistic organization may want to have full control over the design of the disability management program and may place more emphasis on the provision of better benefits for longer service employees. An entrepreneurial organization may allow their employees more flexibility in working arrangements, including the benefits package. The design and funding of the disability benefit plans must fit with the style and culture of the organization and have the full support of the key stakeholders.

## Internal Constraints

There may be many reasons why the use of external consultants or a specific consultant may not be possible. Existing relationships between senior staff and external firms may impact the selection process, or other priorities within the organization may restrict the use of funds for special projects. The authority to proceed with a project, with or without external consultants, should be well defined prior to beginning the project or selecting the consultant.

Other examples of possible constraints impacting particularly on the type of disability plans for an organization include:

1. Whether any of the plans are subject to a collective agreement. Negotiated plans specify the coverage to be provided, restricting the possibility of exploring alternative plan designs;
2. Whether an organization has made a decision to be an industry leader in terms of the type of program to be provided; and
3. Whether the existing program, particularly benefits design, might limit the options to be considered, since a significant decrease in coverage might not be well received by employees.

## External Environment

Although it is difficult to keep pace with the rate of change, awareness of the external environment is essential to the design of any disability management program. Human rights legislation and court decisions have impacted employment practices in Canada. This includes the design and administration of disability benefits such as:

1. The removal of the employer's ability to deny or limit benefits to individuals suffering from a psychiatric condition; or
2. Payment of disability benefits prior to or after the birth of a baby when a woman is medically unfit for work.

The availability of disability benefits through government sponsored plans also impacts disability plan design. Some examples are employment insurance (EI), Canada/Quebec Pension Plan (CPP/QPP), WC, and automobile insurance.

If the disability management program includes insured disability benefits, then the insurance company may have restrictions in available plan design. Insurers have internal underwriting guidelines which are designed to limit their risk and liability. Consultants are able to identify and compare what is available from the insurance marketplace.

Finally, the *Income Tax Act*[3] defines the taxability of benefits from employer-paid disability plans. The rules state:

1. Employer-paid premiums are not taxable to employees;
2. If the employer funds the plan, although the premiums are not taxed, the benefits are taxed once received;
3. If the employee pays for the entire premium for the plan, benefits will be tax-free if the employee becomes disabled. Keep in mind, however, that employee-paid premiums are paid from after-tax dollars; and
4. If the premiums are cost-shared, then the benefit payments paid to the employee are taxed after payments have equaled the premiums paid by the employee.

## DISABILITY BENEFITS PLAN DESIGN

The following section provides a high level overview of a typical insured disability policy contract. Insured benefits (STD, LTD) are income

---

[3]  R.S.C. 1985 (5th Supp.), c. 1.

replacement benefits, where eligibility and the criteria for approval of benefits are outlined in the disability policy contract. The contract also determines and defines disability as it relates to the level of function required to perform a certain job, occupation or a part thereof.

Once the contract has defined the terms of eligibility for benefits, it then defines the expectations of the claimant to mitigate their loss by participating in treatment, co-operating in rehabilitation plans, and providing evidence of ongoing disability for entitlement. A significant component of the disability management program is the design of the STD and LTD disability benefits plan, as they need to be in concert with the overall disability management strategies, providing disability benefits along with incentives to return to work expediently.

Experienced consultants are able to identify the "norm" for the various aspects of a disability plan design, specific features that may best suit the organization's needs and the types of plans offered by competitors. The consultant can also address the costs associated with different alternatives, often a primary determinant of plan design.

## OPTIONS FOR SHORT-TERM DISABILITY PLAN DESIGN

### Salary Continuance

Under a salary continuance program, the employee's salary continues to be paid, in full or in part, most often until the start of LTD. The following is an example of how a salary continuance plan might be designed:

| Length of Service | Percentage | Duration |
|---|---|---|
| Less than 1 year | 100% | first 2 weeks |
| | $66^{2}/_{3}$% | after 2 weeks |
| At least 1 year but less than 5 years | 100% | first 8 weeks |
| | $66^{2}/_{3}$% | after 8 weeks |
| At least 5 years | 100% | until LTD |

For many employers, the ease of administering a salary continuance plan is attractive, but may be offset by the lack of benefits management through claims adjudication and early intervention.

## Weekly Indemnity

The weekly indemnity (WI) arrangement is a disability income replacement benefit where the risk is assumed and underwritten by an insurer. Payments are based on a percentage of weekly income. Many WI policies provide for benefits to begin on the first day of disability if that disability is due to an accident or if hospitalized, and on the fourth or eighth day for other illnesses. Some WI plans are designed to match the federal Employment Insurance (EI) program, since the provision of a WI benefit can reduce the employer's EI premium, if the plan is documented and filed with Human Resources Development Canada.

Employers may favour a WI plan as it places them at arm's length from claims adjudication decisions. This plan also offers the benefit of claims management expertise and resources. The cost attached often varies from seven per cent to 35 per cent of the premium, depending on the size of the plan, its administrative complexity and the specific underwriter. The value of the cost must be considered in conjunction with the full range of disability services provided.

Consultants may recommend to the employer utilization of the same insurance provider for both the insured WI plan and the insured LTD plan. By developing a relationship in this fashion with the insurer, there is potential opportunity to involve the carrier in a purposeful strategy for disability management, including early intervention initiatives. As well, using the same insurer allows for a smooth transition between benefits.

## Accumulated Sick Leave Plan

This type of plan, common in public sector organizations, ties length of service to eligibility for sick leave very precisely. For every month worked, the employee is entitled to a number of days of sick leave. For example, an employee may "earn" 1¼ days per month worked for a total of 15 days a year. These days are "banked" and are used during the LTD qualifying period. Employees may also be able to accumulate days without a maximum or be entitled to payment for unused days at the time of retirement. This STD design has a number of challenges when faced with management and cost containment issues. First, some concerns exist about "entitlement" attitudes which this type of approach seems to encourage. Second, some plan sponsors feel that the lack of benefits for genuinely ill staff with little service is a problem, and indeed in some cases, unions fund hardship cases. Third, the deferred liability attached to plans which allow payout on termination or retirement can be large and insufficiently funded. Public sector employers are becoming more and more concerned about the potential cost of such an approach.

## OPTIONS FOR LONG-TERM DISABILITY PLAN DESIGN

Unlike legislated government sponsored disability programs or compensation plans, insured long-term disability plans are unique and written in part, according to the specifications of the policyholders or plan sponsors. It follows that there are various combinations and choices written into each policy. Understanding the specifics of the applicable policy is necessary to working within that particular system.

### Elimination Period

The elimination period (also called the qualifying period) is the period of time during which employees must be continuously disabled before they are eligible for the disability benefits. The elimination period defined in the disability contract may be as long as a year although 17 weeks or six months are the two most common timeframes. The employee may be receiving sick leave benefits, STD benefits or may have applied for Employment Insurance during the elimination period for LTD.

### Income from Other Sources

Disabled employees may be eligible for (or in receipt of) income from other sources. Almost every LTD plan has a provision which reduces the benefits payable by income from such other sources. In some plans there is a dollar-for-dollar reduction if other disability benefits are payable, such as CPP and Workers' Compensation. Further, the LTD plan may apply an "all source maximum" to the final calculation of the benefit payable to the claimant. Although CPP or QPP disability benefits paid on the behalf of the employee are usually a direct offset, benefits received for dependents may not be considered or may be included in the "all source maximum". Any increases in CPP benefits due to indexing are usually excluded from the offset calculation.

### Mandatory Rehabilitation

Disability plans usually contain a clause which requires the disabled employee to follow a medically-suitable rehabilitation program. The penalty for not following the program is the possible termination of benefits. While this might seem harsh, it is to ensure that the claimant is mitigating his loss by co-operating in vocational rehabilitation, and following recommended treatment plans so the employee can return to meaningful work as quickly and safely as possible.

## Replacement Ratios

The replacement ratio is the net income an employee receives while disabled. This calculation is defined in each disability contract and is expressed as a percentage of the employee's net earnings while actively working. In conjunction with the "all source maximum", the percentage payable to the employee and the resultant "replacement ratio" play a large role in allowing for a monetary incentive to return to work. For some employees this is equal to the "all source maximum" (usually 85 per cent). In other cases, the replacement ratio percentage is higher than the "all source maximum", even without any additional earnings.

This example of over-insurance is most common in employee-paid non-taxable plans. For example, many employee-paid plans with a percentage of $66^2/_3$ per cent will result in a benefit which exceeds 85 per cent of the employee's pre-disability net earnings. The employee will find the premium he or she has been paying will not result in a full benefit. For this reason, many non-taxable plans are designed as graded plans paying $66^2/_3$ per cent of the first, for example, $2000 of monthly earnings, then 50 per cent of the rest, to a monthly maximum benefit. Taxable plans usually pay a benefit of 70 or 75 per cent, to allow for a sufficient replacement ratio, given that the benefit will be taxed.

## Definition of Disability

The definition of disability as defined in the disability contract is the most important issue to understand for any consultant working with the disability management field. This definition is used to compare the employee's level of function due to the medical impairment with the necessary level of function required to engage in either his own job, occupation, or any reasonable and alternate occupation. The definition of disability determines how the claim adjudicator will render a decision as to the employee's eligibility for benefits.

There are two common definitions of disability which are often used together:

1. The "own occupation" definition of disability means that employees are considered "disabled" and eligible for benefits if they are unable to perform the (essential) duties of their "own" occupation due to a medical impairment;
2. The "any occupation" definition of disability means that employees are considered disabled and eligible for benefits if they are unable to perform (due to a medical impairment) the (essential) duties of "any" occupation that is considered "reasonable by way of education, training and experience".

In the determination of "any occupation" disabled, special heed must be applied to the meaning and intent of the terms "reasonable". Often disability contracts and legal precedence have defined that term. Otherwise the commonly understood meaning of an alternate reasonable occupation stands as a test for that determination.

There are variables that further characterize the definitions of disability. The most common characteristic involves timing. Often contracts are written to define the "own occupation" definition for a certain period of time (for example two years), following which the "any occupation" definition of disability is the test for ongoing eligibility for benefits.

Any number of variations and combination can be seen in disability contracts. Some of the more common variations include an "any occupation" definition of disability from the outset, "any occupation" within the company, a five-year own occupation definition and, although rarely used, own occupation coverage to age 65. Obviously, the last definition is extremely expensive in terms of premium costs.

## Limitations and Exclusions

Disability contracts also contain further clauses, called limitations and exclusions, that are critical to the adjudication and administration of the benefit. Limitations generally refer circumstances that limit the benefit to a certain duration of time or amount of money. Exclusions define circumstances that will prevent the entitlement to benefits, such as a "pre-existing conditions" exclusion. For example, if the employee was diagnosed and treated for a medical condition just prior to the effective date of insurance, eligibility for disability benefits for the same cause may be excluded for a certain period of time.

The pre-existing exclusions clause has become aligned with plan management in order to protect the viability of the benefit plan in light of recent human rights decisions and privacy legislation changes. This clause precludes benefit entitlement to any illness/disease for which the individual received treatment, usually in the three months prior to hire. The pre-existing conditions exclusion will then apply for a limited duration, usually 12 months, following the date of hire.

Other exclusions may include those related to self-inflicted injury or participation in a crime.

## Partial/Residual Disability/Rehabilitation

Partial disability is a poorly understood and often misused term in disability benefits. The intent of a partial disability provision is to encourage employees to remain at work, or to return to work on a reduced basis without jeopardizing eligibility for some benefit protection.

It is important to understand that to be eligible for benefit coverage, employees must still meet the definition for total disability. In other words, they must be unable to perform the essential duties of their occupation (for an own occupation definition). However, if the employees are able to perform reduced duties or work reduced hours, they may be eligible for a partial benefit. Partial disability, therefore, can be viewed as a rehabilitation opportunity.

A residual benefit may be included as a provision following a period of total disability. The plan may pay a benefit based on the difference between the pre-disability earnings and the employees' current earning capacity, regardless of whether the employees have actually returned to work.

## Cost of Living Adjustment

One problem for disabled employees is that their income is frequently fixed, except for any indexing under CPP or QPP disability benefits, for the duration of their disability. A few policies have a "cost of living adjustment" (COLA) clause, whereby LTD benefits are increased every year. The increases are linked to the Consumer Price Index (CPI), a defined percentage or a combination of both. The associated increase in premium rates is normally in the range of five per cent for every one per cent of COLA.

## Maximum Benefit Period

Most LTD plans provide employee benefits up to age 65, but there are some exceptions. Some plans have a fixed maximum benefit period, such as five years. Although this approach reduces the cost of the plan substantially, it is relatively unusual.

## FINANCIAL CONSIDERATIONS FOR DISABILITY PLAN DESIGN

The design of a disability benefits plan has a large impact on the cost and, regardless of the type of underwriting (insured, self-insured, retention), the claims "experience" will be the biggest single component of the ongoing cost as claims drive the dollars that must be paid out and "reserved" to ensure ongoing ability to meet these liabilities. Clearly, there is a financial impact associated with claims management and disability management initiatives.

The type of underwriting or funding will also impact costs, and it is important to match the degree of risk with the plan sponsor's ability to accept the ongoing fluctuations in funding needs. Again, an experienced consultant can help assess a company's risk tolerance and choose the most appropriate cost sharing arrangements based on corporate philosophy and budget, taking into account income tax rules.

While this section is primarily focused on disability plans designs and accounting methodologies, it is important to continue to emphasize the corporate financial impact of disability claims management and reiterate the important role the consultant plays in development of the overall disability management strategies. It is not unusual to realize a release of reserve dollars in the six-figure range as a result of effective execution of an overall disability management strategy. As well, the prevention of disability claims experience and the associated costs prompt enormous financial savings.

While using a consultant for plan design issues would add value to the process, many employers have the expertise internally to structure a plan or plans which suit their needs. However, having a consultant analyze and evaluate financing alternatives may still be important, since the liabilities, hidden or otherwise, can be a huge burden on a plan sponsor if not appropriate to the risk tolerance of the organization.

The following section discusses some aspects for consideration in financing a benefits plan.

## Assessing Tolerance for Risk Taking

Risk management under benefit programs is determined by the method of underwriting. The amount of risk absorbed by an organization is often described on a continuum. At one end of the scale are "fully pooled" arrangements, where the insurer assumes all the risk. The plan sponsor pays the premiums, the insurer pays the claims, and there is no process for accounting for any surplus or deficits. The rates fluctuate depending on demographic shifts. This approach tends to be used with smaller employers if the volume of insurance is low, or if the insurer has limited history on which to accurately assess the risk.

At the other end of the scale is self-insurance, where the plan sponsor assumes all the risk. There may or may not be an adjudicator involved but, if there is, the plan is usually called "Administrative Services Only" (ASO). In this arrangement the insurer adjudicates the claims but does not assume the risk. Short-term disability plans are often handled this way, especially with the salary continuance approach. There are fewer self-insured LTD plans, since the potential risk is high and could only be absorbed by larger organizations.

The environmental scan discussed earlier addresses management's tolerance for risk taking and much of the decision about funding the plans comes from that assessment. The insurer's guidelines about its risk taking capabilities is also a key factor.

## ABILITY TO HANDLE RISK AND FLUCTUATIONS IN CASH FLOW

Even when organizations assume as much risk as possible, there are concerns about fluctuations in claims levels and the ability to have the funds on hand in the future to pay out the entire benefit obligation. There are techniques (addressed in the next section) which can assist plan sponsors to "smooth out" the cost of these plans, while retaining the desired level of risk.

## Pooling

When benefits are pooled, the plan sponsor transfers the entire risk to the insurer. To stabilize plan costs, a company can arrange to have the unusually high claims "pooled". This process is more commonly used with LTD versus STD plans because the potential length of a claim increases the plan sponsor's financial risks.

## Refund Accounting

If full self-insurance is not a preferred option, there is a middle ground. Refund accounting is used in insured plans, with or without pooling, to allow the plan sponsor to share in the risk. Every year, the insurance company balances dollars received (premiums) against payments made (claims), obligations incurred (reserves for disabled employees and claims incurred but not yet started) and related expenses. If this calculation results in a surplus, then the surplus can be returned to the plan sponsor, held by the insurer with interest, used for premium holidays, or earmarked as a reserve to offset future deficits. If there is a policy year deficit, a past surplus (if any) can be used to offset the deficit, or the rates in future years will be increased to include a deficit recovery factor. At plan termination, any deficit balance remains the responsibility of the insurer. In this respect, a refund accounting method of underwriting is one of insurance.

## Hold Harmless Agreements

Plan sponsors who wish to have an insured plan but need to reduce their costs and/or accept as much risk as possible, could agree with the insurance carrier to absolve them from responsibility for incurred but unreported reserves or deficits. These "hold harmless" arrangements pass the liability to the plan sponsor for claims incurred prior to, but reported after, the termination of the plan. They also take responsibility for the accumulated deficit on termination, which is normally not repayable by the plan sponsor. By doing this, the premium rate reduces. However, caution should be taken to understand the implications of the additional risk being assumed by this approach. A consultant can identify the risk factor and ensure it is well understood and manageable.

## Administrative Services Only (ASO)

When benefits are self-insured, there is sometimes an insurance company involved providing "administrative services only" (ASO). The plan sponsor pays the insurance company to adjudicate claims and keep appropriate records, but the insurance company plays no part in assuming the risk of the plan. The plan sponsor needs to set aside funds to meet future benefit obligations. A consultant or actuary is needed to value the benefit obligations.

## HOW CLAIMS AFFECT PREMIUM RATES

Except for the smallest of plans, disability claims have a direct impact on the ongoing rating and cost of the plan (premiums). For medium to large groups, the group's own claims experience is taken into consideration in establishing the cost of the plan. The "credibility" or weighting given to claims experience depends on the number of lives covered and the number of years of experience history available to the underwriter. The more lives and the more years of experience, the higher the credibility percentage is. As experience data is collected, the credibility percentage will reach 100 per cent. When this credibility weighting is achieved, a company's own claims experience will be used to determine premium rates at renewal.

Insurers have internal underwriting guidelines and tables to calculate premium rates for disability plans that are less than 100 per cent credible. This is done by blending "average" rates with a company's claims experience.

Again, it is important to link the financial impact of disability management and accounting structures. The disability management consultant can assist a company to better understand how premiums for the organization's disability benefits are determined and what strategies can be developed to reduce and contain premium costs through plan design changes and disability management programs.

## THE SEARCH AND SELECTION OF A "RISK TAKER" OR INSURER

Once the plan design is determined and the preferred funding arranged, the consultant can assist in selecting the most appropriate provider, usually an insurer. Insurers assume the risk, or liabilities associated with the disability insurance plan, and price the risk accordingly. Given that we have noted the financial impact of claims management, it seems reasonable to assess potential partners in a focused and purposeful fashion.

Consultants are adept at analyzing the pros and cons of the many insurers available. Providers of insured services are selected based on criteria unique to each consumer including, but not limited to:

1. The insurer's disability management philosophy;

2. The insurer's service capabilities including the length of time taken to assess and pay claims, location of the adjudication personnel and availability of local representation;
3. Cost;
4. References, particularly from clients of similar size or industry; and
5. Financial stability of the provider, using benchmarks such as industry rating services (*e.g.*, Moody's, Standard & Poor's).

The process of insurer selection often includes the distribution of specifications and requesting proposals or quotes. The consultant champions the review of proposals, assessing them against the established criteria with a focus on the best interests of the client.

## BENEFITS PROGRAM IMPLEMENTATION

If a new plan is to be introduced successfully, or changes are to be made to an existing plan, a communication strategy is critical to prevent and avert negative ramifications. There are consultants who are able to provide direction and implementation protocols for communication strategies befitting the organization and the magnitude of change. Advising employees about change may require a structured approach over a period of time, using various multi-media tools to assist with delivery.

## IMPLEMENTATION OF THE DISABILITY MANAGEMENT PROGRAM

Effectively launching either a new program or modifications to an existing program requires a strategy for communication and a defined action plan. In many cases the launching of the program is added on top of existing responsibilities for internal staff and is therefore difficult to achieve in a timely manner. The consultant can assume some of the time-consuming aspects of the implementation plan, such as the development of the communication guide or documentation of associated policies and procedures. The consultant may also assist in negotiating service agreements with external providers.

## A LOOK TO THE FUTURE

If the primary role of the consultant in the field of disability management is to anticipate and respond to the needs of plan sponsors, then it only stands to reason that the role is not a static one. Consultants add value by anticipating, and in some cases influencing, trends that impact the disability management programs of employers. These trends may be external such as changing legislation, or internal, arising from changing employee needs and demographics.

Certainly government legislation represents a major influence in the design and implementation of employer disability management programs. The delivery of Canadian government sponsored health care programs is undergoing dramatic change at both a federal and provincial level. The concept of universality of health care arising from the *Canada Health Act*[4] has come under significant pressure with the introduction of private organizations offering preferred access to health-related services for individuals and businesses on a fee-for-service basis. Employers are faced with difficult decisions regarding the appropriateness of their role as a purchaser of such services to facilitate an earlier return to work for absent employees as part of their disability management strategy. Consultants can play a role in this decision-making process by helping employers better understand the financial and philosophical impact of their actions. Another role for the consultant is the development of a business case to support the development of a disability management program.

Recent developments in the marketplace have led consultants to widen the list of issues they address. The following section outlines services consultants now provide.

### Changing Benefits Plan Designs

As organizations revisit and revise their corporate and human resources strategy, the design of existing benefits including health, dental, life and disability are under greater scrutiny. The changing nature of work will lead to significant changes in benefit design in the coming years. For example, an increase in contract workers and an aging workforce will result in changing employee benefits needs. As well, it is anticipated that employers will shift more responsibility for benefits costs and decisions to employees. One example of this trend is the rise in flexible benefits programs whereby

---

4    R.S.C. 1985, c. C-6. The five principles of medicare included in the Act are: universality, accessibility, portability, comprehensiveness and public administration.

employees have greater choice in selecting the level and type of benefit that best suits their personal and family needs. The consultant's role in benefits communication and education for employees will continue.

## Outsourcing Benefit Administration and Disability Management

The trend towards outsourcing certain aspects of benefits administration and disability management is likely to continue providing that the outcome measures support the cost-benefit of such a decision. Here, the role of consultants may be in determining the value of outsourcing and the selection of the most appropriate vendor. In addition, many consultant firms provide outsourcing services.

## Preferred Provider Networks

In an effort to speed up access to community health care resources or to negotiate an attractive fee structure, insurers and employers are developing service agreements with preferred providers. Consultants assume the role in the identification of appropriate networks, in the negotiation of service agreements and in the measurement of results.

## CONCLUSION

The role of the consultant in disability management can be tailored to meet the needs of any organization. As outlined in this chapter, the mandate of the consultant in disability management may be project-focused and time limited, or may be broader in scope by providing ongoing advisory services. The consultant can add value by evaluating a current program, designing an approach to disability (including benefits), selecting vendors, implementing the program and measuring the results.

Care should be taken to select the most appropriate consultant considering such factors as the scope of the consultant's mandate, the company's needs and budget, and the consultant's previous experience in the field of disability management. The scope of the consultant's role, the services expected and the associated fees should be negotiated at the beginning of the project. And finally, regular evaluation of the outcomes of the services provided will ensure that the company is receiving value for the dollars spent.

## GLOSSARY

### Commissions:

Commissions are the component in the rates which are payable to a broker, agent or consultant to provide services to the plan sponsor in the design and funding of the plan.

### Cost of Living Adjustment:

The cost of living adjustment (COLA) is applied to payments from a disability income replacement plan. For example, a long-term disability plan may include a COLA provision which increases benefits by the amount of the Consumer Price Index, up to a maximum of three per cent per year.

### Credibility:

This is the percentage of the policyholder's claims which is taken into consideration by the insurance company in setting rates. For example, the claims might be 75 per cent credible (75 per cent of the rate is based on the policyholder's own claims experience and 25 per cent on the insurer's "average" rate).

### Elimination Period:

Also known as the qualifying period, this is the period of time during which an employee has to be continuously disabled, prior to being eligible to receive long-term disability benefits.

### Insured:

Insured means that the insurance company takes the entire risk for any claims eligible under a plan. Although the plan sponsor must pay premiums on an ongoing basis, none of the risk would be assumed by the plan sponsor, but instead, by the insurance company entirely.

### Eligibility:

The entitlement to benefits is determined at the outset of the claim by determination of the individuals for that benefit. Most contracts define eligibility as having to be part of the insured group defined in the policy, and being actively at work, engaging in a minimum number of hours of work during a specified time, at the time of incurred loss. Eligibility does not mean that an individual will be approved for benefits. It means that the individual is eligible to make a claim.

## Plan Sponsor:

The plan sponsor is the organization to which the policy or policies are issued by the insurance company. The plan sponsor could be an employer, an association, a union, or any other similar organization. (Also see Policyholder.)

## Policyholder:

The policyholder is the organization to which the policy or policies are issued (also see Plan Sponsor).

## Premiums:

Premiums are the amount paid to an insurance company on a monthly basis, based on the rate struck by the insurance company at each renewal, times the amount of coverage in place. The rate would normally be held for 12 months at a time, but the premium might vary every month depending on the coverage in place for the employee population at that time.

## Renewal:

Once a year, insurance rates are assessed by the insurance company and "renewed". The renewal process involves a review of the demographics of the group, or the claims experience, or some combination of both. Occasionally, rates are guaranteed for two years for life and long-term disability benefits, but usually renewals are once a year.

## Retention:

Retention is the component built into premium rates which the insurance company "retains" for their administrative and other costs.

## Reserves:

An insurance company is required to establish several reserves. These reserves include:

1. Incurred but not reported reserve (IBNR)
   This reserve is required for claims which are incurred and become the liability of the insurance company, but which may be paid after policy termination;
2. Disabled life reserves (DLR)
   These reserves are established for employees who are disabled to ensure that future claims can be paid for the duration of their disability;
3. Extended death benefits (EDB)
   These reserves set aside dollars to cover the death benefits for disabled employees who have been approved under the life waiver of premium provision.

## Self-Insured:

Compared to an insured plan, the entire risk lies with the plan sponsor and none with the insurance company.

# Chapter 12

# COMMUNICATION STRATEGIES — CONSULTANT'S PERSPECTIVE TO ENHANCE THE DISABILITY MANAGEMENT PROCESS

DIANE MCELROY

## COMMUNICATION — BUILDING A STRATEGIC PLAN

Disability management programs are made up of many interacting components. Successful programs have four common elements. A well thought out design, committed resources, effective administration and a communication plan. Critical to the ongoing success of running a disability management program is the ability to re-evaluate, change and modify the processes in place. Change occurs everyday, and it is essential that the managed care model within an organization keep pace with the times. With re-evaluation and evolutionary strategies, the disability management program will grow and evolve as the organization grows and evolves.

Effective communication is the driver that will take a disability management program from design to effective implementation. Communication challenges loom at every turn in the evolution of a disability management program.

## Role of Communication Consultant

An expert communicator will be crucial in helping to develop and implement a communication plan. The communicator would help to identify the audience groups, identify the issues associated with each, identify the barriers, and help develop communication processes that are practical in the company's environment.

The consultant would help to facilitate the feedback from the various internal and external audience groups. Being an unbiased communicator, the consultant can often help to solve sensitive communication issues in a professional non-confrontational way.

The communication consultant would act as the communication project leader working with the company's disability management team. The consultant would help to pick the communication team, develop the strategy planning process, facilitate each meeting to maximize results, and develop a strategic plan that has buy-in with the right audience at the right time.

## Value of Hiring an Expert Communication Consultant

A communication expert that has extensive experience in disability management can pay big dividends. The consultant will have the experience in dealing with many of the issues and challenges faced by a company. Learning from past experiences is what makes consultants worth their freight. With all the talent in the marketplace, choose a consultant that has a proven track record.

A consultant who brings years of experience will prove invaluable. Pros and cons of real life strategy development and evaluation will go a long way in making sure the communication strategy makes sense in the company's environment. Educating a communicator who hasn't been involved in disability management will not only be frustrating but not very productive.

## Where Would You Find An Expert Communication Consultant?

The best place to start would be to inquire about talented communicators within benefits consulting firms. Communication consultants within benefits consulting firms deal with disability management communication on an ongoing basis. They have worked with plan designers and understand plan design philosophy, disability design components, administration and the very challenging communication issues associated with disability management.

"Fit" is a very important criteria as well. Rapport, trust and a good working relationship often depends on gut feel. Quite often consultants will come into an interview and provide a proposal on the requested services. It is very difficult to ascertain from these short encounters as to whether or not a good fit with the company's team is present. Don't commit to a long-term arrangement from the outset. Usually the first or second planning meeting will give you a good feel about the fit. Don't hesitate to make a switch early in the process.

If budget is a consideration, you can hire a consultant on an advisory basis to help mentor and coach your communication team through the process. This would provide you with the value of the experience but keep costs in check.

## Role of Technical Consultants in the Communication Process

The design or technical consultants also play a very valuable role in the communication process. They can provide the technical review to ensure that the facts communicated are accurate. As well, they often have invaluable input on the communication issues as experienced in their daily roles in the design, administration and implementation of disability management programs.

## Communication Plan Starts at Philosophy Development and Plan Design

Quite often communication comes into play when the plan design is formulated. This is very late in the game. Communication must be an integral part of the design process. By integrating a communication expert as part of your design team, you will be one giant step ahead. A communication expert can help to define your philosophy ensuring that it ties to the company's strategic business goals. As well, the expert can help you to identify the communication issues relative to the components within the design, administration processes and the challenges in communicating to the various audience groups.

One of the most valuable roles that a communicator can add to your team is the ability to provide you with a sound strategy to get buy-in from executives, management, and employees. A company needs to think about the communication process it will follow to get executive management to buy-in. Tied with that will be the buy-in and support of other audience groups integral to the success of the program.

## HOW TO SELL THE EXECUTIVE TEAM ON DISABILITY MANAGEMENT

It is a fact of life that executive teams relate well to the bottom line. Build a solid business case and present it to management. Treat the challenge just like any other business proposal.

Here are the key elements to include in your business case to management:

- Overview of the disability management philosophy;
- Overview of the proposed disability model;
- Advantages for the union, employees, and the company;
- Projected bottom line results;
- Industry-related examples of bottom line savings;
- Resources required;
- Budget required for implementation;
- Overview of the communication plan;
- Overview of what competitors are doing;
- Measures of success.

It is important that the program links to the company's business strategic goals. Executives want human resources programs to complement the strategic goals of the company. This link will also help to build buy-in and support of middle management who will be integral players in making the program work.

### Five Critical Factors That Will Affect Results

There are five factors to success that will require effective, well-planned communication.

### 1. Support and Participation of the Executive Team

Executives must believe in the principles of the disability management program. This support will need to be passed down to other management levels within the company. Executive buy-in will be key to give this group the right motivation to become proactive participants.

The executives support will add credibility and visibility to the program.

### 2. Management Buy-In and Ownership

The management team can only deliver messages they believe in. Management has to buy into the program and be convinced of its benefits.

Management must be prepared to take on some of the ownership of the program. They need to understand the processes, their role and they need the tools to effectively communicate with employees.

### 3. Union Buy-In and Support

In union environments, their participation and support is essential. Include union representatives and seek their input, feedback and involve them in all aspects of implementation.

### 4. Employee Buy-In

Employees need to understand how the program works and the benefits to them. The communication plan must deal with barriers that may cause employee uneasiness or scepticism about the program.

### 5. Communication

A communication plan must be designed to meet the needs of all audience groups. Issues related to each audience group must be examined and dealt with. There are significant barriers and challenges when running or implementing a disability management program. These need to be identified early in the process.

## PLANNING GUIDE FOR DEVELOPING A COMMUNICATION PLAN

The following is a step-by-step guide in developing a disability management communication plan. It is important to get the right level of buy-in and support as you move through the implementation process.

## Choose a Communication Team

Choose a communication team that will help deal with the communication challenges with an existing disability management program or a new one.

The communication team should be made up of at least one senior professional communicator who can help facilitate and manage each step of the communication planning and implementation process. Along with the communication expert, you need to include representatives from each of the identified audience groups.

This group would provide input and feedback as the communication plan is developed and finalized. A typical mix could include human resources, union, employee and management representatives. Depending on the disability model, safety managers, disability co-ordinators, and others who may be involved in the communication process could also be included. The group size should comprise of 10 or less people. Anything larger will impede productivity. External resources tied to the program can be brought in at strategic times in the process for their input. This includes the technical consultants that may be involved in plan design and implementation.

The objectives, roles, responsibilities, deliverables and measures of success need to be defined specifically for the communication plan. As well, a communication project leader must be chosen whose responsibility it will be to ensure that action steps are followed up on and executed. Often, without that focal person, endless meetings of discussion produce little or no results.

Each meeting must have an organized agenda with clear deliverables. The communication project leader would facilitate each session to maximize results and keep the discussion focussed.

## Identify Audience Groups and Disability Providers

The communication team needs to identify the audience groups involved in the disability management process. These are some of the groups or individuals that would need to be considered in any communication planning process.

1. Audience Groups
   (a)   Human Resources Team;
   (b)   Disability Management Team;
   (c)   Executive Team;

    (d)   Management Team;
    (e)   Union Representatives;
    (f)   Safety Manager;
    (g)   Health and Safety Committee;
    (h)   Disability Management Co-ordinator;
    (i)   Employees.

2. Disability Providers
    (a)   Benefits Program;
    (b)   Employee Assistance Program;
    (c)   Short-term/Long-term Benefits Insurer;
    (d)   Safety Experts;
    (e)   Rehabilitation Providers;
    (f)   Occupational Therapists;
    (g)   Physiotherapists;
    (h)   Government support programs;
    (i)   Workers' Compensation;
    (j)   Canada/Quebec Pension Plan.

Identifying the audience groups and disability providers as well as how they interact helps provide a base for the development of a communication plan. A flowchart would be completed as a reference source as to how audience groups and providers interact within the disability management model.

## Identify the Communication Issues Associated with Each Audience Group/Provider

In order to develop communication processes, the issues associated with each audience group or provider should be identified. The communication plan can then deal with these issues when the communication material and methodologies are developed.

These are some issues that traditionally surface in disability management planning sessions for four key audience groups that are found in most disability models.

1. Human Resources Team — What are the issues?
    (a)   How do we get Executive team buy-in?
    (b)   How do we get management support and buy-in?
    (c)   What is our budget?
    (d)   What resources do we have?

   (e)   Who is going to manage or implement the disability management program?
   (f)   What are the administrative issues?
   (g)   How is HR positioned in the process?
   (h)   How can we support management?
   (i)   What is our communication plan?
   (j)   How are we going to measure success?
   (k)   How do we ensure that the program evolves?

2. Executives — What issues will executives want addressed?
   (a)   How much does the disability management program cost?
   (b)   What impact will there be on the bottom line?
   (c)   Is this the right direction?
   (d)   Will the plan work?
   (e)   What are the measures for success?
   (f)   Who is responsible for the management of this program?
   (g)   What resources do we need?
   (h)   What is the competition doing?
   (i)   Do we have the time to do this right?
   (j)   What is expected of the executive team?
   (k)   Will this be a drain on our management staff?
   (l)   Do we have the right experts to make it work?

3. Management — What issues are important to them?
   (a)   Does the executive support this?
   (b)   What is the purpose of this program?
   (c)   What is my role?
   (d)   What are my specific responsibilities?
   (e)   What communication materials or tools do I have to help me?
   (f)   Is there a training program?
   (g)   How will Human Resources support me?
   (h)   Will my participation be rewarded in my performance review?

4. Employees — Education and Training
   (a)   What is disability management?
   (b)   How does the program work?
   (c)   How does it affect me?
   (d)   What is my role?
   (e)   Where do I go for help?
   (f)   How does this program benefit me?
   (g)   If I am not happy with the process, what can I do?

Identifying the issues helps with the next phase of the communication process that will identify communication processes, education and training materials. The group would tailor the communication materials when required to address the identified issues.

## Identify Logistics and Methods of Communication

The communication team has identified the audience groups/providers, and issues related to communication. At this stage, the logistics of communicating to the various audience groups is explored along with the methods of communication factors to consider include: number of locations; number within each audience group; availability of local resources to help handle communication; traditional methods of communication; limitations/challenges in implementing education/training programs.

The feedback from this discussion will help the communication team formulate the communication tools and materials that would be used within the communication plan.

## Communication Processes and Tools

This section would describe the communication processes and tools that would be used to educate, train and communicate with each of the audience groups. As well, each element of the communication plan by audience group would be outlined. This would include the content of the communication, who would handle the communication role with that group, when the communication would occur and how that communication would be delivered.

## Human Resources

This is a sample outline for four identified audience groups — human resources, executives, management and employees.

### 1. Executive Buy-In and Support

- Human Resources team to present to executive team;
- Business case that addresses philosophy, disability management model overview, bottom line impact, resources, timelines, budget for implementation;
- Continued liaison by Human Resources as required.

**Method: Face to Face at regular executive team meetings (Given by the Human Resources team)**

*2. Education and Training Program for Human Resources*

- Training program and training guide developed by disability management team and external providers on how the disability management process works.
- Two-day training program on administrative procedures and guidelines given by disability management team and external providers.
- Training program includes an explanation and documentation of all parties involved in the disability management process, as well as their roles and responsibilities.
- Training program will be updated regularly and will be mandatory for all new hires of Human Resources.

**Method: (Given by disability management team and external providers)**

(a) Face to face by disability management team and external providers;
(b) Training guide in printed form as well as on the company Intranet;
(c) Administration manual documenting processes in detail. Written in simplified language for ease of understanding and reference;
(d) Intranet case study database to help keep track and monitor all disabilities;
(e) Testing of all materials with the human resources team.

*3. Education and Training Program for Management*

- Philosophy, objectives reinforced by the executive team at a management meeting;
- Specific management training program and guide;
- Pared down version of Human Resources training to keep education/training practical for managers;
- Half-day training program on administrative procedures and guidelines given by Human Resources;
- Training program includes an overview of how the disability management process works;
- Training guide includes questions and answers;
- Training program will be updated regularly and will be mandatory for all management new hires.

**Method: (Given by Human Resources)**

(a) Face to face by human resources;
(b) Training guide in printed form as well as on the company Intranet;
(c) Administration forms on Intranet with electronic processing;
(d) Disability management question and answer database on the company Intranet.;
(e) Testing of all materials with the human resources team.

*4. Education Program for Employees*

- Employee meetings to explain program;
- Employee's roles and responsibilies;
- Orientation to disability management (on the Intranet and mandatory for new hires);
- Disability program booklet on the Intranet;
- Disability management questions and answers on the Intranet;
- Reinforcement of program goals by management on a regular basis.

**Method: (Given by human resources and management)**

(a) Face to face;
(b) Booklet, questions and answers forum and orientation on the Intranet;
(c) Reinforcement of the program goals by management.

## Resources

This part of the plan would identify the resources that would be used to implement the communication plan. These could be made up of internal and external resources. A project manager would be assigned to make sure all deliverables are delivered right and on time. Normally, this involves a significant amount of follow-up time and co-ordination with different suppliers.

## Timelines

Timelines need to be developed with buy-in from all suppliers in the process. It is crucial to build in enough time for testing.

## Budget

Budget estimates need to be developed and closely monitored throughout the process.

## Evaluation

In order to continually improve and change your program to keep pace with the times, identify the processes that will help you evaluate each element of the communication program.

## Ongoing Education /Training

Identify a continuing program of education to make sure new hires are fully oriented to the disability management program. Quite often, after a major campaign, communication goes to the back burner. Make sure there is a formal process in place to continue the education with existing employees and new hires.

# Chapter 13

# PHYSICAL REHABILITATION

BRENDA RUSNAK

## INTRODUCTION

### Benefit of Physical Rehabilitation

More and more employers are beginning to realize the benefits of physical rehabilitation for injured employees. These benefits are consistent with those experienced when an employer takes the necessary steps for ensuring a safe work environment. Employers who take the necessary steps increase the likelihood that their workforce will remain healthy and safe from injury, and decrease the likelihood of incurring costs related to injuries and absenteeism. With costs of workers' compensation and disability insurance directly affected by employee absenteeism, employers are realizing they simply cannot afford not to become directly involved in the rehabilitation of injured employees. Physical rehabilitation should be considered whenever it is determined that a physical limitation is preventing work re-entry. For most injuries this can be determined very soon following the injury or incident.

Statistics drawn from the Workers' Compensation Board in Ontario reflect a typical pattern that employers can expect to see when an injury is sustained by a worker. If injured employees are off work for more than six months, the likelihood of them ever returning to work is only 50 per cent. After one year the likelihood is only 10 to 15 per cent, and after two years of being off work the likelihood of returning is close to zero per cent.

Based on these figures, no one can deny the benefit of any intervention that is capable of speeding the process of returning injured employees back to work. Physical therapy has the potential of speeding this process by:

1. Determining immediately following an injury, and at regular intervals throughout the life of a claim, whether individuals are physically capable of safely performing their job;
2. Speeding the healing process and ensuring that the injured tissue heals properly, thus avoiding the onset of a chronic condition; and
3. Ensuring that the individuals are kept in good overall physical condition while they are off work recovering from their injury.

## BENEFITS FOR EMPLOYERS, EMPLOYEES AND FAMILY PHYSICIANS

There is no benefit to anyone in delaying the process of returning an injured individual to a safe work environment as quickly as possible following an injury. Injured employees should receive proper attention, by family physicians and employers, to assist them in this process. Physical rehabilitation provides a mechanism for achieving this common goal.

Family physicians struggle with the responsibility of determining when their patients are capable of safely returning to work. Typically, the family physician relies on a medical history, a medical examination, sometimes diagnostic testing, and subjective information taken from the patient to make this very important decision. If they return the patients to work too soon (*i.e.*, before it is safe to do so), they run the risk of the patients re-injuring themselves. For this reason most family physicians tend to err on the side of caution when making recommendations for returning individuals to work. The result is that most employees will be advised by their family physicians to stay off work longer than is necessary for the safety of the employees. One of the major benefits of the employees' physical rehabilitation for a family physician is the provision of objective information verifying what their patients can and cannot do safely. This information allows physicians to make responsible decisions and to justify their decisions to all parties involved.

Most employees incurring an injury for the first time do not know what to expect from their employer and their family physician. It is, however, fair for them to expect that every effort will be made to return them to a safe work environment as quickly as possible. Their experience within the first few days following an injury sets the stage for the duration of their claim. An expectation for recovery cannot be expressed to an employee, by an employer, without a demonstration of commitment on behalf of the employer. Employers have a small window of opportunity to communicate their expectations to injured workers and to provide these workers with the necessary resources to achieve these expectations. For any physical injury, rehabilitation should be one of the resources available to employees.

The benefit to employers is obvious. There is considerable cost savings by determining if physical limitations are present as soon as possible following an injury, and if so, by assisting individuals in overcoming these limitations. Employers who ensure injured workers receive rehabilitation in a timely fashion experience lower insurance premiums, higher productivity, increased employee morale and fewer absent days over the total employment life of an individual.

## WHAT IS PHYSICAL THERAPY?

### Definition

Physical therapy (physiotherapy) is the process of assisting individuals to reach their highest level of physical function following an injury or illness.

### Who is Qualified to Provide Physical Therapy?

Registered physical therapists (physiotherapists) are professionals specifically educated and trained to provide physical therapy. Training involves a minimum of four years at a recognized university, during which time physiotherapists are educated in the basic health sciences, such as anatomy and physiology, and are taught specific physiotherapy assessment and treatment techniques. This education provides the skills necessary in identifying physical limitations and planning suitable recovery programs for individuals with physical limitations.

In order to be called a "Physical Therapist" or a "Physiotherapist" an individual must hold a degree in physical therapy. Unfortunately, the terms "Physiotherapy" and "Physical Therapy" are not protected titles, and therefore, any individual can claim to be providing these health services. It is, therefore, very important always to ensure that physiotherapy is being provided by a registered physiotherapist and not someone with lesser qualifications.

### How are Physical Therapists Regulated/Licensed?

Each province in Canada has a licensing body most commonly called the College of Physiotherapists. This is the body which develops and enforces the regulations which govern the profession. The Colleges of Physiotherapists have jurisdiction only over physiotherapists (*i.e.*, those with degrees in physical therapy) and therefore do not regulate the practices of non-physiotherapists claiming to provide physiotherapy.

It is common practice for physiotherapists to provide their registration number on invoices for services rendered. This is one way employers can ensure that physiotherapy services are being provided by registered physiotherapists. Caution must be exercised, however, as some physiotherapy facilities have been known to use the registration number of a physiotherapist who is not actually involved in the treatment of patients.

### Principles and Philosophies Behind Physical Therapy

Many people have the misconception that physiotherapy is synonymous with electrical modalities, massage or perhaps exercise. Physiotherapists use many tools both in the assessment and treatment of injured individuals. The skill of physiotherapists lies in their ability to assess an individual's physical limitations, plan a suitable course of action to return this individual to his or her highest level of function, and to implement that plan using a variety of techniques in which the physiotherapist has been specifically trained to provide.

"Assist" and "independence" are the key words in the definition of a physiotherapist. Physiotherapists should "assist", not "provide for" in their treatment. Any type of passive treatment techniques should be short-term and should eventually be terminated and/or replaced with self-administered techniques. The actual path that a physiotherapist chooses to move an individual towards independence varies depending on a number of different factors. However, there should always be a clear path with an identifiable end point in sight.

### WHERE DOES PHYSICAL THERAPY FIT INTO DISABILITY MANAGEMENT?

Several years ago rehabilitation was considered a last resort, initiated only if individuals remained off work several months or years following their injury. Today, a physiotherapy assessment, provided in the very early stages of a disability claim, is recognized as an essential element of any disability management process. A good physiotherapy assessment provides information on an individual's physical abilities and limitations, thus allowing the disability manager to develop a plan, in the early stages of recovery, for overcoming physical barriers that are preventing work re-entry.

Physiotherapy treatment has also gained credibility over the past several years as an effective means of speeding the recovery process, thereby shortening the amount of lost time from work and limiting the likelihood of the injury becoming chronic. It has been observed that when an individual is required to participate actively in a recovery program, often involving a graduated return-to-work initiative, the total lost time from work is reduced. In addition, employers are realizing the importance of ensuring individuals are in good physical condition before returning to work following an injury. Experience shows that one minor injury can lead to a repeated cycle of related and non-related injuries. Therefore, increased efforts are being made to keep employees fit while off work and to use the rehabilitation process as a means of teaching employees how to avoid further injury.

Caution, however, must be exercised in the selection of rehabilitation providers, as not all physiotherapists offer treatment which is consistent with the goals of disability management. Ineffective treatment can prolong the recovery process and foster a chronic dependence on the treatment provider. Although effective physiotherapy is an essential element of disability management, ineffective physiotherapy is of no benefit to this process.

## Assessment versus Treatment

Although a physiotherapy assessment must always precede physiotherapy treatment, a physiotherapy assessment does not always indicate a requirement for treatment. A good physiotherapy assessment should provide information to assist a disability manager in determining barriers to work re-entry that involve the physical nature of the injury and may offer suggestions on how these barriers can be overcome. Suggestions may include modifications to the individual's job, ergonomic alterations, requirements for further medical investigation and recommendations for physiotherapy treatment. With this information in hand a disability manager is in a good position to make appropriate decisions on the most effective means of managing the individual's return to work.

In some cases an assessment should lead to an immediate return to work if it is determined that the individual can safely perform his or her job. If physiotherapy treatment is provided following the initial assessment, reassessment should occur on an ongoing basis throughout treatment.

### When is Each Appropriate and what is the Benefit of Each?

It has been estimated that 80 per cent of all workers' compensation board (WCB) claimants are back at work within two weeks following their injury. Experience has shown that as much as 50 per cent of this population can be converted to non-lost time claims when a physiotherapy functional assessment is provided immediately following the injury. Many of these individuals do not require any time off as, on assessment, they are shown to be capable of safely performing their job or a modified job. Family physicians are more inclined to deny their patient time off for an injury when provided with a report that states that the individual was observed safely performing a number of job functions. Therefore, a physiotherapy assessment should always be considered whenever individuals have sustained a physical injury in which their ability to safely perform their job is in question.

Physiotherapy treatment, on the other hand, should be reserved for times when discrepancies exist between what individuals are capable of performing and what they are required to perform for their job. Treatment is a means in which these discrepancies can be resolved. Treatment should end once the individuals are performing at a physical level equivalent to their pre-injury level of function or when it becomes apparent that the individuals have reached their highest attainable level of physical function.

### A PHYSICAL ASSESSMENT

### Know what is Important

Before a physiotherapy assessment is requested, it is important to have a clear idea of what information the assessment provides and how this information will be used in managing the claim. The type of information required from an assessment depends largely on the stage of the claim. For example, a claim involving an individual who has been off work for several months may require an assessment which looks at that individual's complete physical condition; whereas, an assessment for an acute injury may only need to focus on the injury site. By having a clear idea of the type of information required from an assessment, the disability manager is in a better position to make an appropriate referral for an assessment.

There are various reasons for ordering a physiotherapy assessment. The most common reasons are:

1. To determine whether or not an individual will benefit from physiotherapy treatment, and if so, the type of treatment that should be provided and for how long;
2. To establish which job tasks an individual can safely perform and to place restrictions on those that are not safe to perform;
3. To determine an individual's ability to safely perform a specific job; and
4. To establish an individual's overall general level of disability.

It is important to communicate clearly the type of information that is required from an assessment and to obtain confirmation from the physiotherapist that the assessment he or she is about to perform provides this information. If the expectations of an assessment are made clear before the assessment begins, there is relatively little risk of being disappointed with the results. There is nothing more frustrating than having to pay a bill for an assessment which does not provide the required information.

## Overview of Different Types of Assessments

The following chart provides an overview of the most common types of assessments offered by physiotherapists.

| Type of Assessment | Description |
|---|---|
| Functional Abilities Evaluation (FAE) or Functional Capacity Evaluation (FCE) or Functional Capacity Assessment (FCA) or Functional Abilities Assessment (FAA) | This assessment is known by several different names and acronyms. It is the most comprehensive assessment available from a physiotherapist and involves testing an individual's ability to perform various basic physical tasks. It usually entails six to 10 hours of testing depending on the protocol being followed, and often takes place over two consecutive days. |

| Type of Assessment | Description |
|---|---|
| Ongoing Functional Testing | This assessment tests an individual's physical function over time. It involves an initial assessment of all basic tasks, followed by repeated testing of any task affected by the injury. It is typically provided along side physiotherapy treatment. |
| Work Tolerance Screen | This type of assessment involves the testing of specific tasks required to perform a particular job. |
| Musculoskeletal Assessment | This type of assessment examines the physiological restrictions or dysfunctions of an injured area, for example, joint range of motion and muscle strength. Functional testing is not a standard part of this type of assessment. |
| Musculoskeletal Assessment with Some Functional Testing | This is a musculoskeletal assessment which incorporates the testing of two or three key functional tasks required for the individual's job. |

## Functional Testing

Functional testing involves the objective measurement of an individual's ability to perform basic tasks such as lifting, sitting, standing, walking, squatting, reaching and pushing or pulling. In some cases, functional testing may also involve observed work simulation. If information regarding the employee's general level of disability is required, or recommendations for alternate or modified work are requested, it is imperative that all basic functional tasks are assessed, even those that are not required for the individual's pre-injury job. The testing of a number of basic tasks enables the assessor to estimate the overall disability level of an individual and to make recommendations for alternate employment. When functional testing is being done for the purpose of establishing treatment goals or determining if an individual is capable of performing one or more isolated activities, the testing may be limited to specific tasks.

Testing an individual's function can be achieved by observing the individual performing specific tasks under a controlled environment, or by using special apparatus which simulates the force and movement required to perform specific activities. Under both methods, observations are made to determine if, and when, an individual reaches his or her maximum capacity to perform a task. Some of the ways in which maximum capacity can be determined is through observing changes in body mechanics, watching for signs of muscle fatigue and monitoring the individual's cardiovascular tolerance.

Ideally, the best way to assess an individual's functional tolerance is to assess it on an ongoing basis. This can be done if the individual is receiving treatment on a daily basis, as it allows the assessor to observe changes in the individual's performance over a number of days. Factors such as muscle soreness and cumulative fatigue can then be considered in determining the individual's ability to function on an ongoing basis. If an individual is not receiving daily treatment, the assessment should be conducted over at least a two-day period. This will give the evaluator a more reliable measurement of performance.

The reliability and validity of the test procedure will be enhanced if a standard protocol for testing exists and if that protocol involves retesting or ongoing testing and a check system for consistency of effort. Functional testing should always use the pre-injury status of the individual to determine disability levels, not data taken from normal populations. In order to accomplish this the evaluator must be provided with a detailed description of the physical demands of the individual's pre-injury job.

## Musculoskeletal Assessment

A musculoskeletal assessment does not determine an individual's ability to perform specific tasks. This type of assessment provides information on an individual's physiological limitations such as range of motion and strength. These measurements are normally reported as a percentage of normal and, therefore, can be misleading in determining whether an individual is capable of performing his or her pre-injury job. For example, an individual may not require normal physiological movement to safely perform his or her job and therefore should not be held back from returning to work based solely on physiological limitations. At best, a musculoskeletal assessment provides a physiotherapist with a basis for function testing and/or a means of establishing suitable treatment goals when significant functional limitations do not exist.

## Information That Can Be Expected from an Assessment

The information that can be expected from an assessment is dependent on the type of assessment requested. The following chart provides an overview on the type of information that various assessments should provide.

| Type of Assessment | Information Provided |
|---|---|
| Functional Abilities Evaluation (FAE) or Functional Capacity Evaluation (FCE) or Functional Capacity Assessment (FCA) or Functional Abilities Assessment (FAA) | This type of assessment provides a comprehensive overview of the level at which an individual is functioning. Although this assessment determines if an individual requires physiotherapy and the type of treatment necessary, the real value of this type of assessment is in determining if an individual is disabled and to what extent. It can be used in litigation and arbitration and is generally reserved for proving that an individual is capable of returning to work.<br><br>The report produced from this type of assessment should provide details on an individual's ability to perform a number of specific tasks with an overall assessment of what the individual is capable of performing relative to their pre-injury job. |
| Ongoing Functional Testing | This type of assessment should be provided whenever an individual is involved in a work conditioning or work hardening program. It provides information that can be used to modify the treatment program as the employee progresses and allows work trials to be established based on what the employee is capable of performing at any point.<br><br>The report produced from this type of assessment should highlight the tasks that the individual is not able to perform at his or her pre-injury level and the change in performance over time. |

| Type of Assessment | Description |
|---|---|
| Work Tolerance Screen | This type of assessment is useful just prior to work re-entry or when moving an employee from transitional work to full-time regular work. |
| | The report from this type of assessment should provide details on the individual's ability to perform all required tasks of a specific job with an overall summary of his or her ability to perform the job on an ongoing basis. Any obvious barriers should be summarized with suggestions on how these barriers might be overcome. |
| Musculoskeletal Assessment | This assessment must be provided prior to implementing any physiotherapy treatment program. This assessment alone, however, does not provide sufficient information to plan a suitable treatment program if an individual has significant functional loss. |
| | The report from this type of assessment should highlight any significant physiological limitations or abnormalities. This report should also provide a diagnosis, treatment plan and treatment prognosis. |
| Musculoskeletal Assessment with Some Functional Testing | This assessment determines if physiotherapy is required and provides information that can be used to plan a suitable treatment program. |
| | The report from this assessment should highlight any significant physiological limitations and comment on whether these limitations are consistent with the individual's observed and reported functional limitations. This report should also provide a diagnosis, treatment plan and treatment prognosis. |

## How to Get the Most Out of an Assessment

In order to get the most from a physiotherapy assessment, the purpose of the assessment must be made very clear to the assessor. The above chart can be used to determine the type of assessment that should be requested depending on the information required. It is also important to provide the assessor with clear instructions on the type of summary information that should be provided in the assessment report. All too often disability managers are disappointed with either the lack of recommendations contained in a report or by the initiative taken by the physiotherapist to make recommendations that have not been requested. The information that a disability manager wants contained in a report will be dependent on what the report is to be used for and who will be looking at the report.

When a functional assessment is requested and the assessor is asked to provide his or her opinion on the ability of an individual to perform a specific job, it is imperative for the assessor to have accurate information on the requirements of the individual's job. If this information is not available in the form of a physical demands analysis (PDA), the information should be provided in as much detail as possible. It is often worthwhile to have the assessor conduct a PDA in conjunction with functional testing to ensure an accurate assessment of an individual's ability to perform a specific job.

## When Should the Various Types of Assessments Take Place?

A musculoskeletal assessment with some functional testing should take place immediately following an injury if there is any question as to the individual's ability to safely perform the job. The more information a disability manager has up front, the more effective he or she will be in managing an individual's return to work. Functional information is extremely valuable when it is obtained early in a disability claim. Most family physicians are unaware of the value of this information in reducing the overall cost of a disability claim. Therefore, the disability manager should not rely on the family physician to initiate this process. The disability manager must take the initiative to order this type of assessment as soon as an injury, which may involve lost time, is reported. The information obtained from such an assessment can effectively be used to force the family physician into making some early decisions regarding an individual's ability to return to work.

In most cases a full comprehensive functional abilities evaluation (FAE) is not required in the early stages of disability management. This type of assessment should be reserved when efforts are being made to close a file. If functional information is obtained early and used in the disability management process, the need for a full comprehensive FAE, to close a file, will be limited.

## How to Use the Information Provided from the Assessment

How the information contained in a report is used depends on why the assessment was ordered in the first place. If the purpose of the assessment was to determine if physiotherapy treatment is necessary and to obtain recommendations for a suitable treatment program, the report should be shared with the family physician, the employee and the physiotherapist who will be providing the treatment (if different from the physiotherapist who completed the assessment). In general, this type of report is well received by family physicians who are grateful for any information that helps them better manage their patients. Employees are also usually receptive to reviewing an objective report on their current condition and recommendations for recovery. If the recommended treatment plan is agreed upon by all parties, this report should become the basis for which physiotherapy is provided.

If, on the other hand, the assessment was requested in order to determine if an individual is capable of performing a specific job, the circulation of the report will most likely be restricted according to the instructions of the disability manager.

## TREATMENT

### When is it Necessary?

Physiotherapy treatment should be considered whenever individuals are incapable of safely performing their pre-injury job due to physical limitations. The goal of physiotherapy treatment is to assist the individuals in overcoming these physical limitations in order to be able to return to work in the same capacity as prior to the injury, or in some cases, to be able to return to temporary or permanently modified work.

### Different Treatment Approaches — Active versus Passive

A growing body of literature suggests that an "active" approach is far more effective in returning injured individuals to their pre-injury state than a "passive" approach. In general, an active approach uses a sports medicine model of keeping the individual fit while recovering from the injury. Under this approach the individuals' injuries are explained to them. They are told what to expect and are empowered to take charge of their own recovery. In addition, the focus of an active approach is on improving function rather than on reducing pain.

In contrast, a passive approach requires no active participation on the part of the injured individual and may result in prolonging the patient's recovery time.

Physiotherapists can have a considerable influence on the attitude of the individuals they are treating. A physiotherapist possesses the power to assist an individual to return to work quickly following an injury or to retard this process. Ensuring injured employees are receiving active physiotherapy treatment instead of passive treatment is therefore extremely important in order to avoid the risk of individuals developing a chronic dependence for treatment. Chronic dependence for treatment is usually coupled with long periods of time off work.

The key elements of an active treatment approach are pain management, education, and exercise. Pain management is a very important part of any rehabilitation program. In order to improve an individual's function, it is essential to demonstrate to that individual that his or her pain can be controlled. Acknowledgment by the physiotherapist of the individual's pain also contributes to the trust that individual will have in the physiotherapist. The injured individual must be assured by the physiotherapist that his or her pain is controllable and that it is a natural symptom of the injury. Showing an individual how he or she can, through various techniques, get pain relief proves to the individual that he or she does have some control over the recovery process.

Treatment for pain should be administered as long as the pain is significantly hindering the individual's function and may include a variety of techniques and electrical modalities. Passive pain management techniques should be replaced or discontinued as soon as practical with self-administered techniques (i.e., stretches, mobilizations, heat and ice). In general, treatment for pain should last one to three weeks. Some individuals may never require treatment for pain and therefore should not be given it, even in the early stages of treatment.

Education should begin immediately and continue throughout the length of any treatment program. In the early stages of rehabilitation, individuals must be given information regarding their injury. They also must be taught the basic principles of safe exercise progression. Later education should deal with general health and wellness concepts such as stress management, proper nutrition and injury prevention. In general, education should provide injured individuals with the tools necessary to take responsibility for their own recovery and future injury prevention.

Exercising an injured area is important during the healing process in order to restore or maintain muscle strength and normal joint function. In the acute stages of healing, passive movement and auto-assisted stretching exercises are useful in restoring normal movement and reducing pain. As the injury heals and the pain subsides, strengthening exercises should be provided for the injured area, as tolerated.

Aggressive exercises to non-injured areas of the body can be performed even during the acute stage, providing these exercises do not elicit increased pain to the injured area. Studies clearly indicate that exercise, even when it does not involve the injured body part, significantly increases the speed of healing.

General conditioning exercises should be provided for individuals who have been off work for more than four weeks or who are expected to be off work for an extended period of time. The goal of any active treatment program should be to restore individuals to their pre-injury physical function. This requires keeping the individuals physically fit while they are recovering from an injury.

## Injury Specific Treatment versus Work Conditioning Programs

All of the following three components — pain management, education and exercise — should co-exist in any physiotherapy treatment program (unless pain management is not required). However, the intensity and the degree in which each of these components is provided should be dependent on the length of time the individual has been off work or the expected length of time off work. If an individual has been off work more than four weeks, a more intensive program involving a full exercise conditioning program should be provided. This type of program is known as work conditioning. The total length of time an individual on a work conditioning program spends in physiotherapy should be between two and four hours a day. For an individual who is off work, the requirement to spend two to four hours in physiotherapy is alone one of the key elements which makes this approach so successful. Involving an individual in an activity that occupies a significant portion of the day prevents that individual from developing a passive lifestyle.

## Early Intervention

The majority of physical injuries begin as relatively minor strains or sprains. When these injuries are treated immediately they generally heal within four to six weeks without reoccurrence. Left untreated, any sprain or strain has the potential of becoming a chronic injury as a result of the formation of scar tissue.

When an individual is unable to work as a result of an injury, additional problems begin to manifest within two to three weeks of the injury. These problems are both behavioural and physical in nature and have the effect of complicating the original injury.

It is important that individuals do not fall into a passive lifestyle during the recovery period by developing routines that may in fact hinder the healing process. These passive behavioural patterns are very difficult to reverse and cause the individual to become physically deconditioned.

Early treatment intervention, therefore, should be a standard part of any disability management program. Of course, the very best results are attained when potential problems are identified and addressed before they become claims. True early intervention involves employee education and regular ergonomic job site reviews.

## WHAT TO EXPECT WHILE EMPLOYEES ARE RECEIVING PHYSICAL REHABILITATION

### Communication

Communication among all those involved in working with an injured employee is extremely important. In order to get individuals back to work and ensure that they stay at work following an injury, there must be a direct communication link with the physiotherapist, the family physician, the disability manager and the employer (if different from the disability manager). Good communication helps to provide everyone, particularly the family physician, with the type of information needed to make important decisions about the suitability of returning the employee to work. Direct communication is always preferable, but when this is not possible, due to time constraints or resistance by one party, it is often helpful to introduce a third party to assist in bridging the communication gap. Information regarding the individual's job, medical background and lifestyle must be shared amongst the medical professionals working with the employee if a multi-disciplinary rehabilitation program is being provided.

It is unfortunately the exception, rather than the rule, when a physiotherapist receives information regarding an individual's job requirements from an employer. Ideally, this information should be provided in the form of a PDA. A PDA is a descriptive report on the physical requirements of a specific job, normally prepared by an ergonomist. If a PDA is not available at the time of referral, a job description should at least be prepared and provided to the physiotherapist. Any job description provided by the employer is normally reviewed with the employee to ensure that a common understanding exists of what the job entails.

It is also important that the physiotherapist have a good idea of what, if any, transitional jobs are available to an employee. Very often, if good communication exists between the physiotherapist and the employer, the physiotherapist can assist the employer in modifying the individual's job in such a way that enables the employee to return to work early without risk of re-injury. The mistake that some employers make is to assume that if this type of information is communicated to the family physician, it reaches the physiotherapist. This usually does not happen and so it is essential that this information be communicated directly by the employer or the disability manager to the physiotherapist.

Communication is important even after the employee has been discharged from physiotherapy treatment. The physiotherapist should communicate an anticipated return-to-work date to the family physician and to the employer several weeks in advance in order to ensure there is ample time to reinstate the individual's job and complete any necessary paperwork. A co-ordinated effort by the employer, physiotherapist and family physician should provide the encouragement that may be needed by the employee during what can be a difficult transition from treatment to work.

Once the employee has returned to work the physiotherapist should be prepared to be on-call for minor problems that may arise. This transition stage often results in minor flare-ups which, if handled correctly, should not cause the employee any set backs. Often these situations simply require assurance or a reminder, by the physiotherapist, of coping mechanisms. If handled incorrectly, these situations can lead to the employee being advised by the family physician to take additional time off work.

## Functional Progress

It is essential that progress be demonstrated for any individual receiving physiotherapy treatment. The speed in which progress is experienced varies among individuals dependent on a number of different personal characteristics, including the type of injury. When progress is not evident, it is the responsibility of the physiotherapist either to change the treatment being provided or to make appropriate recommendations for alternate medical intervention.

At any point in time the physiotherapist should be aware of the employee's functional level and which physical functions do not meet the requirements of the individual's job. If progress is occurring, the individual's function, as it relates to the job requirements, should be improving. It is improvement in the individual's functional level, not his or her subjective account of pain, which should be used to determine if progress is being made.

## Transition Back to Work

Transitional work trials are essential to ensure that skills acquired during rehabilitation are transferred to the workplace. Work hardening centres, although appropriate in some cases, do not effectively reproduce a workplace setting for an individual. Important psychosocial factors such as work induced stress, work relationships and attitudes towards work cannot be reproduced in a clinical setting. Therefore, transitional work trials are important and can only be accomplished with good communication at every step of the rehabilitation process.

## WHAT TO EXPECT ONCE AN EMPLOYEE IS BACK AT WORK

### Maintenance Treatment versus Follow-up

There is an important difference between maintenance treatment and follow-up sessions. Maintenance refers to an ongoing need for the physiotherapist to maintain an individual at a specific physical level. It implies a need for continued treatment and therefore is not consistent with the goal of assisting an individual to become functionally independent. If a maintenance program is recommended, it should not require the involvement of a physiotherapist. The physiotherapist should instruct the individuals in the maintenance program and encourage them to carry out this program on their own.

Follow-up sessions, on the other hand, are pre-arranged dates in which the physiotherapist plans either to contact the individual or meet with the individual to ensure that continued progress is being made. Follow-up sessions are appropriate for individuals who return to work on modified or transitional work duties. They are intended to encourage independence while ensuring that progress is being made. If progress has not been made, the follow-up session should include a thorough investigation of why and provide suggestions for how this might be addressed.

## Long-Term Success

The success of rehabilitating an injured employee must not be based solely on the number of lost days the employee incurred during the initial injury, but rather on his or her return-to-work work performance and long-term injury re-occurrence rate. A truly successful case is one in which an individual returns to work and remains at work with no re-occurrence of the original injury and no new injury claim. When an employee is off work for a prolonged period of time, many physical changes as well as attitudinal changes occur. Rehabilitation, therefore, must address these issues and ensure that when the individual returns to his or her job, not only is the injured area functioning properly, but the individual is also in good physical condition and is motivated to return to work. When an individual's general wellbeing is not taken into consideration during prolonged absenteeism from work, the individual often returns to work only to sustain a second unrelated injury. This is often a result of the individual not being physically and/or emotionally fit to return to work. This unfit condition predisposes the individual to further injury. Attention must be paid, therefore, to the long-term effectiveness of various rehabilitation approaches, in order to evaluate if true success is being experienced.

## WHAT KIND OF CONDITIONS AND EMPLOYEES ARE APPROPRIATE FOR PHYSICAL ASSESSMENTS AND REHABILITATION?

Any type of physical injury is appropriate for physiotherapy. Although the most common types of injuries seen by physiotherapists are sprains and strains, more serious injuries such as fractures, dislocations, head injuries and burns also fall under the scope of physiotherapy.

Many disability managers are now facing a growing problem of how to deal with stress-related disorders and conditions such as chronic fatigue syndrome and fibromyalgia. Physiotherapy can be appropriate for these conditions, however, care must to taken to seek out physiotherapists who have the necessary skills and experience to deal with this special population.

## SELECTING APPROPRIATE PROVIDERS

There has been a substantial growth in the number of rehabilitation facilities over the past decade. Although disability managers now have a greater choice in treatment facilities, it has become more of a challenge to determine which treatment providers offer the best service and produce the best long-term results. Rehabilitation providers should be accountable to the disability manager, the patient and the family physician. This is a new concept for most health care practitioners, who in the past have viewed their only responsibility to be with the end-user or patient.

A trend that is beginning to develop among employers and disability managers is a movement to identify preferred service providers. Dealing with a select group of providers enables employers and disability managers to develop a close working relationship with providers who have a good understanding of the physical requirements of their jobs. It also provides disability managers and employers with a consistent quality of service and reduces the requirement to monitor continually a seemingly limitless number of rehabilitation facilities.

### The Physical Space

In order for a facility to provide an active treatment program, it must be equipped with at least some exercise equipment. The clinic does not have to have an entire gym, however, a few essentials should be present. These essentials include: at least one piece of cardiovascular equipment such as a treadmill, stationary bike, rowing machine or step machine; and at least two pieces of muscle strengthening equipment (ideally one for exercising the upper extremities and one for exercising the lower extremities) such as pulley systems or Nautilus-type equipment. In addition, if a clinic is claiming to be able to provide functional assessments, the facility must have, at minimum, equipment such as adjustable shelving units, crates and push/pull apparatus. To ensure that a clinic has sufficient equipment to conduct functional testing, the staff of the clinic should be asked to demonstrate how various physical tasks such as lifting, reaching, pushing and pulling are tested at the clinic.

The physical space should be inspected. Although the size of a clinic should not be a criterion for selecting an appropriate clinic, it is important to keep in mind that the space necessary to house the minimum required equipment is at least 1000 square feet. The physical space needs to be well ventilated and clean. The brightness of the facility should also be considered, keeping in mind that it is important that employees enjoy going to the clinic and that they perceive attendance at the clinic as a positive step towards their recovery.

## Qualifications of the Provider(s) and Conflict of Interest

In order to ensure that a registered physiotherapist is providing the physiotherapy treatment, the disability manager should always request the registration number of the treating practitioner. Unfortunately, being provided with a registration number does not guarantee that an employee will be treated by a physiotherapist. To ensure that employees are in fact being treated by a registered physiotherapist, the disability manager should inquire as to the ratio of physiotherapists to auxiliary staff (including kinesiologists) at the clinic. The ratio should never be greater than one physiotherapist for one auxiliary staff. In addition, the disability manager should insist on regular communication with the treating physiotherapist and that all reports be written by the treating physiotherapist.

Disability managers should also ensure that physiotherapy facilities in which employees are receiving treatment are not involved in any conflict of interest. A conflict of interest is generally classified as a situation in which a health care professional or a member of his or her family, a corporation owned or controlled by the professional or a member of his or her family, receives any benefit, directly or indirectly from a supplier to whom the professional refers his or her clients. This encompasses health care products, as well as professional services such as physiotherapy. Unfortunately, conflict of interest situations are on the increase in Canada, the most common being self-referral (*i.e.*, referring patients to facilities owned or partially owned by the referrer).

Studies that have addressed the issue of self-referral to physiotherapy facilities clearly indicate that conflict of interest situations result in a large number of individuals being referred for unnecessary physiotherapy treatment and a higher than average number of treatments being provided. This situation has the potential of increasing the total cost of disability, for the longer individuals are kept in treatment the longer they will be incurring days lost from work.

## Assessment and Treatment Protocols

Physiotherapy facilities that have documented assessment and treatment protocols generally have better treatment outcomes. Protocols should be based on a consensus of which treatment approaches are the most effective and substantiated by statistical data if available. When protocols do not exist there is no mechanism in place for providers to draw from a collective body of knowledge and experience.

## Commitment to Communicate

Communication does not mean writing lengthy reports when required to do so. It means successfully conveying information to another individual. Disability managers should choose providers who are committed to communication. When a physiotherapist resists communication it is often an indication that he or she has a different agenda, or that he or she has not been monitoring the employee's progress and therefore has nothing to communicate.

## Outcomes

Outcome data should be tracked by both providers and disability managers. When physiotherapists collect and analyze their own outcome data, it demonstrates an interest in self-evaluation and a commitment to continual improvement. Unfortunately, the analysis of data by an individual treatment provider or an individual disability manager in isolation does not provide a valid means of evaluating his or her effectiveness relative to others. It is therefore imperative for disability managers and physiotherapists to be able to access a data pool in order to give the data they are collecting some relevance. Providers who are unwilling to participate in the pooling of data and to be evaluated for the effectiveness of their treatment are people who should evoke suspicion. On the other hand, any providers willing to risk this type of exposure must be given the assurance that outcome data will be collected for the purpose of improving overall quality.

## Employee Satisfaction

If employees do not buy into the concept of participating in rehabilitation programs, disability management will not be successful. Employee satisfaction is extremely important to the success of any disability management process and therefore should be monitored closely on an ongoing basis. Employee satisfaction is one of the determining factors in long-term success. Any physiotherapist can demonstrate effectiveness in rehabilitating an individual and making a recommendation for that individual to return to work. However, it is the physiotherapists that are liked and trusted by employees who will be successful in returning employees to work and keeping them at work. A simple questionnaire sent out randomly to employees who have received physiotherapy coupled with outcome data will provide the disability manager with a very clear idea of which physiotherapists should be used.

## HOW TO DETERMINE IF PHYSICAL ASSESSMENTS AND REHABILITATION WILL SAVE MONEY

### Simple Cost Benefit Analysis on a Case-by-Case Basis

In order to use physiotherapy services effectively, it is necessary for a disability manager to assess, on a case-by-case basis, whether physiotherapy is likely to be effective in returning a particular employee to work. The ability to make such a prediction must be based on the experience of the disability manager, recommendations of the physiotherapist and historical data if available. The disability manager must decide if money spent on physiotherapy will result in decreased lost time. When physiotherapy is effective the total cost of a disability claim should be reduced. That is, the cost of physiotherapy should be outweighed by the savings in lost wages. Ineffective treatment leads to increased costs not only associated with the cost of physiotherapy but with the potential for increased lost wages if treatment results in a chronic dependence.

### General Cost Analysis

In general, a disability management program that involves early functional physiotherapy assessments decreases the total number of lost time claims and decreases the average number of lost work days per lost time claim. The reduction in lost work days appears to be a direct result of an early start on rehabilitation and, consequently, an earlier completion of treatment and return to work. Referrals made by physicians for physiotherapy are on average 45 days post-injury. When disability managers routinely refer employees earlier than 45 days, a decreased number of lost work days is experienced. The reduction in the total number of lost time claims appears to be a result of family physicians being prepared to deny time off work when an objective assessment proves that the employee can safely perform the job required.

Cost savings are also experienced by employers when recommendations for ergonomic improvements are followed and when there is an increased awareness of health and safety issues among employees. Savings appear to be the result of decreased occurrences in back injuries, and a levelling off of injuries such as repetitive strain injuries.

## Future Trends

Improvement through past experience is a concept that most people readily accept and experience throughout their lifetime. The key to *significant* improvement, however, is learning not only from one's own experience, but also learning from others' experiences and being able to apply new knowledge in a systematic way. The generally accepted method for accomplishing this in the rehabilitation industry is through the standardization of measurement tools and the development of treatment protocols and clinical practice guidelines. In fact, some observers have estimated that practice guidelines can save as much as 25 per cent of health care dollars. In order to experience any cost savings associated with the development and application of clinic guidelines, a system for information sharing must be in place. The challenges one faces in developing such a system lie in the collection and dissemination of information.

In order to draw valid conclusions and develop practice guidelines from pooled information, large quantities of information must be collected. The pooled information must be complete and accurate. Standards must be developed to ensure the information being collected is reliable. Also, the integrity of the data entering the system must be secured by the use of filters, which allow only data meeting certain criteria to be entered. The stronger the filter system, the more confidence one can place in the accuracy of the information that the system yields.

A system of data collection must also protect the confidentiality of the data sources. Individuals contributing to an information system must be assured that they will not be identified in the data pool. This includes protecting the identity of the patient, the provider, and in some cases, the payer. Providers will look for assurance that their data will not be used against them, but instead will be used in a constructive way to promote the best practices within their profession. While such a system may allow the performance of various providers and institutions to be compared against norms, provider profiling should always involve the provider and include information on procedure-specific outcomes, patient satisfaction, recurrence rates and complication rates.

The development of guidelines cannot be based solely on data but must also involve a thorough review of how clinic results are achieved and the "real life" limitations of clinical practice. This approach allows continual improvement in the quality of care being provided, supports the continual development of less expensive ways of providing this care, and ensures the acceptance of guidelines by rehabilitation professionals.

Of equal importance is a system that allows information to be disseminated to the providers in such a way that they can apply it in their clinical practice. Practice guidelines can only influence practice patterns to the extent that they are followed, and there is plenty of evidence that suggests that merely creating a guideline and disseminating it does not guarantee changes in practitioner behaviours. A printed guideline does not provide a dynamic system in which information about what's happening in the present can be compared to norms for a specific population. In other words, guidelines need to be accessible in *real time*. Ideally, practitioners should be able to access the guidelines before and during treatment in order to ensure that norms or benchmarks are being reached at each stage of the recovery process. Guidelines not only need to be meaningful, but readily accessible to providers, case managers and payers. The only way to accomplish this is through automation.

How much data is required to begin seeing patterns and developing practice guidelines? Population specific guidelines require a sample size of at least 10,000 files. Actuaries state that at least 120 months of data is needed that tracks people longitudinally before a good measurement of outcomes is possible. The bottom line is that the sample size of data is an important factor in determining how much confidence disability managers have in making decisions based on the data. In addition to the sample size, enough data must be collected on each individual file to produce population-specific outcomes and cost information. The more specific the data is to a particular population, the more effective the practice guidelines will be in assisting clinicians to use the best practices.

The collection of data and development of guidelines also have inherent benefits to disability managers. It is often difficult to predict if an individual will benefit from a particular type of treatment and at what point in the recovery process a specific treatment intervention should be initiated. Pooled data assists in this decision-making process by providing information on the likelihood that a particular patient population will benefit from a particular intervention. Disability managers will therefore be in a better position to select the most appropriate type of treatment on a patient specific basis. This will reduce the incidence of paying for treatment which turns out to be ineffective.

Information pooling also enables providers and disability managers to recognize specific areas of expertise. This process helps to identify practitioners who excel in the treatment of certain types of patients. Specialization will be a natural outcome within various professions as providers and payers begin to realize that certain practitioners are more successful than others with certain patient populations. This will strengthen the movement toward preferred provider arrangements as disability managers naturally seek out practitioners who are able to provide cost-effective high quality treatment.

The future offers significant opportunity for growth among physiotherapists and disability managers. The key to growth is information sharing. Dramatic advancements in technology over the past five years have made information sharing possible. All that is required now is a commitment among health care professionals to share information, on the basis that the information will be used for the purpose of improvement. Improvement cannot occur in isolation. Once information is readily available, those who choose to learn from it will reap the benefits. Those who choose to ignore it will not be able to keep pace in a very dynamic, quality driven, disability and health care environment.

# Chapter 14

# EMPLOYEE ASSISTANCE PROGRAMS

*WARREN SHEPELL, PH.D.*

## INTRODUCTION

Because employees are an organization's greatest competitive strength, when that element is weakened, business suffers. The far-reaching benefits of a quality Employee Assistance Program (EAP) are based on one simple equation: *strong employees equal stronger companies.*

From a business and employee relations perspective, building the right EAP for an organization is highly beneficial. When it is built to fully integrate and reflect the organization's core values and strategic objectives, and is characterized by unconditional respect in the treatment of all employees, it can be vital.

For any manager, supervisor or group head, a distracted or emotionally distraught employee poses a potential problem to the company's operations and bottom line. Very often, that employee turns out less than acceptable work — and less of it. Such a person tends to be late or absent more than the rest of the group. The troubled employee may spend a lot of time on the job worrying about his or her problem, and talking about it with others at work — taking up the supervisor's and co-worker's time. Sometimes, this employee begins to take sick days, frequently leading to a short-term disability claim. This trend has an adverse effect on the workload and on the morale of other employees. In some work areas where safety is a concern, a chronic personal problem, an addiction or distracted attitude can be dangerous for everyone, including customers and clients.

In its 1999 Statistical Report on the Health of Canadians, Statistics Canada reports that 12 per cent of adult Canadians (2.5 million people) suffer from depression that would benefit from treatment. Severity ranges from two weeks or more of functional impairment to severe clinical depression. It is estimated that between 10 to 15 per cent of all employees are troubled and distracted by a serious concern or problem in any given year. And an additional 5 to 10 per cent of the people in any given work force are preoccupied with some sort of personal problem causing some distractions that, if left unaddressed, can lead to a serious problem. Therefore, up to a total of 25 per cent of people at work will be experiencing a personal problem in any given year. The scope of the problem suggests heavy personal and professional costs. A 2001 study co-authored by Natacha Joubert, Mental Health Promotion Unit, Health Canada, Ottawa, concludes that the economic burden of mental health problems in Canada — both medically treated and not — is $14.4 billion annually. In the same year, Benefits Canada magazine reported that "Many companies are enjoying a return on investment of between 15% to 20% from their EAP dollars." If organizations are serious about cost containment and meeting corporate objectives, they must develop strategies to deal with employees experiencing these types of problems.

What are some of the issues facing employees and what kind of impact do they have on the organization?

**These five scenarios help explain:**

### 1. Addressing Personal Loss

Sarah had been working in her new job as customer service representative only three months when her mother died suddenly. When she told her manager, he expressed his sympathy and informed her about the company's bereavement leave policy. When she returned to work, Sarah found she couldn't concentrate. Her quality of work was slipping dramatically and, no matter how hard she tried, she could not capture her former level of energy, commitment and accuracy. Her colleagues began to resent Sarah for not pulling her weight and customers found she wasn't able to meet their needs. Within six months of Sarah's personal loss, the company itself had lost one good employee, a number of customers and the strong positive culture it had worked so hard to create.

> *With one phone call to her EAP, Sarah could have got help dealing with her grief and found ways to successfully cope at work through professional, short-term counselling, before it became a debilitating problem for her and her employer.*

## 2. Tackling Hidden Stress/Addictions

Jack had finally built his division's team to the point where he could take some time for himself. He gave his most senior manager, Norm, a promotion to department director and he began taking Fridays off for himself and his family. A few months after this organizational change took place, Jack started noticing a steady decline in productivity. His employees didn't seem to be as relaxed and open with him as they once were, and Norm didn't appear as confident. Then he happened to overhear two employees talking about Norm's drinking. His production and employee records confirmed what he suspected — production meetings had been cancelled, quality assurance practices had been ignored and employees were calling in sick on a more regular basis. Jack came across liquor bottles in Norm's office and when confronted with the situation, Norm resigned.

*With one phone call to his EAP, Norm could have found professional, confidential support to deal with the stress of his new work responsibilities and strategies to address his dependence on alcohol, before it became an unmanageable problem.*

## 3. Urgent Problem Resolution

Mary, CEO of a medium-sized manufacturing company, couldn't have been happier with the contributions of each of her senior staff. Things were moving along smoothly until Nadia, her manager of operations, got a call from her nanny, saying she'd quit. Mary expected Nadia back the next day, then the day after that but, because Nadia could find no one she knew or trusted to sit with her toddlers, she was away almost an entire week. Other employees were asked to cover, but they were neither comfortable nor capable doing so. Finally, Nadia was back on Monday, with a temporary babysitting agency in place, but was distracted on the job — making costly errors and spending too much time on the phone arranging permanent child care. Mary was fielding calls from customers, suppliers and staff looking for direction and wondering what happened to Nadia. She wanted to support Nadia, but had no solutions to offer. She simply had to demand Nadia's full attention, no matter what was going on at home.

*With one phone call to her EAP, Nadia could have received immediate support for her predicament and resources on reputable temporary and permanent child care in her area through the EAP's extended work/family service, before her family responsibilities interfered with her responsibilities at work.*

## 4. Management Support

As line manager, Carlos was frustrated with two staff members in particular. One was chronically late in the mornings, no matter how many warnings she got. Another had become uncharacteristically belligerent and was consistently failing to meet his quota. Together, they were disrupting the workplace and lowering productivity. By not addressing these issues, Carlos knew he was sending a dangerous message to other staff. But he simply wasn't sure what to do. He didn't want to threaten to fire them because he'd already been directed to reduce the company's high turnover rate. Nor did he feel comfortable asking anything of a personal nature to determine if they were facing problems at home. Carlos wanted to prove to his boss that he could handle employee issues himself, so didn't ask her advice. More time went by, more damage was done and, still, Carlos was both frustrated and undecided about what to do.

*If this company had an EAP in place, Carlos could have called his EAP account manager for support and advice in addressing employee performance issues, and could have comfortably made his own staff aware of EAP counselling for personal problem resolution.*

## 5. 24-7 Counselling and Information

Claude was the company's top performing salesperson. He travelled extensively, had boundless energy and could always be counted on to inspire others. Lately, though, Claude was finding job stress was getting to him, and had been for the past few months. He was feeling insecure about his targets — something he'd never felt before. He didn't have the same motivation, was nervous most of the time and concerned about his health. It was in Europe that he first felt stabbing abdominal pain. He panicked, not knowing if it was appendicitis or simply a bad case of indigestion. He had an important meeting to get to, but decided to close his laptop and start looking for immediate medical care close to his hotel. It took hours for the concierge to arrange for him to see a doctor, who told him there was nothing to worry about — it was probably a temporary stress-related illness. Claude had missed the big meeting, and the opportunity to close a huge sale. His stress level continued to climb, until he went on Short-Term Disability.

*With one phone call to his EAP, from anywhere in the world, Claude could have received immediate medical advice from a Registered Nurse through the EAP's telephone medical advice service. And he could have started dealing with his stress and mental health issues months earlier by tapping into confidential in-person, telephone or Internet-based counselling, well before Claude lost his confidence and the company lost the sale.*

## WHAT IS AN EMPLOYEE ASSISTANCE PROGRAM?

Employee assistance programs are designed to provide immediate help, including accurate assessment of the problem areas, and effective counselling to employees and their family members who may be experiencing personal or work-related problems, including addictions, personal, emotional, social, family and work/career-related difficulties.

Today, a large number of companies offer some form of EAP as an employee benefit, just as they offer medical or dental plans. An EAP provides quick access to help for troubled employees, in the form of highly qualified, specialized counselling, plus well-founded practical information and direction.

In most cases, EAP counselling is based on a short-term therapeutic model for prompt problem resolution. By discussing their problem(s) in a confidential and supportive environment, employees can expect to see improvements in their sense of well being and a reduction in the intensity of the problem. This often leads to improved work performance within a short period of time. Similarly, the supervisor can expect to see marked improvements in an employee's attitude and work performance, including attendance, within weeks.

EAP counselling can cover a broad range of personal and work-related problems. The many types of issues employees can bring to an EAP and the many ways an EAP can help employees and supervisors will be covered later in this chapter.

Figure 1

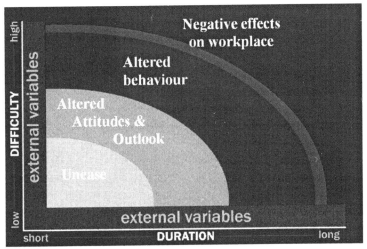

As figure 1 indicates, from a clinical perspective, the impact of an employee facing personal problems can be broken down into stages. On this graph, one axis reflects the difficulty of a problem and the other indicates the length of time a problem takes to resolve.

An employee's ability to function well in the workplace is also influenced by variable outside factors — such as poor physical or mental health, changes in the workplace, willingness to get help and accessibility of help. These factors can be problems in themselves and they can increase the difficulty and duration of all other personal problems.

The first stage an employee enters when challenged by a problem — whether it's financial hardship or marital discord or child care — is the state of unease, where it becomes increasingly more difficult to stay focused on the job. At this stage, information, support and resources may serve well to resolve the problem quickly and completely.

If no help is received, the employee can enter the next stage, with unease turning to altered attitudes and outlooks. Without intervention to help the employee identify and take responsibility for resolving the problem at this stage, an inability to focus on the job can turn to a high level of stress, a disregard for duties and costly errors.

If still no help is offered, the employee can enter the third stage, where individual behaviour is altered in degrees ranging from exhibiting uncharacteristic traits to erratic attendance to acts of aggression.

It's at this stage that the workplace — in addition to the employee — can truly suffer. Negative consequences from employee problems, such as disruption, inaccuracies, absenteeism and conflict, begin severely impacting the business — through lower productivity, poisoned morale, rising disability costs and workplace trauma.

Early intervention with support, information, resources and counselling through an EAP makes the difference between an employee resolving a problem at the first stage of unease, rather than the later stage of negative effects on the workplace. Having an EAP in place, even when an employee isn't facing problems can help strengthen the workplace by reducing the negative affects of variable outside factors.

## BACKGROUND

Originally, most forms of employee guidance and assistance were services administered from within the company. A high employee absentee rate or serious alcohol abuse were the most common reasons for counselling in the earlier days. Most sessions of this kind were held at the workplace, in an office or area where some privacy was ensured. Very often, an employee who had been treated successfully for alcoholism returned to the company to become a resident counsellor. Companies that did not have any sort of counselling very often fired the employee facing difficulties or the employee went on short- and then long-term disability.

## A NEED THAT GREW ... AND GREW

It soon became apparent that the underlying causes for deteriorating performance or chronic absenteeism were many and varied. Company counsellors often found themselves trying to give assistance that was either beyond their capabilities or beyond the practical limits of their job function. For example, what does one say to an employee who has witnessed an accidental death at the plant and who now often stays away from work because of fear and high anxiety levels? What words can be offered to the faithful 15-year employee who suddenly starts taking afternoons off to sit with a daughter who has a painful, lingering form of cancer? How does one provide on-the-job assistance to someone whose early childhood experiences are just now beginning to affect his or her marriage and family relations?

In the past, many companies believed the words "you're fired" were their only solution to some of these workplace problems. However, dismissal meant that employees who once were high performers were gone for good. Also, when faced with the abrupt firing of a colleague, remaining employees often became fearful, resentful and less productive. This usually led to a "them" and "us" mentality that created more discontent in the workplace and lower levels of productivity and morale.

To their great credit, many of those early in-house counsellors struggled to perform a service for employees with little corporate support. Those who were successful were able to change long-held attitudes of both management and labour. They extended their companies' EAPs by recognizing that a wider range of personal problems was affecting employee performance. In some cases, organizations would make the decision to hire a professionally educated and clinically experienced counsellor. There are still a few fine EAPs being administered in-house today that are considered to be effective and professionally staffed.

## EMPLOYEE ASSISTANCE PROGRAMS TODAY

In the late 1970s, an EAP was provided in Canada for the very first time by a group of professional counsellors who were employed by a professionally based company other than the employer organization. It was the start of off-site EAPs. Since then, external EAP services by independent firms have become far more numerous than in-house EAPs. Today, the majority of EAPs implemented in companies are being offered by independent, external EAP providers whose only business is supplying EAP services. One of the largest EAP firms in the country is Warren Shepell Consultants, which has been providing EAP services since 1979.

External EAP services offer one major benefit over internal EAPs: confidentiality. The counselling locations are away from the workplace. No one at the company ever sees employees going for their appointments. The counsellors are not employed by the employer and, in fact, company management never learns which employees make use of their EAP unless, of course, the employee has decided to reveal his or her EAP participation. Counselling files of the employee are kept away from the workplace and the employer and off-premises EAPs allow for family members to easily access the EAP services. Very few family members would feel comfortable coming to their spouse's or parent's workplace for counselling.

Because deeply personal problems cannot be left at the door when the employee enters the workplace, they are a significant cost to Canadian business and industry. This is where an organization can make a difference, by providing an EAP service to its employees. This is where an EAP provider can make a difference by delivering quality counselling and problem-solving to the employees who need and use the service. This is where a supervisor can make a difference by promoting the EAP services to his or her employees.

## WHAT DOES AN EMPLOYEE ASSISTANCE PROGRAM OFFER?

### Services for the Organization

A quality EAP helps strengthen an organization on two levels: by providing services to promote employee wellness and by providing expert consultation and services to promote management effectiveness and overall organizational health. Below are some of the elements that can be integral to group support services:

**What is a quality EAP?**
- Accessible
- Voluntary
- Anonymous
- Confidential
- Comprehensive
- Ethical
- Client-focused
- Held to the highest professional standards

- Employee Assistance Program management;
- Consultation with management on employee-focused programs;
- Monitored employee referrals;
- Management training and consultations;
- Harassment policies and issues;
- Workplace violence services;
- Workplace change and transition services;
- Conflict management and dispute resolution services;
- Substance abuse program;
- Wellness initiatives;
- Disability management program;
- Stress management program;
- Coping with change;
- Mediation.

Having an EAP in place allows an organization to address its humanitarian as well as its "bottom line" accountabilities. By implementing an EAP for employees and their family members, an organization and its management can truly say, "We care about you and your family. We know that, from time to time, you or your family will run into personal difficulties and we want to make sure you have quick access to excellent professional counsellors who can help."

Through early intervention, employee issues do not become big and complex problems, which are much more likely to lead to lower productivity, chronic absenteeism and high health care and disability costs.

Group services that help a business improve its organizational health across the board can make a significant difference in its strength and future success. An EAP provider, with solid knowledge and experience in workplace issues, will be able to provide far-reaching support in maintaining a safe and healthy workplace. For example, violence in the workplace is an issue no business can ignore. In some cases, for federally regulated industries in some provinces, it's the law. An EAP provider should be a source of information around legislation for issues such as these, but also serve as an effective resource.

In the fall of 2000, the Canadian federal government passed new legislation for prevention of violence in the workplace and the protection of employees. These amendments to Chapter Two of the Canadian Labour Code require the employer to create a "safe" environment for all employees.

The legislation is a direct result of the Coroner's inquest into the tragedy that occurred at Ottawa-Carleton Transpo in the Spring of 1999, when a former employee shot six former colleagues and then killed himself. This episode of workplace violence prompted the government to take the steps it did.

Through consultation and the provision of expert advice and services, an EAP should enable the employer to set templates for:

- high standards in a code of conduct at work;
- zero-tolerance policy and procedures for all employees;
- education and training of managers, supervisors and all staff on the ramifications of zero-tolerance;
- awareness sessions on the notion of what constitutes a respectful workplace;
- sourcing about liability issues regarding national and provincial legislation.

A model EAP should be a source of expert consultation regarding recommendations, training and education, policy formulation and procedural matters regarding issues, such as workplace violence, that impact the organization as a whole.

## Services for Supervisors

Supervisors are in the role of managing people because the company believes they can inspire others to work well in a team and to give their best. However, supervisors are not selected for the position because they have in-depth counselling expertise or because they are able to know instinctively what to do to help troubled employees. When an effective EAP is in place, most of these burdens are removed from a supervisor's shoulders. The EAP gives supervisors the opportunity to help employees obtain professional help quickly and efficiently to resolve their problems. By getting employees help when they need it, supervisors gain more time to guide work performance by practical advice, demonstration and example.

Author Paul M. Roman, Ph.D., Director for the Center for Research on Deviance and Behavioral Health, reports in *Workplace Managed Care Research: Successful EAP Models*, that companies with EAPs in place find:

- Depression is lower among their employees;
- Self-esteem is significantly higher among their employees;

- Job satisfaction is significantly higher among their employees.

By improving employee wellness, an EAP helps make the job of supervisor easier. The supervisor becomes more efficient and, as well as the employee, benefits from increased wellness. They tend to take home fewer problems and have more time to relax.

In addition to providing training and consultation around all workplace and management issues, an EAP provider offers specific training programs for supervisors and managers to help them fully understand the practical aspects of the EAP and how to use it for the employees' and the company's benefit.

These programs are designed to help managers recognize cases where employee counselling would be useful. They also show ways to help increase the acceptance and use of EAP benefits among employees. It is important to remember that employees cannot be forced to use an EAP, but there are many ways a supervisor can make them aware of the services and benefits available to them.

## Services for Employees

The following is an overview of the kind of help employees can obtain from today's most advanced EAP companies. This section of the chapter is deliberately detailed so that supervisors can help their employees appreciate the wide-ranging experiences and events that lead to a problem. Very often, co-workers, supervisors and managers dismiss others' problems when they hear about them. Even families and friends can do the same thing. If the problems were not important to the individual, they would not have been identified as problems in the first place.

A high quality EAP can achieve significant success rates within a relatively brief period of time using a short-term counselling approach. Following is a discussion of the strategies and approaches that may be used to address some of the problems.

## Personal/Emotional Problems

In our experience, close to 20 per cent of employees accessing EAP services are those with personal problems. Employees who are experiencing emotional problems connected with impatience, frustration, anxiety, fears, worries and disappointments, sadness, depression, panic attacks or loneliness can feel so "stuck" or lost in their feelings that their preoccupation becomes detrimental to their current relationships, including those at work. As well, their job performance usually deteriorates.

Very often these emotions stem from the harsher experiences of life. These include such things as early sexual abuse, parental neglect, loss of loved ones, rejection, bereavement, relocation, demotion, job loss, uncertainty and change.

## Marital and Other Close Relationship Problems

Of all the employees to contact their EAP, in our experience close to 25 per cent seek help for relationship problems. When an employee's primary relationships are threatened or in disarray, work performance, including attendance, is likely to fall from priority.

EAP counsellors can help employees (and their partners) resolve such issues as jealousy, anger, household spending, sexual politics, poor communication, personal differences, obnoxious habits, mood swings and domestic violence.

Counsellors can help clear up misunderstandings and resentments before the rift between the couple becomes serious. However, EAP counsellors work with the couple any way the trio feels is most effective; either to help enhance their future relationship, or to prepare the most stress-free ways to face the challenges of living apart.

## Family Turmoil

Close to 17 per cent of all EAP users seek advice about problems within the family. These problems usually centre on several issues: opposing ideas about child-rearing including disciplinary methods, sibling rivalry, second marriages, family integration problems, strong differences of opinions between teens and parents (including runaway threats), school concerns (school choice, learning problems, low-grades, bullies, teacher/parent relations), behavioural and/or developmental concerns, the problem child or problem parent, abuse (physical, verbal or emotional), encroachments of relatives, friends, and career or family privacy.

Effective EAPs have counsellors on staff who are specifically trained to resolve a broad range of family issues.

## Stress and Depression

Unavoidable situations that are commonly experienced as stressful are among the toughest, most persistent problems in today's workplace. Stress is being caused by the increasing rate of change in today's work and home environments. Introducing its book *Stress at Work*, The National Institute for Occupational Health & Safety states that, "The nature of work is changing at whirlwind speed. Perhaps now more than ever before, job stress poses a threat to the health of workers and, in turn, to the health of organizations."

Balancing all the demands placed on employees—not only in the workplace but also from family, community and financial obligations—can be an additional source of stress. When the demands of childcare and eldercare are factored in, coping becomes even more difficult.

According to Health Canada, 75 to 85 per cent of care received by seniors in the community is provided by family and friends. Statistics Canada reports that 50 per cent of caregivers agree that helping others has caused them to have repercussions at work.

This commitment is taking a toll on caregivers. Health breakdown is the most severe change that caregivers experience, including lack of sleep and other physical and psychological symptoms of stress.

One employee interviewed by an EAP counsellor said that even taking a vacation was now a stressful event. "You must work longer hours to clean up before you go, and longer hours to catch up when you get back," she said. In addition, the advance of communication technologies frequently prevents us from the benefits of a true vacation while on vacation.

When employees seek help in this area, the EAP counsellor first determines their specific causes of stress. The counsellor assesses the employee's coping skills as well as reactions that actually may make coping more difficult, such as excessive alcohol use or overeating.

The EAP counsellor can then help the employee manage the revealed stress areas in several ways. The counsellor discusses effective changes in attitude and lifestyle that help to avoid stress situations or to acknowledge and cope with those events that usually trigger stress reactions.

Through counselling, employees discover those events they can do something about, such as rearranging priorities, eliminating some self-imposed obligations, and becoming appropriately assertive in those situations where the employee can develop some control over his or her life. Employees are taught to recognize times of personal stress overload and how to deal with them by using a variety of practical techniques. In situations when employees have no influence or control, EAP counsellors help employees deal with their stress reactions directly in such a way that employees improve their stress-coping skills.

One EAP firm has introduced a self-help, Internet-based stress management program called Mastering Stress. Employees can help manage their stress by logging on to the interactive program and, at their own pace, determining the stressors in their lives and possible solutions. The 30-day program is based on well-researched data and is designed to be user friendly.

## Adjustment to Work Counselling

One result of today's rapid changes in technology and corporate structure is a heightened level of employee concern about job security. Since many organizations have rationalized production and management, these concerns can be well founded. In some families, one or both wage earners may be seeking new employment. Teenage family members may be having serious doubts about their future opportunities, as well as the earning potential of their education. EAP counselling can help people make better informed, more realistic decisions about their work futures.

Counselling, in addition to providing highly useful vocational assistance, will help people adjust to current changes within the company, suggest ways to acquire new work skills, and direct employees to the appropriate departments and their staff for internal assistance. Also, EAP counsellors can be very helpful for employees adjusting to geographical moves and/or career changes.

EAP counsellors also help employees address problems with co-workers, supervisors and those being supervised. Conflict with co-workers can be an ongoing source of stress and disruption in the workplace, and counselling can help one or both parties move in a positive direction.

## Addictions — Counselling and Treatment

A small but significant number of employees regularly use alcohol and/or other drugs to excess. In our experience, four to six per cent of employees using EAP services seek help with an alcohol or drug-related problem. Untreated addictions account for huge losses of work time and productivity, as well as incurring enormous insurance costs for both short- and long-term disabilities and health-care costs.

Abuse of alcohol, tobacco and prescription drugs has created hazards to both safety and health in many workplaces. In some instances, the problem is so serious that many safety-sensitive companies (transportation, steel production, heavy metal working, pulp mills, petroleum plants, *etc.*) have adopted drug-free policies backed by drug testing programs.

But the greatest losses of all are borne by the user. Untreated addictions lead to loss of friends, family, possessions, career, and ultimately one's own health.

## Treatment of alcohol and drug addictions

An effective EAP provider employs counsellors who are trained in addiction counselling. These people are trained to assess the individual's degree of substance misuse and/or abuse and gauge the severity of the associated problems.

Because of possible serious consequences to the employee and others, this is one of the few times, depending on the policies of each organization, when the individual may be directly confronted with a hard choice: seek help with the addiction or face dismissal. Later in this chapter, the monitored referral procedures will be explained, outlining how a supervisor can increase the likelihood of an employee seeking help through the EAP.

An EAP has specialists who know the best ways to motivate alcohol and drug abusers to address their addictions successfully. Then, the EAP counsellor maintains regular after-care contact during the following year to reinforce, resolve and help prevent a relapse.

Similar employee performance problems and related organizational costs are experienced with addictions other than substance abuse. They include gambling, eating and sex. Again, an EAP will have counsellors and access to specialists in all types of addictions in order to successfully treat the addiction.

## Fast Response to Employee Trauma

In addition to working with employees who have developed problems over time, there are occasions when EAP counsellors need to provide support and intervention just after a major incident has occurred. This can have lasting effects on employees, customers and the "brand".

There is a wide range of trauma-causing events that can occur in the workplace, on the streets or at home. These include being a witness to murder, suicide and accidental death, or being a witness to or unwilling participant in a robbery, rape, assault, bombing, fire, hostage-taking or accidental dismemberment. About two-thirds of all people involved in these and other terrifying events develop some form of post-traumatic stress if they do not receive immediate psychological counselling.

Many people will deny the depth of the personal shock they experienced and belittle its ongoing impact in their lives. This denial leads to a general numbing of their emotions and feelings. They experience a variety of symptoms:

- listlessness and fatigue;
- loss of trust in others;
- suspicions and paranoia;
- loss of appetite;
- reduced mental powers and ability to concentrate;
- loss of sex drive;
- below-normal performance levels in all areas of life.

Victims and witnesses often begin having unwanted recall of the most vivid images connected with what happened in the form of flashbacks and nightmares.

When a traumatic event occurs in the workplace, untreated employees can develop any or all of the above symptoms. As a result, they tend to avoid being where the tragedy took place. Increased absenteeism, decreased output and eventual resignation are common outcomes. In all cases, the sooner people are treated for trauma, the better. That is why an EAP Trauma Response Team should be ready for immediate action, 24 hours a day, any day of the week. In the case of workplace trauma experienced by a group of people, the team should hold its first counselling session, a guided group session, within 24 hours.

Employees who are traumatized are encouraged to talk about the incident and to release their feelings of shock, horror, fear and disgust. Those most closely involved can do this with a skilled and sympathetic listener who has been specially trained and certified by the National Organization for Victims' Assistance (NOVA). NOVA is the only licensing body for trauma intervention and treatment in North America.

Another counselling session will be held for all employees who work at the trauma site. This group "airing" gives immediate victims another opportunity to express themselves about the event. It helps to normalize their fears and terrors, due to group acceptance. This session also helps to settle things in the minds of co-employees who were not present. They too have a need to hear all the details and to discuss them.

Those who continue to suffer trauma symptoms after the first series of discussion treatments are advised to enter one-on-one therapy with a member of the EAP trauma team.

Other types of traumatic events that often require treatment are downsizes, corporate restructuring and geographic relocations. These may not be as dramatic as physical violence, but they can leave deep and lasting scars.

## EXTENSION OF EMPLOYEE ASSISTANCE PROGRAM SERVICES

Sometimes the problem that doesn't require counselling can be just as distracting to an employee, and just as disturbing. Our ability to concentrate on work — or even to show up to the workplace — can often be compromised by family and personal obligations. Work/Life Consultation Services have an integral role to play in an EAP because they provide timely solutions to these problems. Professional and up-to-date services — covering the topics that are most relevant to today's employees — are most conveniently accessed through a central toll-free line. The cost of these extended EAP services and any advice the employee receives may be included in the overall EAP cost paid by the organization.

### Legal Consultations

In our experience, the average employee's knowledge of the law—and of the help lawyers can offer—is extremely low. On average, 48 per cent of employees encounter legal problems that cause them to take some time off work. A legal consultation service accessed through a company's EAP can save individual employees time, as well as hundreds or even thousands of dollars. The employee can obtain free legal information and clarification over the phone, given by a fully-qualified lawyer with solid experience in the caller's type of problem. A single call to a qualified lawyer enables the employee to determine whether or not there really is a legal aspect to the problem, and what to do about it.

These free advice areas include domestic violence, separation, divorce, summons/warrants/subpoenas, wills and trusts, motor vehicle accidents, personal injury, and consumer protection. For an EAP service to remain responsive to both the organization and the employee, *employment legal concerns cannot be addressed through this service.*

If follow-up legal work is required, the EAP legal counsellor supplies a list of law firms in the caller's area that are well qualified to handle the case. In some plans, if one of the law firms on the list is consulted, the first 30 minutes of the initial meeting are free of charge. If subsequent meetings are required, a 25 per cent fee reduction applies.

## Financial "Problem Area" Consultations

Each year, many employees need expert advice about a financial crisis situation. Many EAPs offer rapid telephone access to this type of help.

There are three major areas where financial emergencies often occur:

- debts and credit problems;
- estate situations;
- termination of employment.

In each case, the general analysis of the caller's problem, useful information about it, and sound budget planning is immediately available from a highly-qualified financial firm of accountants and financial planners. Regular EAP counsellors are usually not qualified to provide this financial advice. There is no cost to the employee, and the service is included in the overall EAP costs to the employer.

Of course, some financial woes are so complex they can only be resolved through an ongoing series of face-to-face consultations. On the other hand, some employees who are financially comfortable seek non-urgent help in planning rosier fiscal futures. In both of these cases, the employee is offered a choice of nearby financial planners who can provide well-qualified, in-depth personal service at an hourly rate.

## Dependent Care Counselling and Information Services

Most adults in society are caught between two sets of responsibilities. Even though both members of the working couple have to work to maintain home and family, they must provide full care and support for their children. In our experience, many of these working couples (over 50 per cent of them) also feel responsible for the care of their aging parents. This two-way stretch can lead to almost intolerable levels of stress, deep preoccupations while at work, frequent telephone check-ups or arrangements, and regular absences from the workplace. It is very difficult to stem such activities, because doing whatever it takes to maintain the family is exactly why most employees are working.

Many companies understand this deep-rooted feeling and have included dependent care services in their EAP packages. These services need to be offered by specialists trained and qualified in areas around parenting, childcare and eldercare. Traditional EAP counsellors should not offer them. Both types of service have three levels:

1. An employee can call the EAP number to discuss a particular problem with a skilled dependent care expert. For example, "We changed to a day care centre that is nearer to work, but since then, Johnny has started wetting the bed again. What can we do?"
   Or
   (a) "My mother-in-law won't move from her own home, but we spend most of our weekends keeping house for her. And I've decided I'll move out if she moves in with us. Could you help us iron this out?" or
   (b) "My dad refuses to wear a hearing aid, but he's become dangerously deaf. Will counselling help?" or
   (c) "My wife and I have so many family matters to handle, we're starting to quarrel about them. What can we do to relieve the pressure?"

2. Once the problems have been talked out, the counsellor helps the employee gain a clear idea of the sort of outside assistance needed to make life easier. The EAP counsellor then arranges for an information package to be delivered to the employee. The package will be based on a local search of the type of privately operated services required, and will contain details about a number of possible providers.

3. Although there is no charge for assessment, consultation and information, the employee does pay for any service that the employee engages beyond the EAP. The EAP counsellor can provide immediate support and education to employees and access to the latest resources on topics related to all life stages, from pre-natal to palliative care, such as:
   (a) Childcare: day care; nursery schools; in-home and nanny care; after-school supervision and care; programs for children with special needs, summer care.
   (b) Eldercare: in-home support services; seniors' accommodations; senior day care programs; seniors-helping-seniors programs; geriatric health services; long-term care facilities, and social and educational programs.

(c) Parenting: infertility; new parent support; infant and child development; parenting challenges; teenage issues; education options; health concerns.

## Telephone Medical Advice

Health advice and information by telephone around-the-clock. Providing 24-hour access to a registered nurse is a service that informs and advises people who need help concerning common general health problems such as fever, minor rash or itch, cough, headaches, sore throat, stomach ache, diarrhea, vomiting, ear-ache, and general aches and pains.

The service gives employees and family members quick, 24-hour-a-day telephone access to one of many registered nurses. Each nurse has over five years of work experience in a clinic or hospital. These nurses also have emergency room or intensive care experience.

As an EAP service unit, the nursing team is supported by the expertise of a medical doctor with extensive experience in emergency care. The health care information and guidelines that can be accessed through the nursing group were developed by a panel of medical doctors and are regularly reviewed by these MDs.

The potential for this type of service to reduce lateness, absenteeism and poor concentration at work is enormous. Approximately 20 per cent of all Canadians visit a hospital emergency ward in any given six-month term. Forty per cent of these visits are non-urgent. In non-urgent cases, a competent nurse could have handled the health problems over the telephone.

## Home Care Services

The service is set up to allow employees to call the EAP number for access to home care professionals who are available round-the-clock for immediate telephone assessment and consultation. Home care professionals address emergency and non-emergency childcare, eldercare, nursing and other homemaking service needs right in the employee's home. The service provides everything from simple household help to complex nursing care.

In emergency situations where the employee needs to be at work but needs someone to provide home care to a family member, an appropriate caregiver can arrive at the employee's home within a one- to three-hour time frame.

## Accessibility and Responsiveness

Employees who most need to reach out for help are often the ones who find it hardest to do so. As vital as providing professional counselling and resources to those who call into an EAP is the mandate to make that care as accessible as possible. Innovative systems and a variety of gateways should bring services directly to employees and their families — no matter what country they're in or what time of day or night they need help. The following components heighten the level of accessibility and responsiveness in an EAP:

- 24-hour call centre;
- Centralized appointment scheduling;
- Counselling access options;
- Counselling environment.

## 24-Hour Call Centre

Professional counsellors should be available to respond to an employee's *first call* — 24 hours a day, 365 days of the year. A bilingual toll-free hotline staffed by experts who can either handle a crisis if the call is urgent or book an appointment immediately is fundamental both from a clinical and a customer service point of view.

The optimal scenario would be to offer a 24-hour seamless, one-step process for access to all counselling and consultation services. In the interest of time and confidentiality, employees should not expect callbacks to book appointments, or the use of answering machines or answering services. Call centre technology should be advanced, dependable and have 24-hour back-up systems. English and French language lines, and telephone devices for the hearing impaired should be available, and service standards for average speed and call abandonment should be well-above average.

## Centralized Online Appointment Scheduling

To ensure a client-focused approach, an appointment scheduling system should allow call centre staff to access all counsellors' schedules. An acceptable standard of appointment booking is *same-day in-person counselling sessions for urgent matters and within five working days for non-urgent situations.*

## Counselling Access Options

Long-term problem resolution through short-term counselling is an attainable goal that can be achieved for a greater number of employees when a greater number of access formats are offered. The format is ultimately dictated by clinical needs, but for employees considering counselling, a choice of formats can lessen or eliminate barriers to access.

Traditional face-to-face counselling is a vital format that should be made widely available to staff in all locations. Maintaining a large network of salaried as well as affiliate counsellors provides excellent and dependable coverage for clients with a widespread workforce. Having the structure in place to quickly match the network to growing employee populations is an important feature and ensures that, no matter where employees are working, they can access consistent, standardized, quality in-person counselling services.

Telephone counselling establishes an ongoing, short-term relationship between the client and one counsellor and is an excellent service for employees who find this method the most comfortable choice in resolving personal problems. It's becoming increasingly popular as it offers a high level of convenience, flexibility, anonymity and ease of use.

New and innovative ways to connect employees to counselling is important today. One EAP firm has recently introduced Internet-based e-counselling, which has proven to be another excellent choice for employees who find they express themselves well in writing and prefer to communicate with their counsellor in a text-based manner, rather than face-to-face. The ability to log on anywhere there is Internet access allows an employee to gain the same benefits as they would from any form of professional counselling, with the additional capability of rereading their conversations with the e-counsellor whenever they feel the need to review or reconnect. If an employee's situation is complex, or if he or she is facing deep emotional problems, online counselling may not completely address their needs, and the online counsellor should always be ready to recommend an alternative form of help.

## Counselling Environment

The quality of the EAP service environment, as dictated by the Employee Assistance Society of North America (EASNA), is:

- Safe;
- Clean;

- Handicap accessible;
- Free of fire hazards;
- Child friendly;
- Professional.

The environment should reflect a high level of inclusion and accessibility. Counselling services should be available in the language of choice for the employee; diversity should not only be tolerated but welcomed; and human rights and safety should be respected above all else. In the case of face-to-face sessions, a maximum 30-minute travel time from the employee's home or workplace to the counselling location is an acceptable standard.

## WHO IS ELIGIBLE?

Once an EAP begins to serve a company, its services are freely available to every defined employee. A broad range of these services is also free to members of each employee's immediate family. These include spouses, children, and stepchildren—usually the same people that are covered by the employee's company benefits such as the medical or dental plan.

## MAKING SURE EMPLOYEES KNOW ABOUT THE EAP

EAP providers encourage organizations to publicize the program. Initially, orientation sessions are offered to the entire workforce group by group. These sessions are delivered by the professional staff from the EAP provider. Brochures, printed pieces and other communication materials that describe the full range of EAP services are always freely available to all employees. Employees should also have ready access to an informative videotape presentation of specific EAP services. Some EAP providers will have produced and personalized a video specific to the services they offer. These tapes contain real-life examples and encourage the viewer to follow the same easy steps of the EAP to resolve similar problems. Managers should encourage employees to take the tape home and discuss it with others in their households. Managers could also show the tape at staff meetings.

Well-publicized EAP "Wellness Information" workshops are held at regular intervals. These enable interested employees (and managers) to become better informed about health-promoting lifestyles and various services provided by their EAP. The EAP provider should make a list of wellness topics available to the employer.

Some EAP providers also develop and distribute regular newsletters on a company-wide basis. These cover additions or changes to the overall program, along with topics that promote health and wellness. Employees are encouraged to take these newsletters home to share with others in the household. Usually, at least once annually, the EAP provider and the company will co-ordinate a mailing directly to the employee's home. The mailing can include a description of the services, a list of new services, a newsletter, a fridge magnet or wallet card. This is done to ensure family members are made aware of, and are reminded of, the services available to them through their EAP.

The "best practices" EAP provider will have a website that allows employees and family members to obtain the most recent information on the EAP's services, as well as the latest information on wellness topics such as managing stress, family issues, parenting, and maintaining a healthy lifestyle. The more progressive EAP providers will also allow the company to have a link to their website that provides e-counselling and details on wellness programs, benefits and plan items, as well as initiatives and announcements that managers want their employees to access. The EAP provider should collaborate with the company to make this service as timely and relevant as possible.

All employees should receive an EAP wallet card to carry with them at all times. One can be caught in a conflict or emotionally upsetting situation that requires professional help anywhere and at any time.. The card should contain a 24-hour access telephone number and an outline of the very simple steps to obtain service. Some EAP providers have professionally trained counsellors (with a master's degree in psychology or social work) available via the telephone at all times. There should be no waiting, no callbacks, and, especially, no answering service.

Unlike the medical or dental plan that employees use as needed, the EAP requires regular promotion. Many employees forget about the EAP after its introduction, and, worse, when they are troubled or besieged by personal problems. Therefore, regular promotion will catch the attention of those employees that need it.

The EAP provider should offer the above methods to a company to assist the manager in promoting the EAP services. The provider should work closely with the company's account manager on an ongoing basis to develop, implement and maintain the EAP promotion program best for the company.

## LET THE ACCOUNT MANAGER PROMOTE THE EAP

Every off-site EAP service provider appoints a specific EAP account manager to be the key contact for each company. The supervisor or manager should record the name of the company's account manager on his or her EAP wallet card. First and foremost, a company's account manager helps promote the EAP services to the employees. However, an account manager can do so much more to contribute to the health of the organization. Account managers can help make a supervisor's or manager's job easier in many ways.

When a question arises about any aspect of the EAP services or eligibility, a call to the account manager will help. When managers need a second opinion about handling a problem within the work group, the account manager will get an expert in the problem area to talk with them. When managers require coaching and support in approaching an employee with personal problems, the account manager can review the steps to be taken. If one of the employees complains about anything concerning an EAP Service (quality, speed of contact, follow-up, effectiveness, *etc.*), the manager or employee can call the account manager to get things straightened out quickly. In summary, just as the EAP counsellor is there for the employees, the EAP account manager is there for managers whenever they have a workplace or EAP-related issue or concern.

## HELPING EMPLOYEES USE THE EMPLOYEE ASSISTANCE PROGRAM

Even with all the above reminders, it is very hard for many people to take that first step in contacting their EAP centre for help. That is why managers should try to help employees get over this hurdle. When employees talk to managers about personal problems, managers should identify the company's EAP as an excellent problem-solving option.

## EARLY INTERVENTION

The sooner supervisors can assist the troubled employee, the more easily and quickly the problem can be resolved. Everyone has "up" days and "down" days, but employees who are starting to have more and more "down" days, including increased sick days and improbable explanations for absence, should be identified early. Managers are expected to help motivate the work team to do their jobs, to be productive and to be at work. And each EAP can be a manager's ally if he or she deals with the performance fall-off and the subtle but increasing absence and/or sick days earlier rather than later. This can be accomplished by addressing the observations directly with the employee, asking for change and encouraging the employee to access the EAP for professional help. Managers should talk about the EAP in a positive, upbeat manner and emphasize that the EAP is there for the employee "just in case" the employee may have personal problems that are affecting work performance and/or work attendance.

## WHEN EMPLOYEE PERFORMANCE STARTS TO DECLINE

Managers should talk to their supervisors about the situation and ask for advice and guidance before they address the problem with the employee. As well, managers may need to familiarize themselves with the company's policies and procedures concerning decreased performance and lowered attendance. Once managers are clear about the policies, then they may also want to call their EAP provider and talk with a counsellor for some support and clarification about how to approach the employee and how to suggest the use of EAP services.

The human resources group and the company's EAP provider and counsellors are ready to guide managers every step of the way when they are dealing with a troubled employee. Of course, if managers talk with the employee and this encouragement motivates the employee to call the EAP provider and seek professional counselling and help so much the better. In these situations, managers will not know whether the employee has accessed the service because the EAP must maintain confidentiality. If performance or attendance fall-off continues then managers may choose a monitored referral procedure which is described in the next section.

## HOW TO GET THE EMPLOYEE INTO COUNSELLING IF PERFORMANCE CONTINUES TO DETERIORATE

There are times when, despite all efforts at early intervention, a supervisor or manager encounters an employee with a steady deterioration in performance and/or attendance. The problem is usually related to chronic alcohol or drug abuse, or to unresolved and worsening emotional turmoil.

When managers see the development of a downward spiral—increasing tardiness, indolence, days absent, accidents and low output—they must talk with their supervisor, human resource contact, or occupational health nurse. Managers should also contact their EAP provider. Usually, the key person in human resources or occupational health will meet with the employee face-to-face, or coach managers on how to conduct such an interview. A series of steps to correct the work problem will be strongly recommended, including the recommendation that the employee obtain professional counselling through the EAP.

In these cases, the human resources or occupational health person will request that the employee sign a release that permits the counsellor and company contact to be regularly informed as to whether the employee uses the service and follows the treatment plan. The counsellor makes a thorough assessment of the case, then develops and implements a treatment plan. Regular progress reports about the onset of treatment, appointment times, employee attendance, *etc.*, are shared with the contact in the company directly concerned with the outcome. However, what goes on in the counselling sessions, including the topic of discussions between the employee and counsellor, are not revealed unless required by law in situations where there is a threat of violence. The content of the discussions remains confidential. No employee can be forced into taking the recommendation to use the EAP service. Employees can choose not to follow the recommendation, or they may choose to address and to correct the performance and/or attendance issues in some other manner. Many agree to seek help to avoid almost certain dismissal if they do not improve or correct their performance and/or attendance.

This procedure, usually called a monitored referral, enables ongoing treatment of an employee to proceed in a caring but firm manner.

The EAP offers special training to help managers recognize when, and if, monitored referral procedures should be employed. Managers should always have any in-depth talk with their supervisors and the HR and/or Occupational Health group, including any EAP counsellor, about such a situation. Managers should find out more about how an EAP can help in these particular situations. If continued performance fall-off and absenteeism are not addressed, the likelihood of a disability claim is inevitable.

## DISABILITY MANAGEMENT

The Institute of Work and Health reports that every 10-12 minutes, a Canadian employee is disabled due to injury, illness, disease or other cause. What's the result?

### Direct Costs of Disability:

* premiums (WSIB/WCB, STD/SALARY CONTINUANCE, LTD)

### Indirect Costs

* high turnover;
* recruitment costs (interim, long-term);
* retraining;
* low productivity;
* diminished morale;
* opportunity costs.

A Watson Wyatt study entitled *Staying@Work: Value Creation through Integration* lists these six drivers of disability costs:

* poor plan design;
* lack of supervisor involvement in RTW;
* history of sick leave abuse;
* job dissatisfaction;
* preventable health problems;
* inadequate provider involvement.

According to the National Institute of Disability Management, in 1997, direct payroll costs for workers' compensation, STD and LTD were $11 billion in Canada. The cost of failure to effectively re-integrate injured/disabled workers in B.C. alone in 1994 was $3.6 billion. Cost is projected to be $30.5 billion by 2006.

The Canadian Human Rights Commission's 1998 Annual Report reveals Canada labour force participation for persons with disabilities is 2.3 per cent (down from 1997). This indicates that re-integration — once attachment to the pre-disability employer is lost — becomes increasingly difficult.

Social Security statistics from 1994-1995 indicates there were 430,000 injured workers or dependents receiving workers' compensation benefits throughout Canada. $1.9 billion was paid in temporary disability benefits. Human Resources Development Canada reports that, with indirect costs (productivity loss, retraining, *etc.*), the combined total is in excess of $9.9 billion per year.

## WHAT THE EAP PROVIDER CAN CONTRIBUTE TO DISABILITY MANAGEMENT

Employers want to put a stop to the dramatic increase in both the direct and indirect costs of disability and, as experts in organizational health, effective EAP providers are in a strong position to provide strong solutions.

Because more than one-half of short- and long-term disability claims fall within the mental health area, a disability management focus and practice is a natural extension of EAP services. As we have suggested earlier, every issue facing employees is an issue facing business. From infertility to caring for a sick child to money problems to depression, unresolved personal problems can create significant barriers to business success by the impact they have on absenteeism and disability.

From a clinical perspective, whether a business is addressing an employee's growing absenteeism, helping its managers be more effective or trying to cut its disability claims in half, a deep understanding of human psychology is vital. This expertise, matched with a rich history of solving diverse workplace issues, make an effective EAP provider a good choice for disability management consultation.

An EAP provider may have extensive involvement in providing disability management consultation either directly through its own professionals, or through a strategic alliance with a disability management company. The EAP provider may have created a process to work closely with an insurer throughout the disability management process, or they may have developed a comprehensive and custom program to manage all aspects of disability — from policy-making to workplace education to meeting facilitation to medical involvement to return-to-work plans.

Responding to the great need in Canadian organizations to get disability costs under control and to increase organizational health, Warren Shepell Consultants has recently launched an innovative disability management program, called back@work, that successfully integrates disabled employees into the workplace by:

- facilitating communication between the employee and manager;
- co-ordinating medical and other specialized expertise and intervention;
- providing issue-specific management training, coaching and consultation;
- resolving complex disability claims through intensive case management and rapid specialist referral.

Generally, the three essential components of disability management include prevention, early intervention, and prompt return to work. This section reviews each of these components to illustrate how EAPs can assist in helping employees get back to work.

## PREVENTION

It has been identified that there is a need for programs targeted at risk areas in the mental health area such as addictions and depression. Further, these programs need to target individuals who are at risk of developing health problems, for example, stress management programs for employees in high-stress work areas or high-stress companies.

EAP professionals can help an organization review and identify the strategies that would be appropriate for the organization and its employees and that would become an ongoing and effective preventative component of the disability management program.

## WHAT ROLE DOES AN EAP PLAY IN PREVENTION?

The most significant preventative aspect of a disability management program is the EAP. Every employee should be aware of the EAP services and every employee should feel comfortable and confident about accessing the EAP services no matter how small the problem. Today, organizations tend to experience an annual usage rate of approximately 8 per cent. To be truly effective in improving a workforce's level of wellness, usage should be twice that, at a minimum. As mentioned earlier, up to 25 per cent of an employee group could use professional counselling in any given year because they are experiencing problems.

An organization should celebrate high usage rather than be concerned about the extra costs that the higher usage may incur. An organization should want all employees to use the EAP services when they have a problem. Organizations should want to prevent small problems from becoming big problems, which lead to higher rates of absenteeism, sick leave, accidents on or off the job and maladaptive coping such as misuse of alcohol and drugs, gambling and overeating. Of course, all of these issues lead to short- and possibly long-term disability. The cost of an excellent and highly used EAP is a small price to pay for the tremendous cost savings obtained in the long run.

## Early Intervention

Reaching employees before the initiation of a benefits claim for disability is essential for effective disability management. This is where the supervisor plays a key role and where he or she can make a big difference as to whether the troubled employee will file claims.

## Using the EAP to Prevent Disabilities

When it comes to short- and long-term disability, an ounce of prevention is worth a pound of cure. An alert supervisor can use the company's EAP to help prevent the troubled employee from developing a disability, especially in the mental health or emotional arena. Many disabilities don't "just happen".

As soon as an employee with a "productivity problem pattern" is identified, he or she should be discussed with the internal resources such as a manager, the HR or Occupational Health group. Poor communication or even lack of communication between supervisors and employees concerning chronic lateness, absenteeism or low productivity has often been the start of a chain of events that led to a psychological disability claim.

Also, the EAP provider should be called for expert advice on ways to talk about the problem with the employee and perspectives on the issues surrounding the situation. The EAP provides expert coaching on what things to say, how to say them, and when is the best time to say them.

If the problem persists after the first discussion with the employee, the EAP consultant, along with the HR or occupational health contact should be called again for tactful but effective ways to recommend EAP counselling. If the problem still persists after the talks with the employee, in-depth assistance is needed. At this point, the HR or occupational health department should be fully involved. A skilled and coached person can confront the employee and get him or her to agree to a monitored referral process described earlier in this chapter. Very often employees cannot improve without professional help.

If the employee refuses counselling and a performance problem persists, then termination of employment may be one of the only alternatives left before the employee goes on disability. If this must happen, managers will at least know that they tried every alternative first. Of course, the termination must be compliant with the organization's and legislative policies and procedures.

When the above steps are followed, the EAP can eliminate a high percentage of supervisors' concerns surrounding employees with serious performance and attendance fall-off long before they have a chance to develop into a disability. The best solution for managers, the organization and the employee who is struggling is one that restores the employee to full productivity. The EAP plays an integral role in helping to do this.

## Prompt Return to Work

If, after following all the above steps, the employee has gone on disability, he or she must be actively engaged in a comprehensive rehabilitation program to facilitate the return to work as soon as he or she is capable. It is not the nature or severity of the disability as much as the duration of disability that determines whether an employee will return to work. The longer the period, the less likely the employee will return to work — therefore, it is important to act quickly. An employee who has returned to work may not be 100 per cent productive, but even if the employee is able to fulfil only 60 per cent of the job's demands right away, he or she is still more productive than an employee sitting at home collecting benefits.

## HOW CAN THE EAP ASSIST IN A PROMPT RETURN TO WORK?

An EAP provider, in collaboration with a group of professionals (psychologists, vocational rehabilitation counsellors, social workers, rehabilitation counsellors, occupational health nurses, occupational therapists and various medical personnel) will develop a treatment plan to move the employee from an attitude of "I need to be away from the workplace" to "I want to be back at work". Once this occurs, the EAP provider and its disability management team can work with the employer to prepare for the employee's return, including any accommodations that may be necessary.

The psychological readiness of the employee, of the supervisory staff and often of the co-workers needs to be in place for the employee's return to work to be successful. The EAP professional's assistance helps to get everything needed into place and to facilitate communication between the workplace and the employee. It's important for all parties to understand that the employee's privacy can remain protected at the same time as the team, and the employee, determines his/her readiness to return to work — modified or otherwise. The EAP, through this process and the insight it has into the company and its employees saves the organization money, helps the supervisor re-establish a full and productive workforce, and improves the self-esteem of the employee.

## HOW TO EVALUATE THE EAP PROVIDER

Off-site EAP firms come in a variety of structures, sizes, and service levels. This chapter has mentioned a number of elements that many EAP providers have in common. This section explores some of their important differences.

The following factors should be considered by any organization before appointing or changing an EAP firm. Several of these items will have a direct bearing on the levels of help that can be expected for members of the work group and its supervisors.

### Accessibility

The best EAP providers give the employee immediate 24-hour access to fully-qualified counsellors. Only a few providers ensure that there is a counsellor readily available at any hour who can begin to offer treatment on that very first call.

A call to the EAP hot line can be a desperate one, but especially desperate are those calls made in the middle of the night. Employees should know exactly what level of access they can expect from this highly important aspect of the EAP Service and should be discussed with the potential provider. Evidence of access should be sought.

### Depth of Professional Qualifications

Almost every EAP provider has staff members with doctorate levels in counselling or social services, and most have some with degrees in psychiatry or psychology. The excellent provider will only employ these professionals who also have a minimum of five years of actual practice in their chosen fields. The best providers will have teams of professionals, with each experienced team member providing highly specialized consulting skills.

The exceptional EAP will also have counsellors with first-hand knowledge of the particular stresses related to a company's business. The better EAP counsellors have been educated in helping families and individuals and organizations. A company should ensure it has an EAP provider that has an in-depth understanding of organizations and, specifically, their own industry. Managers should determine the depth of professional expertise offered by the company's EAP provider.

The excellent providers have dedicated full-time counsellors working for them. The EAP providers with full-time counsellors receive greater accountability, loyalty, priority and consistency in quality from their counsellors than EAP providers who use part-timers and subcontractors. Exceptional EAP firms also have their own counselling offices across the country.

## Geographical Coverage

When organizations contract with an EAP firm, it is their responsibility to ensure that all of the company locations are well matched by the physical facilities of the provider. If your company is truly nationwide or international in size, it requires an EAP firm with offices across Canada and in other countries where there are employees. However, each supervisor's geographical EAP concerns only apply to one particular location and one specific group of employees. Supervisors will want to know how close the EAP provider location is to the workplace, and how easily it can be accessed.

Other questions that should be asked are:

1. Is there a choice of locations?
2. Does each offer employees private, confidential access?
3. If the work site is not in or very near a major population centre, what depth of service can employees expect?

## Employee Assistance Society of North America Certification (EASNA)

EASNA is a professional association that sets the ethical practices, service standards and operating guidelines for professional EAP providers. It also monitors those firms who are accredited EASNA members. To obtain EASNA certification, an EAP organization must meet a long and detailed list of requirements. In many ways, the process is like ISO certification. It can take months to complete, and many providers do not become accredited on their first attempt.

Once acquired, EASNA accreditation is valid for a three-year term. Then, the organization must go through the process again. "Is this a fully accredited member of EASNA?" is one of the most important questions management can ask any EAP provider. In the author's opinion, no company should hire an EAP supplier that is not fully recognized and certified by this group.

## Pricing of Services

EAP providers will generally provide a quote based on a per employee per year basis. This pricing would normally be based on the EAP providers delivering a certain number or bank of EAP cases per year. At the point in the contract year that the organizational client exceeds this bank of cases, the organization would be charged a flat fee per case delivered.

The number of cases that would be delivered on an annual basis would be determined by the EAP provider based on the organizational client's industry statistics, change occurring within the organization, the promotion of the EAP program by the client, as well as many other factors related to usage of the program. EAP providers are considered to be experts in determining the expected usage rate of EAP within an organization.

It is important to be sceptical when an EAP firm offers a flat rate for unlimited usage or full or unlimited number of cases. It may be quoting a low fee to get the business. However, you have to be curious as to how they fund the extra usage. If you are paying for 100 cases and your usage for the year is 150 cases — who pays for the extra 50 cases? What happens if that offer is extended to most of the firm's organizational clients? Something has to suffer. It is my professional opinion that, as an employer, you should pay for all your cases — no matter what the level of usage. If your employee needs professional help, he or she should receive it completely and fully, with no corners cut. If your employee gets the help he or she needs, it will result in dollars saved.

## Service Offerings

An effective EAP service offers a range of products. An EAP service that provides opportunity to reach the largest number of people is the most effective. Some people may not be comfortable with face-to-face counselling and require telephone or Internet-based services. Others may just need basic information with consultation around elder or childcare. The service provider must be able to address everyone's need in the ways that work best for them. Some EAP services have utilized information resources on the web in order to increase awareness about issues. In our experience providing access to information without a method of resolving an issue can lead to lost productivity and absentiseem.

## EAP and Return on Investment

The dollars savings expected to be delivered to an organization due to the implementation of an EAP program is a question frequently posed to the EAP provider. The published research studies that have attempted to measure the return on investment (ROI) to a client have indicated returns or dollar savings of between three times the cost of the EAP program to a return as high as 10 times the cost of the program.

The studies that have been published have been survey-based studies. Leading EAP providers are now moving towards studies that are non-survey based and those studies that target actual cost savings in areas such as employee absenteeism, employee productivity, long-term disability costs, as well as other areas that the client believes is generating costs that may be large in nature and difficult to control in many cases.

## Frequency of Referrals

The best EAP companies base their quotes on their ability to achieve desirable results using only their own staff in about 90 per cent of all the cases they encounter. In other words, referrals to outside specialists should occur in only 10 to 15 per cent of the cases. A company should ask its EAP about the referral rate and ask for evidence. If it is above 10 to 15 per cent, a performance contract to bring it down to acceptable levels should be requested. A high referral rate from an EAP service suggests the provider is trying to keep its costs down by encouraging employees to go outside the EAP for fee counselling.

Employees referred by an EAP provider to an outside service may choose not to pay or may not have the money to pay; therefore, they drop out of counselling. Or, if the extended health plan pays for subsequent counselling that is referred, a company would then be requested to pay higher premiums based on the higher claims experience.

## Focus on Short-Term Results

In order to be competitive (and to give client companies optimum returns on their EAP investment), most pay-per-service EAP companies are focused on results-oriented, short-term treatment of employee problems with minimal referral. They make every possible attempt to resolve the difficulties and restore the employee to full wellness and productivity within their EAP services and counsellors. Because their professional staff is trained to achieve this goal, they fully control the pace of treatment in about 90 per cent of all the cases they handle.

## Readiness for an Audit

How does one investigate the quality of an EAP provider when most services are confidential? Has the EAP supplier actually treated all the people claimed? Has it lived up to its promises concerning professionalism, depth of involvement, success rates, and well-structured case management? How can management tell?

The answer is for the company to have a complete audit of the EAP activity. This means that a recognized firm of auditors is called in for third-party verification of all services rendered, along with close scrutiny of the EAP firm's internal operation. The provider's case tracking system and records, its professional credentials and managerial facilities are all examined.

A thorough audit is the only way to get an accurate assessment of the value of the service to a company. Some providers will not permit an audit on the grounds that it breaches confidentiality. Others may try to frustrate the auditor's search. A company must be most concerned about those EAP providers that will not allow an auditor to verify user names and files against employee lists to confirm the validity of the users and the usage levels for which the organization is also paying. A company should not contract with an EAP provider who does not agree, in writing, that verification of users will be allowed for each contract term.

The best EAP providers are ready for an audit at all times. Every step of each case they handle is on record—from the first phone contact to itemized details of treatment to the last callback. Confidentiality is maintained because only the auditors will see those details, and only they have the right to make random checks among employees to verify them. The auditors are sworn not to divulge any of this information to the employer. Breaking this trust would cost them a great deal of money and could also cost them their professional licence.

## Ways to Measure Effectiveness

Besides a thorough audit, there are other ways to tell if a company's EAP is effective. Management should make use of these strong indicators.

### 1. Year-to-year Productivity Comparisons

Management will have detailed company records of lateness, absenteeism, accidents, and disability leaves and productivity levels. If the EAP has not made a favourable difference to these figures after its first two years of operation, it may not be an effective program.

The author has stipulated a two-year trial because employees need time to accept and use EAP services. Also, the positive effects of all well-administered EAPs are cumulative. The problems that result in the first year are most likely not to be repeated by the same employees in the second year.

### 2. Industry-wide Comparisons

The productivity factors listed above are recorded by most of the companies in a particular industry. Each year, these figures are averaged and are then published as productivity norms. It is an easy matter for a company's top executives to make year-by-year comparisons between the industry averages and the numbers achieved by their own company. All other parameters being equal, with an effective EAP, an organization should look better over time because there is a less troubled and healthier workforce—which usually translates into improved productivity.

### 3. Return on Investment

EAP providers are moving towards studies that will provide organizations with return-on investment measurement. Partnering with an EAP provider who will work with you to identify metrics that will produce an ROI will lead to evidence of improved productivity.

### 4. Employee Feedback

There are three ways that employees can discuss their EAP:

1. General observation: superintendents, the occupational health staff, and the HR department are among the first to notice a lighter, happier company atmosphere when an effective EAP service is well-entrenched.
2. Confidential surveys: Some firms take anonymous user and opinion polls where unsigned employee comments about their EAP and other issues are written on cards and dropped into locked ballot boxes or mailed to an outside evaluator.
3. Provider records: an effective EAP firm will measure employee satisfaction levels with the service during a follow-up call. This usually takes place two or three months after treatment is initiated.

The employee is asked to rate several key aspects of provider performance from excellent to poor. Other questions asked in the follow-up may include: (1) the number of days (if any) the employee's problem caused him or her to be away from work prior to counselling; (2) the number of days the employee estimates might have been lost without counselling; (3) whether or not the employee would recommend company EAP services to fellow employees. The first two measurements give some insights into the costs saved by reducing absenteeism. The third measure gives a good indication of the value and confidence employees would place in the EAP services.

Although employee reactions are more subjective than numerical comparisons, their opinions can give a strong picture of the program's overall effectiveness and its likely future.

## MAKE THE EMPLOYEE ASSISTANCE PROGRAM WORK

The author believes a group supervisor or manager has one of the toughest jobs in the company. They are right on the front line where productivity needs and people needs often clash. They play a key role in identifying early signs of difficulty and in promoting early solutions. A group supervisor or manager advises employees of the many different services the EAP provides and they must ensure that every employee fully understands the many forms of help the EAP offers. Supervisors and managers should also take advantage of the immediate advice, guidance and support the EAP offers. Supervisors and managers can further their careers, improve their companies' strengths, meet company objectives and improve the well-being of their people by recommending the EAP at every opportunity. An effective EAP can be a supervisor's, an employee's and an organization's best friend. And it can play an important role in effectively managing disability into ability and strength in the workplace.

# Index